*The Process
of Biology:
Primary Sources*

The Process
of Biology:
Primary Sources

JEFFREY J. W. BAKER, Wesleyan University
GARLAND E. ALLEN, Washington University

ADDISON-WESLEY PUBLISHING COMPANY

Reading, Massachusetts • Menlo Park, California • London • Don Mills, Ontario

This book is in the
Addison-Wesley Series in Life Science

John W. Hopkins III
Consulting Editor

Preface

One of the most exciting aspects of studying any science is to follow the thought processes of its great investigators. Although it is never possible to recapture exactly the sequence of ideas which a man encountered as he sought the solution to a problem, some of the initial excitement can be experienced, albeit vicariously, through a reading of original research reports. These papers provide a means of analyzing the hypothesis (or hypotheses) which a worker has developed, the experiments which have been designed to test the hypothesis, and the way in which conclusions have been drawn from specific data. There are few better ways to come to a full understanding of scientific principles in any field than to follow carefully the line of reasoning which carried an investigator from his hypothesis through his data to his conclusions.

In a previously published textbook, *The Study of Biology,* the authors emphasized the rigorous and critical analysis of scientific conclusions. To thoroughly understand how a particular piece of research was conceived and carried out, and its conclusions related to the data, a student must learn to seek out and read critically the investigator's original reports. The present collection of papers provides a means of learning this process. In reading these selections, the student must apply the "If . . . then" reasoning pattern, and ask himself continually whether the data on which an author bases his conclusions have been obtained in a controlled and valid way, and whether the conclusions based on those data are justified. To get the most out of original papers, the student must develop not only such skills of analysis, but also those of careful and attentive reading. Few of the papers in this collection can be skimmed with any profit. Only through active participation in the reading and thinking process can the reader understand the full significance of most of these papers.

Our choice of papers for this anthology was dictated by three considerations. First, we selected those papers which dealt with important biological problems discussed in *The Study of Biology.* While this collection could be used with almost any other textbook, the papers follow in sequence the broad sweep of ideas in *The Study of Biology.* This arrangement provides the student with an opportunity to investigate particular problems in greater depth. Second, we have tried to include articles which were both interesting and within the comprehension of the average college freshman. Third, we have included, for the most part, papers which are not readily available in a number of other anthologies. Thus, some papers of great significance to one or another area of biology have been omitted because they have already been reprinted elsewhere.

We have abridged some papers in order to bring their length to manageable proportions, without, we hope, altering the original meaning. In the case of selections from whole books, we excerpted in such a way as to preserve the flavor and context of the original, larger work as much as possible. When feasible, however, we have reprinted a paper *in toto,* rather than in a pre-digested form in which only the most meaty and relevant parts have been preserved. Selecting the more important from the less important parts of any written material is one of the skills which working with original papers can most profitably teach.

The papers included here can be approached in several different ways. For example, the growth of an idea or the approach to a single problem could be studied through the work of a number of different investigators. (The papers in Section IV, Development, lend themselves well to this approach.) Here, the emphasis would be on seeing how different men approached the same problem, what new assumptions they brought to it, what newly developed techniques gave their work its special slant, what kinds of answers—theoretical, especially—they were willing to accept as explanations for the phenomena they observed. On the other hand, individual papers could be analyzed in great detail for the purpose of understanding the internal logic and organization leading to a single concept. In this approach emphasis would be placed on close reading, on careful analysis of data, and on understanding the point of view which the author takes. (Is he a mechanist or a vitalist? Is he dogmatic or skeptical? And so on.) Both approaches are valid and valuable ways of grasping the intellectual excitement and critical thinking behind great discoveries in science.

Many individuals have advised us in the selection of these papers, and for their help we are sincerely grateful. We, however, take full responsibility for sins of omission and commission in both the final selection and the editing process. We would like to express our thanks especially to three people who have assisted immeasurably in the tedious problem of securing permissions to reprint the various articles in this collection: Mrs. Susan Allen, Mr. Martin Goldstein, and Mrs. Louise Qualls. Without their assistance this anthology would have remained nothing more than an intriguing list of titles on a memo pad.

San Juan, Puerto Rico   J. J. W. B.
St. Louis, Missouri   G. E. A.

Contents

Section IV   Development: The Nature of Cell Differentiation

Section V   Ecology, Species, and Evolution

Section VI   The Origin of Life

Section I
Method and Communication in Science

Introduction

Three approaches to problem-solving in biology are illustrated by the papers in this section. The first paper, Spallanzani's work of 1785, involves a series of very simple observations and experiments—the kind that virtually anyone, with no specialized training whatsoever, could carry out. The second, Bayliss and Starling's paper of 1902, shows a highly rigorous, experimental approach, involving a high degree of technical competence, and carrying the problem into a number of closely related questions. The third, by Weil, Zinberg, and Nelsen (1968), demonstrates simple aspects of statistical analysis, while raising the broader problem of designing valid and controlled experiments using human subjects.

Despite the wide range of historical periods, and the different approaches which they represent, these three papers have some important points in common. All recognize the existence of several alternative interpretations to the phenomena which they have observed; in each case the author(s) set out to provide evidence which would help distinguish between rival theories or concepts. Second, each of the papers presents a relatively unbiased view of the alternative explanations. None starts out with a preconceived idea as to which of several possible ideas must be *the* correct one. Third, each author(s) draws conclusions which are within the range of permissible inference from the data at hand. None of the papers extends general conclusions into speculation or dogmatic theory-building, despite the several instances in which this could have been a temptation. (For example, Bayliss and Starling could have concluded that *all* digestive glands were triggered to secrete digestive fluids by blood-borne chemical agents; or, Weil, Zinberg and Nelsen could have claimed that smoking marihuana was *perfectly safe* and should be encouraged for *all* people.)

Spallanzani's paper was written to answer the question: Is the spermatic fluid, or the solid material in it, the agent of fertilization? In the eighteenth century, it was not known what role sperm cells played in the process of

1

fertilization. Spallanzani himself believed that the unfertilized egg contained a completely preformed adult, a concept which we do not accept today. To Spallanzani, either the solid matter of whole semen (sperm cells plus various gelatinous suspensions) or the spermatic fluid itself served to trigger the growth of the egg. His simple observations and well-planned experiments led Spallanzani to conclude that the spermatic fluid alone was not enough to cause fertilization, that the solid part of the semen was indeed a necessary, and perhaps sufficient, agent. Interestingly enough, however, Spallanzani did not associate the sperm cells themselves with the act of fertilization. He was under the erroneous impression, though understandable for its day, that whole semen, minus the sperm cells, was still capable of triggering the growth of an egg.

The work of Bayliss and Starling began with the recognition of two conflicting hypotheses advanced to explain a single phenomenon. It was noted in the later nineteenth century that when food passed out of the stomach into the duodenum, the pancreas shortly thereafter began secreting pancreatic juice. The question was: What mechanism triggered the pancreas at just the right time? One hypothesis suggested that a nerve pathway carried the stimulus from the duodenum (via the solar plexus and vagus nerve) to the pancreas. Another claimed that when stimulated by the entrance of food from the stomach, the duodenum walls secreted a substance which triggered the pancreas by way of the blood stream. Bayliss and Starling designed a "crucial experiment" to distinguish between these hypotheses. In addition, they extended their experiments and conclusions beyond the initial hypotheses, by showing where in the duodenum the blood-borne messenger substance was produced, by stimulating duodenal cells *in vitro* to produce the substance, and by chemically characterizing it as a protein, *secretin*. The elegant experimental techniques and the careful preparation of control experiments (such as monitoring the blood pressure) indicate the value of thoroughness in carrying out any scientific investigation.

The article by Weil, Zinberg, and Nelsen was chosen not only for the timely interest of its subject (the supposed ill-effects of smoking marihuana), but also because of its clear presentation of statistical data and controlled experimental procedure. Because they used human subjects, and were investigating to some extent psychological phenomena, Weil and his colleagues were restricted in the kinds of experiments which they could perform. For example, they were forced to rely upon a subject's description of the sensations he perceived. The various methods which the investigators employed to compensate for or minimize individual differences provide a useful model for understanding how biologists (and particularly psychologists) try to ensure that their experimental results are true measures of the phenomena being investigated. The use of statistics and the determination of reliability of data forms an important aspect of data analysis as presented in this paper.

Scientific work in general, and biological work in particular, is often caught up in subjects of intense practical or medical interest to society at large. The work of Weil, Zinberg, and Nelsen is a particular case in point. A considerable amount of erroneous information has circulated in recent years about the effects of the hallucinogenic or "mind-expanding" drugs. Weil and his colleagues set out to explore some of the measurable physiological and psychological responses of individuals under the influence of one of the most widely used of these drugs, marihuana *(Cannabis)*. Their investigations were stimulated by the need to have objective and highly controlled experimental evidence. Although the investigators have taken no side in the arguments for or against the use of marihuana, they have shown clearly that many of the supposed ill or side effects of the drug have no basis in physiological fact.

Experiments
Upon the Generation
of Animals and Plants

by LAZZARO SPALLANZANI

Is fertilization effected by the spermatic vapor?

It has been disputed for a long time and it is still being argued whether the visible and coarser parts of the semen serve in the fecundation of man and animals, or whether a very subtle part, a vapor which emanates therefrom and which is called *aura spermatica,* suffices for this function. It cannot be denied that doctors and physiologists defend this last view, and are persuaded in this more by an apparent necessity than by reason or by experiments. They rely upon the observations of some anatomists who have found the vagina of some pregnant women very narrow or perfectly closed; they dwell upon other observations which would have one believe that the semen does not penetrate into the uterus. They reflect upon the orifice of the egg canals or the Fallopian tubes, so narrow that a very fine probe cannot enter there, and which can hardly allow the passage of air; from which they conclude that the seminal liquid of the male, ejaculated into the organs of generation of the females, cannot arrive at the ovaries where the embryos are lodged;[1] but that they must be fertilized by the part of the semen which evaporates, and which they call *aura spermatica.* They further believe that this fertilization must be accomplished by the vapor which communicates with the ovaries by means of the circulation, or by the opening of the uterus and the tubes. Despite these reasons, many other authors hold the contrary opinion, and believe that fertilization is accomplished by means of the material part of the semen. They suspect that the entrance of the vagina and the tubes is enlarged by the heat produced during copulation, and they confirm this suspicion by the finding of semen in the uterus and in the ovaries—they take no account of observations which show that often the uterus of females is without seminal liquid even after copulation, whether because the uterus has been examined too late

[1] It was not known then that fertilization takes place in the oviduct. [Editors of *Great Experiments in Biology.*]

after mating, and the seminal liquid has already left, or because the quantity of this liquid which penetrates the uterus is so small that it has escaped observation.

These reasons advanced for and against do not appear to me to resolve the question; for it has not been demonstrated that the spermatic vapor itself arrives at the ovaries just as it is not clear whether the material part of the semen that arrives at the ovaries and not the vaporous part of the semen is responsible for fertilization. Therefore, in order to decide the question, it is important to employ a convenient means to separate the vapor from the body of the semen and to do this in such a way that the embryos are more or less enveloped by the vapor; for then if they are born, this would be an evident proof that the seminal vapor has been able to fertilize them; or, on the other hand, they might not be born, and then it will be equally sure that the spermatic vapor alone is insufficient and that the additional action of the material part of the sperm is necessary. This procedure, which seems to me to have been completely ignored, is that which I have deemed it necessary to employ.

I have elsewhere demonstrated that the seminal liquid continues to fertilize even though it is diluted with a very large quantity of water, a small drop of water of $^1/_{50}$ of a ligne [1 ligne = 2.25 mm] drawn from a volume of water of 18 oz, in which there had been infused 3 grains of semen, is quite adequate to fertilize a tadpole[2] [egg]. This experiment seemed to favor the spermatic vapor idea since spermatic vapor is nothing but the semen itself extremely attenuated; but the facts which I am going to relate evidently prove the contrary.

In order to bathe tadpoles thoroughly with this spermatic vapor, I put into a watch glass a little less than 11 grains of seminal liquid from several toads. Into a similar glass, but a little smaller, I placed 26 tadpoles [eggs] which, because of the viscosity of the jelly, were tightly attached to the concave part of the glass. I placed the second glass on the first, and they remained united thus during five hours in my room where the temperature was 18°. The drop of seminal liquid was placed precisely under the eggs, which must have been completely bathed by the spermatic vapor that arose; the more so since the distance between the eggs and the liquid was not more than 1 ligne. I examined these eggs after five hours and I found them covered by a humid mist, which wet the finger with which one touched them; this was however only a portion of the semen, which had evaporated and diminished by a grain and a half. The eggs had therefore been bathed by a grain and a half of spermatic vapor; for it could not have escaped outside of the watch crystals since they fitted together very closely. But in spite of this, the eggs, subsequently placed in water, perished.

Although the experiment overthrows the spermatic vapor theory, it was nevertheless unique and I wished to repeat it. One grain and a half of this vapor, taking example from the spermatic liquid, should have been able to fertilize several thousand eggs, and surely, by consequence, 26. I tried to increase the dosage and I succeeded, using the same technique, simply by increasing the

---

[2] In conformity with his preformationist views, Spallanzani uses "tadpole" for the unfertilized as well as the fertilized egg. [Editors of *Great Experiments in Biology*.]

atmospheric temperature. I therefore put 11 grains of this semen into a larger watch glass and I attached, by means of their jelly, 26 eggs to the concavity of another smaller glass, taking care that the spermatic drop and the eggs corresponded perfectly, and were both in the middle of the glasses; I then placed them one on the other, as in the previous experiment, and I exposed them to the sun in a window, tempering its action by an interposed sheet of glass which prevented the heat from exceeding 25° so as not to hinder fertilization in case this could take place. At the end of four hours the eggs were so bathed with this vapor that they were covered with very noticeable droplets; but in spite of this, they did not develop. I again repeated this second experiment in the same circumstances, not only to assure myself of the result but in order to see whether the remainder of this semen, of which a part had been reduced to vapor, had preserved its fertilizing power. Half of these eggs, bathed by the spermatic vapor, perished in the water into which I placed them; but the other half, which I had taken care to moisten with the residue of the semen after evaporation, succeeded well; all the tadpoles hatched. I draw two conclusions from these facts; one, that the spermatic vapor of the semen of the toad is incapable of fertilization; the other, that the remainder of the semen, after a considerable evaporation, entirely preserves its fertilizing powers. . . .

Having previously used spermatic vapor produced in closed vessels, I wished to see what would happen in open vessels in order to eliminate a doubt produced by the idea that the circulation of air was perhaps necessary to fertilization; but fertilization did not succeed any better than in the preceding experiments.

The last experiment of this type was to collect several grains of spermatic vapor and to immerse a dozen eggs in it for several minutes; I touched another dozen eggs with the small remnant of semen which remained after evaporation, and which did not weigh more than half a grain; eleven of these tadpoles hatched successfully although none of the twelve that had been plunged into the spermatic vapor survived.

The conjunction of these facts evidently proves that fertilization in the terrestrial toad is not produced by the spermatic vapor but rather by the material part of the semen. As might be supposed I did not do these experiments only on this toad, but I have repeated them in the manner described on the terrestrial toad with red eyes and dorsal tubercles, and also on the aquatic frog, and I have had the same results. I can even add that although I have only performed a few of these experiments on the tree frog, I have noticed that they agree very well with all the others. . . .

Shall we, however, say that this is the universal process of nature for all animals and for man? The small number of facts which we have does not allow us, in good logic, to draw such a general conclusion: One can at the most think that this is probably so, more especially as there is not a single fact to the contrary, and the question of the influence of the spermatic vapor in fertilization is at least definitely decided in the negative for several species of animals, and with a great probability for the others.

Having succeeded in artificially fertilizing several viviparous animals which are naturally fertilized outside the body of the female [sic], it remained for me therefore to see whether it was possible to fertilize artificially animals which are naturally fertilized only in the body of the females and to seek for this purpose an animal which was large, like a cat, a sheep, or a dog. I did not believe this very difficult, after my success with silkworms, which are fertilized within the body of the female, and I resolved to make the attempt upon a bitch.

The bitch which I chose was a water spaniel of medium size. She had previously whelped, and I suspected that she would not be long in coming into heat; I immediately enclosed her in a room where she was obliged to remain a long time, and in order to be sure of the results I myself fed and watered her: I alone kept the key to the door which imprisoned her; at the end of the thirteenth day of this confinement, the bitch gave evident signs that she was in heat, as was apparent from the swelling of the external genital organs, and by a flow of blood; from the 23rd day, she appeared to have a strong desire to mate: it was then that I attempted the artificial fertilization in the following manner. I had at that time a young dog of the same species [breed]; he supplied me, by spontaneous emission, with 19 grains of seminal liquid, which I injected without delay into the uterus of the bitch, with a small sharply pointed syringe, introduced into the uterus; and since the natural temperature of the seminal liquid is perhaps a necessary condition for the success of the fertilization, I took the precaution to bring the syringe to the temperature of the seminal liquid of the dog, which is approximately 30° Réaumur. Two days after this injection, the bitch ceased to be in heat, and at the end of twenty days the belly appeared swollen; therefore on the 26th day I set her at liberty. The belly continued to grow, and 62 days after the injection of the seminal liquid the bitch delivered three very lively puppies, two male and one female, which by their form and their color resembled not only the mother, but also the male which had furnished me with seminal liquid. The success of this experiment gave me a pleasure which I have never experienced in any of my philosophical researches.

A Sperm Suspension, Filtered Through Various Bodies, Loses its Fertilizing Power

Filtration produces upon a sperm suspension in water the same effect as shaking. If one filters water containing a suspension of sperm through cotton, through rags, or through cloth, it loses much of its fertilizing power and it loses it entirely if one filters it through several blotting papers. If one filters this water through two papers, and if one fertilizes tadpole eggs with the filtered water not as many tadpoles are born as when it has not been filtered. They are born in still fewer numbers if one has filtered the water through three papers. The diminution of births is greater still if one filters this water through four papers. Finally, filtration performed through six or seven layers of paper prevents the birth of tadpoles fertilized by this water.

If the paper through which there has recently been filtered a sperm suspension is squeezed out into pure water where one puts unfertilized eggs, these hatch out very successfully, which proves that the filtration deprives a sperm suspension of its fertilizing power, insofar as the seminal liquid which it had contained remains upon the blotting papers; then one causes it to come out by squeezing it.[3]

[3] Despite the fact that these results point so clearly to the spermatozoa as the agents of fertilization, Spallanzani failed to associate the residue on the filter paper with spermatozoa, having previously come to the erroneous conclusion that semen devoid of spermatozoa was still capable of fertilization. Later workers (Prévost and Dumas, 1824; Newport, 1851) repeated and confirmed this experiment and drew the conclusion that to our twentieth century hindsight seems so obvious. [Editors of *Great Experiments in Biology*.]

The Mechanism of Pancreatic Secretion

by W. M. BAYLISS and E. H. STARLING

I. HISTORICAL

It has long been known that the activity of the pancreas is normally called into play by events occurring in the alimentary canal. Bernard[1] found that the pancreatic secretion could be evoked by the introduction of ether into the stomach or duodenum, and Heidenhain[2] studied the relation of the time-course of the secretion to the processes of digestion going on in the stomach and intestines.

Our exact knowledge of many of the factors determining pancreatic secretion we owe to the work of Pawlow and his pupils,[3] who have shown that the flow of pancreatic juice begins with the entry of the chyme into the duodenum and is not excited directly by the presence of food in the stomach itself. The exciting influence of the chyme is due chiefly to its acidity, and a large secretion can be brought about by the introduction of 0.4 percent hydrochloric acid into the stomach, whence it is rapidly transferred to the duodenum. Pawlow found, however, that other substances, *e.g.* water, oil, introduced into the stomach had a similar, though less pronounced, effect. In each case the effect was produced only when the substances had passed into the duodenum. Pawlow has, moreover, drawn attention to a remarkable power of adaptation presented by the pancreas, the juice which is secreted varying in composition according to the nature of the food which has passed into the duodenum. Thus, with a diet of meat the tryptic ferment

Abridged from W. M. Bayliss and E. H. Starling, "The Mechanism of Pancreatic Secretion," *Journal of Physiology* **28** (1902), 325–353. Reprinted by permission.

[1] *Physiologie expérimentale,* II. p. 226. Paris, 1856.
[2] Hermann's *Handbuch d. Physiologie,* V. p. 183. 1883.
[3] *Die Arbeit der Verdauungsdrüsen.* Trans. from Russian, Wiesbaden. 1898. Also *Le travail des glandes digestives.* Paris, 1901.

is present in relatively largest amount, while a diet of bread causes the preponderance of the amylolytic ferment, and a diet of milk or fat that of the fat-splitting ferment.

Pawlow regards the secretion evoked by the presence of acid in the duodenum as reflex in origin, and ascribes the varying composition of the juice in different diets to a marvellous sensibility of the duodenal mucous membrane, so that different constituents of the chyme excite different nerve-endings, or produce correspondingly different kinds of nerve-impulses, which travel to the gland, or its nerve-centres, and determine the varying activity of the gland-cells.

In searching for the channels of this reflex, Pawlow has shown that, if proper precautions be taken, it is possible to excite a secretion of pancreatic juice by excitation of the divided vagus or splanchnic nerves. The vagus nerves, also, according to him, contain inhibitory fibres.

The question as to the mechanism by which a pancreatic secretion is evoked by the introduction of acid into the duodenum has been narrowed still further by the independent researches of Popielski[4] and of Wertheimer and Lepage.[5] These observers have shown that the introduction of acid into the duodenum still excites pancreatic secretion after section of both vagi and splanchnic nerves, or destruction of the spinal cord, or even after complete extirpation of the solar plexus. Popielski concludes, therefore, that the secretion is due to a peripheral reflex action, the centres of which are situated in the scattered ganglia found throughout the pancreas, and ascribes special importance to a large collection of ganglion cells in the head of the pancreas close to the pylorus. Wertheimer and Lepage, while accepting Popielski's explanation of the secretion excited from the duodenum, found that secretion could also be induced by injection of acid into the lower portion of the small intestine, the effect, however, gradually diminishing as the injection was made nearer the lower end of the small intestine, so that no effect at all was produced from the lower two feet or so of the ileum. Secretion could be excited from a loop of jejunum entirely isolated from the duodenum. They conclude that, in this latter case, the reflex centres are situated in the ganglia of the solar plexus, but they did not perform the obvious control experiment of injecting acid into an isolated loop of jejunum after extirpation of these ganglia. They showed that the effect was not abolished by the injection of large doses of atropin, but compared with this the well-known insusceptibility to this drug of the sympathetic fibres of the salivary glands.

The apparent local character of this reaction interested us to make further experiments on the subject, in the idea that we might have here to do with an extension of the local reflexes whose action on the movements of the intestines we have already investigated.[6] We soon found, however, that we were dealing with an entirely different order of phenomena, and that the secretion of the pancreas is normally called into play not by nervous channels at all, but by a chemical

---

[4] *Gazette clinique de Botkin* (Russ.) 1900.
[5] *Journal de Physiologie,* III. p. 335. 1901.
[6] This *Journal,* XXIV. p. 99. 1899.

substance which is formed in the mucous membrane of the upper parts of the small intestine under the influence of acid, and is carried thence by the blood-stream to the gland-cells of the pancreas.[7]

II. EXPERIMENTAL METHODS

All our experiments were made on dogs which had received a previous injection of morphia, and were anæsthetized with A.C.E. mixture during the course of the experiment. In order to keep the animals' condition constant, artificial respiration was usually employed, a procedure which is especially necessary when both vagi are divided, the anæsthetic bottle being introduced in the course of the blast of air from the pump. The animals had received no food for a period of 18 to 24 hours previously. In the earlier experiments, where a considerable degree of preliminary operative manipulation was required in the abdominal cavity, the animals were placed during the remainder of the experiment in a bath of warm physiological saline, the level of the fluid being above that of the abdominal wound. This method was found to keep them in such good condition throughout a long experiment that it was adopted as a routine practice in all cases. The arterial pressure was always recorded by means of a mercurial manometer connected with the carotid artery in the usual way. The pancreatic juice was obtained by placing a cannula in the larger duct which enters the duodenum on a level with the lower border of the pancreas. To the cannula was connected a long glass tube filled at first with physiological saline; the end of this tube projected over the edge of the bath so that the drops of the fluid as they were secreted fell upon a mica disc cemented to the lever of a Marey's tambour, which was in connection, by means of rubber tubing, with another tambour which marked each drop upon the smoked paper of the kymograph.

III. THE EFFECT OF THE INJECTION OF ACID INTO THE DUODENUM AND JEJUNUM

It is unnecessary to describe at length the results obtained under this heading. We are able to confirm the statements made by our predecessors. The result of injecting from 30 to 50 c.c. of 0.4 percent hydrochloric acid into the lumen of the duodenum or jejunum is to produce, after a latent period of about two minutes, a marked flow of pancreatic juice. Further, this effect is still produced after section of both vagi, section of the spinal cord at the level of the foramen magnum, destruction of the spinal cord, section of the splanchnic nerves, or extirpation of the solar plexus, or any combination of these operations.

Fig. 1 will serve as an illustration of the fact. In this case the spinal cord was destroyed from the 6th thoracic vertebra downwards, and both vagi and splanchnic nerves were cut. At the period of time marked by the signal, 50 c.c. of acid were injected into the duodenum, about 2 minutes from the beginning of the injection

[7] A preliminary abstract of the main results of this work was published in the *c. Roy. Soc.* LXIX. p. 352. 1902. The experiments, of which an account is given in the present paper, were completed in March, 1902, their publication being delayed by extraneous circumstances.

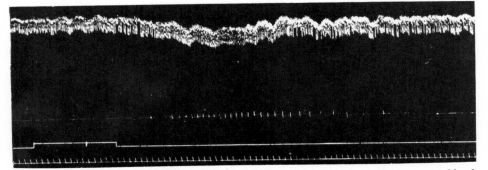

Fig. 1. *Effect of injection of acid into duodenum after destruction of cord. Upper curve—blood-pressure. Uppermost of three lines—drops of pancreatic secretion. Middle line—signal marking injection of 50 c.c., 0.4% HCl. Bottom line—time in 10″. Blood-pressure zero = level of time marker.*

the first drop of secretion is recorded, and a rapid series of drops commences at 4 minutes, to last for some 3 or 4 minutes and gradually cease after 11 or 12 minutes.

In two or three of these experiments we noted an effect which is perhaps worth recording. During the injection of repeated doses of acid, the effect of each dose was less than that of the preceding one, and sooner or later a point was reached at which no effect was produced, even by 1.6 percent HCl. On now injecting into a vein about 50 c.c. of 3 percent sodium carbonate solution a considerable flow of juice was obtained without any further injection into the duodenum.

Intravenous injection of sodium carbonate solution, without previous introduction of acid into the gut, had no effect on the pancreatic secretion.

Our experiments, therefore, confirm those of previous observers in so far as we find that after exclusion of all nerve-centres, except those in the pancreas itself, a secretion of pancreatic juice is obtained by the introduction of acid into the duodenum. But, as pointed out above, the *experimentum crucis* of taking an isolated loop of intestine, dividing the mesenteric nerves supplying it, and then injecting acid into it, had not been performed.

It is plain that this experiment cannot be performed on the duodenum for anatomical reasons. Fortunately, however, as Wertheimer and Lepage have shown, the jejunum, separated by section from the duodenum, is also capable of exciting the pancreas to activity, when acid is introduced, and in this case the centre for the "reflex" must be in the cœliac or mesenteric ganglia. The possibility of our crucial experiment is given here, and the results are contained in the next section.

IV. THE CRUCIAL EXPERIMENT

On January 16th, 1902, a bitch of about 6 kilos weight, which had been fed about 18 hours previously, was given a hypodermic injection of morphia some 3 hours before the experiment, and during the experiment itself received A.C.E. in addition. The nervous masses around the superior mesenteric artery and cœliac axis were completely removed and both vagi cut. A loop of jejunum was tied at both ends and the mesenteric nerves supplying it were carefully dissected out and divided, so that the piece of intestine was connected to the body of the animal merely by its arteries and veins. A cannula was inserted in the large pancreatic duct and the drops of secretion recorded. The blood-pressure in the carotid was also recorded in the usual way. The animal was in the warm saline bath and under artificial respiration.

The introduction of 20 c.c. of 0.4 percent HCl into the duodenum produced a well-marked secretion of 1 drop every 20 secs. lasting for some 6 minutes; this result merely confirms previous work.

But, and this is the important point of the experiment, and the turning-point of the whole research, the introduction of 10 c.c. of the same acid into the enervated loop of jejunum produced a similar and equally well-marked effect.

Now, since this part of the intestine was completely cut off from nervous connection with the pancreas, the conclusion was inevitable that the effect was produced by some chemical substance finding its way into the veins of the loop of jejunum in question and being carried in the blood-stream to the pancreatic cells. Wertheimer and Lepage have shown,[8] however, that acid introduced into the circulation has no effect on the pancreatic secretion, so that the body of which we were in search could not be the acid itself. But there is, between the lumen of the gut and the absorbent vessels, a layer of epithelium, whose cells are as we know endowed with numerous important functions. It seemed therefore possible

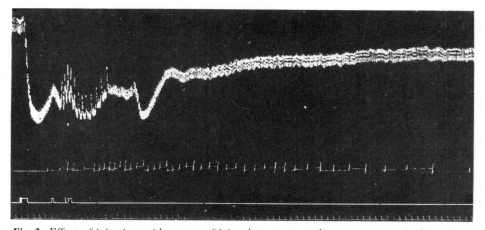

Fig. 2. *Effect of injecting acid extract of jejunal mucous membrane into vein. Explanation as Fig. 1. The steps on the drop-tracing are due to a gradual accumulation of secretion on the lever of the drop-recorder, which fluid falls off at intervals. Blood pressure zero = level of drop-recorder.*

---

[8] *Journal de Physiologie*, III. p. 695. 1901.

that the action of acid on these cells would produce a body capable of exciting the pancreas to activity. The next step in our experiment was plain, viz. to cut out the loop of jejunum, scrape off the mucous membrane, rub it up with sand and 0.4 percent HCl in a mortar, filter through cotton-wool to get rid of lumps and sand, and inject the extract into a vein. The result is shown in Fig. 2. The first effect is a considerable fall of blood-pressure, due, as we shall show later, to a body distinct from that acting on the pancreas, and, after a latent period of about 70 secs. a flow of pancreatic juice at more than twice the rate produced at the beginning of the experiment by introduction of acid into the duodenum. We have already suggested the name "secretin" for this body, and as it has been accepted and made use of by subsequent workers it is as well to adhere to it.

In the same experiment we were able to make two further steps in the elucidation of the subject. In the first place the acid extract was boiled and found undiminished in activity, secretin is therefore not of the nature of an enzyme. In the second place, since Wertheimer and Lepage have shown that the effect of acid in the small intestine diminishes in proportion as the place where it is introduced approaches the lower end, so that from the last 6 inches or so of the ileum no secretion of the pancreas is excited, it was of interest to see whether the distribution of the substance from which secretin is split by acids is similar in extent. Fig. 3 shows the result of injecting an extract from the lower 6 inches of the ileum made in the same way as the jejunum extract. The fall of blood-pressure is present, but there is no effect on the pancreas. Another preparation from the ileum just above this one also had no effect on the pancreas. A preparation from the jejunum below the previous one had a marked effect, but less than that of the loop above. The distribution of "prosecretin," as we have proposed to call the mother-substance, corresponds therefore precisely with the region from which acid introduced into the lumen excites secretion from the pancreas.

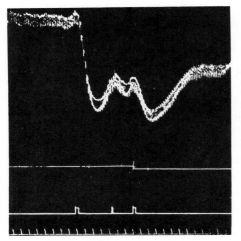

Fig. 3. *Effect of acid extract of lower end of ileum. Explanation as before.*

In reply to the objection of Pflüger to this experiment,[9] we admit that it is difficult to be certain that all nerve-channels were absolutely excluded, since the walls of the blood vessels were intact, but we submit that since the result of the experiment was such as has been described it does not in the least matter whether the nerves were all cut or not; the only fact of importance is that it was the belief that all the nerves were cut that caused us to try the experiment of making an acid extract of the mucous membrane and that led to the discovery of secretin.

As to the further objection of Pflüger that it is in no way extraordinary that a body should be extracted from intestinal mucous membrane capable of acting as a stimulant to gland activity since there are many such bodies known, our reply is that secretin, as will be shown more fully later on, is of an entirely specific nature; the experiment described above shows that even from the ileum no such substance can be obtained, and subsequent experiments showed that from no other part of the body could any body be extracted which caused secretion in the pancreas. And further no other substance known to us, even pilocarpin, which acts so powerfully on most glands, has any effect on the pancreas at all comparable with that of secretin; nor has secretin any action on glands other than the pancreas, except perhaps to a small degree on the secretion of bile.

V. PROPERTIES AND ACTION OF SECRETIN

Some physical and chemical characters. Having shown that boiling an acid extract of the mucous membrane does not destroy its activity, we proceeded to test whether the reaction had any effect in this way and found that a short boiling in either acid, neutral or alkaline solution was harmless. Since a preparation containing less proteid and more easily filterable can be made by neutralizing while boiling, our final routine method of preparing an active solution for ordinary purposes is the following. The duodenum and jejunum are cut out, slit up with scissors, washed under the tap, the mucous membrane scraped off and well rubbed with sand and a little 0.4 percent HCl in a mortar, allowed to stand under about 2 or 3 times its volume of 0.4 percent HCl for some minutes, the whole boiled over free flame in a porcelain dish, and while boiling brought to the alkaline side of neutrality by strong caustic soda, then made slightly acid by acetic acid, strained and pressed through muslin and filtered through paper. The solution thus obtained contains very little proteid, but becomes slightly turbid on cooling, partly owing to a trace of albumoses, but chiefly to gelatin.

In order to obtain a purer preparation we attempted to precipitate the solution by alcohol, and were somewhat surprised to find that the active substance is soluble in alcohol, at all events in alcohol of a strength up to 90 percent. Dr W. A. Osborne, who is engaged in investigating the chemical nature of secretin, found later that it is insoluble in absolute alcohol, as also in ether. Fig. 4 will serve to show the fact of the solubility in alcohol. A solution of secretin made as above was mixed with 5 times its volume of absolute alcohol, a little ether added to

[9] *Pfluger's Archiv*, XC. p. 32. 1902.

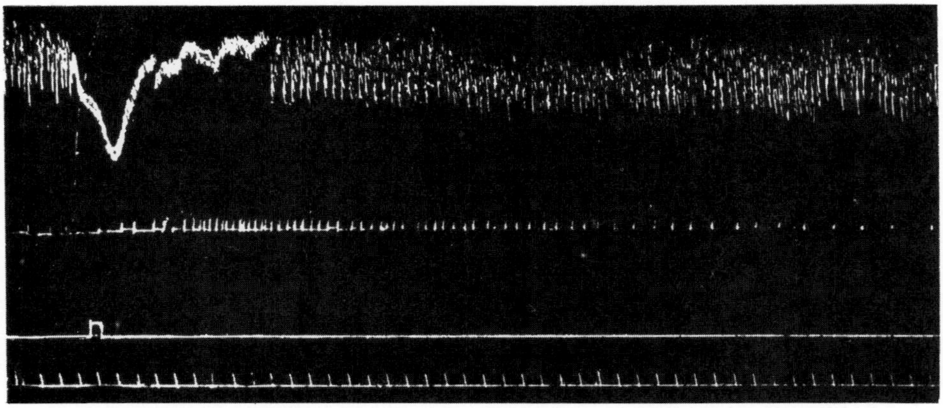

Fig. 4. *Effect of saline extract of dried residue from alcoholic solution of secretin. Explanation as before. There was a certain amount of secretory activity already present owing to a previous injection, the effect of which had not passed off. Blood-pressure zero 20 mm. below time-marker.*

cause agglomeration of the precipitate, filtered, the filtrate evaporated in dryness under diminished pressure and various extracts made of the residue. The effect of the saline extract is shown in the figure. It will be noticed that there is very little fall of blood-pressure. The alcoholic and ethereal extracts of the above residue were evaporated to dryness, taken up again in saline, and the facts as to solubility already given were made out.

Although short boiling does not destroy it, on concentrating a weak solution by prolonged evaporation at atmospheric pressure the activity was found to disappear, this we think was due to slow oxidation, and in fact the activity of a strong solution is very readily abolished by weak potassium permanganate. Dr Osborne finds also that any attempt to precipitate a solution of secretin by the addition of metallic salts such as those of mercury, lead, or iron, or by phosphotungstic acid leads to destruction of the active body, since it has disappeared from both filtrate and precipitate. Tannin may be used, however, and a very pure preparation may be obtained by precipitating the excess of tannin in the filtrate by gelatin, and the gelatin afterwards by alcohol. The effect of such a solution is shown in Fig. 5. It will be seen however that by this treatment alone the body causing fall of blood-pressure is not removed.

Secretin is non-volatile, it does not appear in the distillate obtained by passing steam through its solution.

It dialyses through parchment paper, but not readily.

The action of its solutions does not depend on their inorganic constituents, since the ash, prepared for us by Dr Osborne, has no effect on the pancreas.

It is destroyed by digestion with active tryptic solutions for one hour; the effect of peptic solutions is somewhat uncertain, digestion with gastric juice from the dog for one hour did not destroy the activity of a solution of secretin, but considerably diminished it.

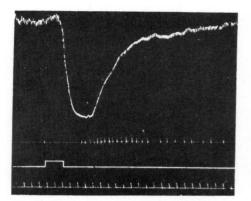

Fig. 5. *Effect of filtrate from precipitating secretin solution by tannin. Explanation as before. Blood-pressure zero 15 mm. below time-marker.*

Taking these facts together it will be seen that we cannot as yet give any definite suggestion as to the chemical nature of secretin, its solubility in alcohol and diffusibility point to its being a body of low molecular weight; since it is not destroyed by boiling it is not a ferment; and that it is not of the nature of an alkaloid or diamino-acid is shown by the fact of its not being precipitated by tannin. . . .

VI. THE ACTION OF SECRETIN ON SOME OTHER GLANDS

Salivary glands. Secretin does not excite secretion in these. In one experiment we noted a slow thick secretion from the cannula in the submaxillary duct, but this was abolished at once on cutting the sympathetic on the same side of the neck. This result shows the caution necessary in these experiments and the absolute necessity of taking a blood-pressure tracing, since the explanation of the phenomena was given at once by the blood-pressure curve. The secretin preparation used contained a considerable admixture of depressor substance, and there can be no doubt that the fall of blood-pressure was sufficient to excite the nerve-centre by anæmia, and so produce the flow of sympathetic saliva.

Stomach. No effect, so far as we were able to make out from the absence of gastric juice after a number of injections of secretin.

Succus entericus. Also no effect.

Bile. Since the secretion of bile is very much influenced by the blood-pressure, the depressor substance in our ordinary secretin preparation would tend to obscure any simultaneous excitatory effect of the secretin itself; and on the other hand the bile-salts contained in it would increase the rate of secretion of bile, so that it was necessary to use a purified preparation. Neglect of this precaution makes the results of Victor Henri and Portier[10] of little value. . . .

The preparation used was made from mucous membrane which was ground

---

[10] *C. R. Société de Biologie,* 6 Juin, 1902, p. 620.

up with sand, and extracted by several changes of alcohol in the cold. It was then boiled in alcohol, and a secretin preparation made in the usual way from the dried membrane by extraction with acid, etc. The alcohol from the last extraction was evaporated to dryness, and the residue tested for bile-salts by Pettenkofer's test with no result. It will be noted that there was still present a small amount of depressor substance, and no doubt it is owing to this that the first effect of the injection is a slowing of the bile-flow. In order to neutralize the effect of this it is advisable to count the drops for a considerable time before the injection, and also afterwards. In this case there were in the 900 secs. preceding the injection 27 drops, and in the 700 secs. afterwards 42 drops, that is, the rate of secretion was almost doubled. We have made several similar experiments and obtained more or less acceleration of the secretion in all.

The question arises whether the substance exciting the liver is the same as that exciting the pancreas. It would be appropriate that the same body should perform both functions, but we must leave the question at present undecided.

Other "secretins." The point raised in the last paragraph leads naturally to the thought that there are similar mechanisms in relation to other secretions. We have tested the question to some extent with respect to the salivary glands, stomach, and succus entericus, by investigating the action upon them of extracts made in various ways from the tongue, salivary glands, pyloric and cardiac ends of stomach, and various parts of the small intestine, but have hitherto obtained no definite results. It is quite possible that in the case of the anterior portions of the alimentary canal the nervous mechanism is the most important one. In the case of the succus entericus, according to Pawlow's investigation, the pancreatic juice acts as an excitant; in our language we should say then that pancreatic juice is the "secretin" for the succus entericus, but the subject needs further work. As regards the stomach, an article of interest was published recently by Popielski,[11] in which it is shown that the digestion of meat proceeds normally in the stomach separated from the central nervous system, and this fact is taken to prove that the gastric juice is secreted in response to a peripheral reflex from ganglia in the walls of the stomach. We regard it as unfortunate that the possibility of a "secretin" being produced was not considered, and that so good an opportunity of testing the hypothesis was neglected.

Other chemical sympathies. It will suffice to call to mind the well-known relation between the uterus and mammary glands, as also the production of a lactase in the pancreatic juice of adult dogs after feeding with milk, and we do this to call attention to the advisability of a renewed investigation of these facts from the point of view of the production of bodies analogous to our pancreatic secretin.

VII. THE ACTION OF DRUGS AND OTHER EXTRACTS ON THE SECRETION OF THE PANCREAS

In the course of our experiments we have tested the effect of the intravenous injection of a large number of substances on the pancreas. The only bodies found

---

[11] *Centralbl. f. Physiologie*, XVI. p. 121. June 7th, 1902.

to be active were pilocarpin and physostigmin, as indeed has been long known. The bodies found to be inactive were pancreatic juice itself, succus entericus, gastric juice, extracts, neutral and acid, of both ends of the stomach, peptone, ether in solution in physiological saline, various extracts of submaxillary glands and tongue, and of the spleen.

As regards *peptone* Gley[12] has obtained secretory effects, but the doses needed were large and the effect small, 1 c.c. of juice in 5 to 10 minutes; the ordinary rate produced by secretin is, on the contrary, 6 c.c. in 10 minutes, and this is often exceeded.

Pilocarpin produces a slow secretion of a thick juice, which is stated to be active without enterokinase, a point on which we are engaged at present. The maximum flow obtained by the injection of 7 c.c. of 1 percent solution was 10 drops in 160 secs., that is at the rate of 1 c.c. in 8 minutes, since 30 drops were equal to 1 c.c., but only 10 drops were obtained in all. The secretory effect of pilocarpin, as of physostigmin, is at once abolished by a small dose of atropin, a drug which has no influence on the secretory effects of secretin injections.

On two occasions we noticed the rapid flow of a few drops of secretion on injecting *curare,* but since a second dose had no effect we concluded that this effect was due to some subsidiary cause, perhaps contraction of ducts or squeezing out secretion by vascular dilatation.

Taking all the above facts into consideration we think we are justified in the conclusion that the mode of action of bodies like pilocarpin and peptone is of a totally different nature from that of secretin, which is a specific substance, acting only on the pancreas, and perhaps the liver, whereas all the other active substances produced an effect on all glands indiscriminately. . . .

VIII. SUMMARY OF CONCLUSIONS

1. The secretion of the pancreatic juice is normally evoked by the entrance of acid chyme into the duodenum, and is proportional to the amount of acid entering (Pawlow). This secretion does not depend on a nervous reflex, and occurs when all the nervous connections of the intestine are destroyed.
2. The contact of the acid with the epithelial cells of the duodenum causes in them the production of a body (secretin), which is absorbed from the cells by the blood-current, and is carried to the pancreas, where it acts as a specific stimulus to the pancreatic cells, exciting a secretion of pancreatic juice proportional to the amount of secretin present.
3. This substance, secretin, is produced probably by a process of hydrolysis from a precursor present in the cells, which is insoluble in water and alkalis and is not destroyed by boiling alcohol.
4. Secretin is not a ferment. It withstands boiling in acid, neutral or alkaline solutions, but is easily destroyed by active pancreatic juice or by oxidising

[12] *Bull. du Muséum d'Hist. nat.* III. p. 244, 29 Juin, 1897; see also Camus and Gley, *C. R. Société de Biologie,* 7 Mars, 1902.

agents. It is not precipitated from its watery solution by tannic acid, or alcohol and ether. It is destroyed by most metallic salts. It is slightly diffusible through parchment paper.

5. The pancreatic juice obtained by secretin injection has no action on proteids until "enterokinase" is added. It acts on starch and to some extent on fats, the action on fats being increased by the addition of succus entericus. It is, in fact, normal pancreatic juice.

6. Secretin rapidly disappears from the tissues, but cannot be detected in any of the secretions. It is apparently not absorbed from the lumen of the intestine.

7. It is not possible to obtain a body resembling secretin from any tissues of the body other than the mucous membrane of the duodenum and jejunum.

8. Secretin solutions, free from bile-salts, cause some increase in the secretion of bile. They have no action on any other glands.

9. Acid extracts of the mucous membrane normally contain a body which causes a fall of blood-pressure. This body is not secretin, and the latter may be prepared free from the depressor substance by acting on disquamated epithelial cells with acid.

10. There is some evidence of a specific localized action of the vaso-dilator substances which may be extracted from various tissues.

Clinical and Psychological Effects of Marihuana in Man

by ANDREW T. WEIL, NORMAN E. ZINBERG, and JUDITH M. NELSEN

In the spring of 1968 we conducted a series of pilot experiments on acute marihuana intoxication in human subjects. The study was not undertaken to prove or disprove popularly held convictions about marihuana as an intoxicant, to compare it with other drugs, or to introduce our own opinions. Our concern was simply to collect some long overdue pharmacological data. In this article we describe the primitive state of knowledge of the drug, the research problems encountered in designing a replicable study, and the results of our investigations.

Marihuana is a crude preparation of flowering tops, leaves, seeds, and stems of female plants of Indian hemp *Cannabis sativa* L.; it is usually smoked. The intoxicating constituents of hemp are found in the sticky resin exuded by the tops

Andrew T. Weil, Norman E. Zinberg, and Judith M. Nelsen, "Clinical and Psychological Effects of Marihuana in Man," *Science* **162** (December 13, 1968), 1234–1242. Copyright © 1968 by the American Association for the Advancement of Science. Reprinted by permission.

of the plants, particularly the females. Male plants produce some resin but are grown mainly for hemp fiber, not for marihuana. The resin itself, when prepared for smoking or eating, is known as "hashish." Various *Cannabis* preparations are used as intoxicants throughout the world; their potency varies directly with the amount of resin present *(1)*. Samples of American marihuana differ greatly in pharmacological activity, depending on their composition (tops contain most resin; stems, seeds, and lower leaves least) and on the conditions under which the plants were grown. In addition, different varieties of *Cannabis* probably produce resins with different proportions of constituents *(2)*. Botanists feel that only one species of hemp exists, but work on the phytochemistry of the varieties of this species is incomplete *(3)*. Chronic users claim that samples of marihuana differ in quality of effects as well as in potency; that some types cause a preponderance of physical symptoms, and that other types tend to cause greater distortions of perception or of thought.

Pharmacological studies of *Cannabis* indicate that the tetrahydrocannabinol fraction of the resin is the active portion. In 1965, Mechoulam and Gaoni *(4)* reported the first total synthesis of $(-)$-Δ^1-*trans*-tetrahydrocannabinol (THC), which they called "the psychotomimetically active constituent of hashish (marihuana)." Synthetic THC is now available for research in very limited supply.

In the United States, the use of *Cannabis* extracts as therapeutics goes back to the 19th century, but it was not until the 1920's that use of marihuana as an intoxicant by migrant Mexican laborers, urban Negroes, and certain Bohemian groups caused public concern *(3)*. Despite increasingly severe legal penalties imposed during the 1930's, use of marihuana continued in these relatively small populations without great public uproar or apparent changes in numbers or types of users until the last few years. The fact that almost none of the studies devoted to the physiological and psychological effects of *Cannabis* in man was based on controlled laboratory experimentation escaped general notice. But with the explosion of use in the 1960's, at first on college campuses followed by a spread downward to secondary schools and upward to a portion of the established middle class, controversy over the dangers of marihuana generated a desire for more objective information about the drug.

Of the three known studies on human subjects performed by Americans, the first (see *5*) was done in the Canal Zone with 34 soldiers; the consequences reported were hunger and hyperphagia, loss of inhibitions, increased pulse rate with unchanged blood pressure, a tendency to sleep, and unchanged performance of psychological and neurological tests. Doses and type of marihuana were not specified.

The second study, known as the 1944 LaGuardia Report *(6)*, noted that 72 prisoners, 48 of whom were previous *Cannabis* users, showed minimum physiological responses, but suffered impaired intellectual functioning and decreased body steadiness, especially well demonstrated by nonusers after high doses. Basic personality structures remained unchanged as subjects reported feelings of relaxation, disinhibition, and self-confidence. In that study, the drug was administered orally as an extract. No controls were described, and doses and quality of marihuana were unspecified.

Williams *et al.* in 1946 *(7)* studied a small number of prisoners who were chronic users; they were chiefly interested in effects of long-term smoking on psychological functioning. They found an initial exhilaration and euphoria which gave way after a few days of smoking to indifference and lassitude that somewhat impaired performance requiring concentration and manual dexterity. Again, no controls were provided.

Predictably, these studies, each deficient in design for obtaining reliable physiological and psychological data, contributed no dramatic or conclusive results. The 1967 President's Commission on Law Enforcement and the Administration of Justice described the present state of knowledge by concluding *(3)*: "... no careful and detailed analysis of the American experience [with marihuana] seems to have been attempted. Basic research has been almost non-existent. ...." Since then, no other studies with marihuana itself have been reported, but in 1967 Isbell *(8)* administered synthetic THC to chronic users. At doses of 120 μg/kg orally or 50 μg/kg by smoking, subjects reported this drug to be similar to marihuana. At higher doses (300 to 400 μg/kg orally or 200 to 250 μg/kg by smoking), psychotomimetic effects occurred in most subjects. This synthetic has not yet been compared with marihuana in nonusers or given to any subjects along with marihuana in double-blind fashion.

Investigations outside the United States have been scientifically deficient, and for the most part have been limited to anecdotal and sociological approaches *(9–12)*. So far as we know, our study is the first attempt to investigate marihuana in a formal double-blind experiment with the appropriate controls. It is also the first attempt to collect basic clinical and psychological information on the drug by observing its effects on marihuana-naive human subjects in a neutral laboratory setting.

RESEARCH PROBLEMS

That valid basic research on marihuana is almost nonexistent is not entirely accounted for by legislation which restricts even legitimate laboratory investigations or by public reaction sometimes verging on hysteria. A number of obstacles are intrinsic to the study of this drug. We now present a detailed description of our specific experimental approach, but must comment separately on six general problems confronting the investigator who contemplates marihuana research.

1. Concerning the route of administration, many pharmacologists dismiss the possibility of giving marihuana by smoking because, they say, the dose cannot be standardized *(13)*. We consider it not only possible, but important to administer the drug to humans by smoking rather than by the oral route for the following reasons. (i) Smoking is the way nearly all Americans use marihuana. (ii) It is possible to have subjects smoke marihuana cigarettes in such a way that drug dosage is reasonably uniform for all subjects. (iii) Standardization of dose is not assured by giving the drug orally because little is known about gastro-intestinal absorption of the highly water-insoluble cannabinols in man. (iv) There is considerable indirect evidence from users that the quality of the intoxication is different when marihuana or preparations of it are ingested rather than smoked. In particular, ingestion seems to cause more powerful effects, more "LSD-like" effects, longer-lasting effects, and more hangovers *(12, 14)*. Further, marihuana smokers are accustomed to a very rapid onset of action due to efficient absorption through the lungs, whereas the latency for onset of effects may be 45 or 60 minutes after ingestion. (v) There is reported evidence from experiments with rats and mice that the pharmacological activities of natural hashish (not subjected to combustion) and hashish sublimate (the combustion products) are different *(14)*.

2. Until quite recently, it was extremely difficult to estimate the relative potencies of different samples of marihuana by the techniques of analytical chemistry. For this study, we were able to have the marihuana samples assayed spectro-photometrically *(15)* for THC content. However, since THC has not been established as the sole determinant of marihuana's activity, we still feel it is important to have chronic users sample and rate marihuana used in research. Therefore, we assayed our material by this method as well.

3. One of the major deficiencies in previous studies has been the absence of negative control or placebo treatments, which we consider essential to the design of this kind of investigation. Because marihuana smoke has a distinctive odor and taste, it is difficult to find an effective placebo for use with chronic users. The problem is much less difficult with nonusers. Our solution to this dilemma was the use of portions of male hemp stalks *(16)*, devoid of THC, in the placebo cigarettes.

4. In view of the primitive state of knowledge about marihuana, it is difficult to predict which psychological tests will be sensitive to the effects of the drug. The tests we chose were selected because, in addition to being likely to demonstrate effects, they have been used to evaluate many other psychoactive drugs. Of the various physiological parameters available, we chose to measure (i) heart rate, because previous studies have consistently reported increases in heart rate after administration of marihuana (for example, *5*); (ii) respiratory rate, because it is an easily measured vital sign, and depression has been reported *(11, 17)*; (iii) pupil size, because folklore on effects of marihuana consistently includes reports of pupillary dilatation, although objective experimental evidence of an effect of the drug on pupils has not been sought; (iv) conjunctival appearance, because both marihuana smokers and eaters are said to develop red eyes *(11)*; and (v) blood sugar, because hypoglycemia has been invoked as a cause of the hunger and hyperphagia commonly reported by marihuana users, but animal and human evidence of this effect is contradictory *(6, 10, 11)*. [The LaGuardia Report, quoted by Jaffe in Goodman and Gilman *(18)* described hyperglycemia as an effect of acute intoxication.] We did not measure blood pressure because previous studies have failed to demonstrate any consistent effect on blood pressure in man, and we were unwilling to subject our volunteers to a nonessential annoyance.

5. It is necessary to control set and setting. "Set" refers to the subject's psychological expectations of what a drug will do to him in relation to his general personality structure. The total environment in which the drug is taken is the setting. All indications are that the form of marihuana intoxication is particularly dependent on the interaction of drug, set, and setting. Because of recent increases in the extent of use and in attention given this use by the mass media, it is difficult to find subjects with a neutral set toward marihuana. Our method of selecting subjects (described below), at the least, enabled us to identify the subjects' attitudes. Unfortunately, too many researchers have succumbed to the temptation to have subjects take drugs in "psychedelic" environments or have influenced the response to the drug by asking questions that disturb the setting. Even a question as simple as, "How do you feel?" contains an element of suggestion that alters the drug-set-setting interaction. We took great pains to keep our laboratory setting neutral by strict adherence to an experimental timetable and to a prearranged set of conventions governing interactions between subjects and experimenters.

6. Medical, social, ethical, and legal concerns about the welfare of subjects are a major problem in a project of this kind. Is it ethical to introduce people to marihuana? When can subjects safely be sent home from the laboratory? What kind of follow-up care, if any, should be given? These are only a few specific questions with which the investigator must wrestle. Examples of some of the precautions we took are as follows. (i) All subjects were volunteers. All were given psychiatric screening interviews and were clearly informed that they might be asked to smoke marihuana. All nonusers tested were persons who had reported that they had been planning to try marihuana. (ii) All subjects were driven home by an experimenter; they agreed not to engage in unusual activity or operate machinery until the next morning and to report any unusual, delayed effects. (iii) All subjects agreed to report for follow-up interviews 6 months after the experiment. Among other things, the check at 6 months should answer the question whether participation in the experiment encouraged further drug use. (iv) All subjects were protected from possible legal repercussions of their participation in these experiments by specific agreements with the Federal Bureau of Narcotics, the Office of the Attorney General of Massachusetts, and the Massachusetts Bureau of Drug Abuse and Drug Control *(19)*.

SUBJECTS

The central group of subjects consisted of nine healthy, male volunteers, 21 to 26 years of age, all of whom smoked tobacco cigarettes regularly but had never tried marihuana previously. Eight chronic users of marihuana also participated, both to "assay" the quality of marihuana received from the Federal Bureau of Narcotics and to enable the experimenters to standardize the protocol, using subjects familiar with their responses to the drug. The age range for users was also 21 to 26 years. They all smoked marihuana regularly, most of them every day or every other day.

The nine "naive" subjects were selected after a careful screening process. An initial pool of prospective subjects was obtained by placing advertisements in the student newspapers of a number of universities in the Boston area. These advertisements sought "male volunteers, at least 21 years old, for psychological experiments." After nonsmokers were eliminated from this pool, the remaining volunteers were interviewed individually by a psychiatrist who determined their histories of use of alcohol and other intoxicants as well as their general personality types. In addition to serving as a potential screening technique to eliminate volunteers with evidence of psychosis, or of serious mental or personality disorder, these interviews served as the basis for the psychiatrist's prediction of the type of response an individual subject might have after smoking marihuana. (It should be noted that no marihuana-naive volunteer had to be disqualified on psychiatric grounds.) Only after a prospective subject passed the interview was he informed that the "psychological experiment" for which he had volunteered was a marihuana study. If he consented to participate he was asked to sign a release, informing him that he would be "expected to smoke cigarettes containing marihuana or an inert substance." He was also required to agree to a number of conditions, among them that he would "during the course of the experiment take no psychoactive drugs, including alcohol, other than those drugs administered in the course of the experiment."

It proved extremely difficult to find marihuana-naive persons in the student population of Boston, and nearly 2 months of interviewing were required to obtain nine men. All those interviewed who had already tried marihuana volunteered this information quite freely and were delighted to discuss their use of drugs with the psychiatrist. Nearly all persons encountered who had not tried marihuana admitted this somewhat apologetically. Several said they had been meaning to try the drug but had not got around to it. A few said they had no access to it. Only one person cited the current laws as his reason for not having experimented with marihuana. It seemed clear in the interviews that many of these persons were actually afraid of how they might react to marihuana; they therefore welcomed a chance to smoke it under medical supervision. Only one person (an Indian exchange student) who passed the screening interview refused to participate after learning the nature of the experiment.

The eight heavy users of marihuana were obtained with much less difficulty. They were interviewed in the same manner as the other subjects and were instructed not to smoke any marihuana on the day of their appointment in the laboratory.

Subjects were questioned during screening interviews and at the conclusion of the experiments to determine their knowledge of marihuana effects. None of the nine naive subjects had ever watched anyone smoke marihuana or observed anyone high on marihuana. Most of them knew of the effects of the drug only through reports in the popular press. Two subjects had friends who used marihuana frequently; one of these (No. 4) announced his intention to "prove" in the experiments that marihuana really did not do anything; the other (No. 3) was extremely eager to get high because "everyone I know is always talking about it very positively."

SETTING

Greatest effort was made to create a neutral setting. That is, subjects were made comfortable and secure in a pleasant suite of laboratories and offices, but the experimental staff carefully avoided encouraging any person to have an enjoyable experience. Subjects were never asked how they felt, and no subject was permitted to discuss the experiment with the staff until he had completed all four sessions. Verbal interactions between staff and subjects were minimum and formal. At the end of each session, subjects were asked to complete a brief form asking whether they thought they had smoked marihuana that night; if so, whether a high dose or a low dose; and how confident they were of their answers. The experimenters completed forms on each subject.

MARIHUANA

Marihuana used in these experiments was of Mexican origin, supplied by the Federal Bureau of Narcotics (20). It consisted of finely chopped leaves of *Cannabis,* largely free of seeds and stems. An initial batch, which was judged to be of low potency by the experimenters on the basis of the doses needed to produce symptoms of intoxication in the chronic users, was subsequently found to contain only 0.3 percent of THC by weight. A second batch, assayed at 0.9 percent THC, was rated by the chronic users to be "good, average" marihuana, neither exceptionally strong nor exceptionally weak compared to their usual supplies. Users consistently reported symptoms of intoxication after smoking about 0.5 gram of the material with a variation of only a few puffs from subject

Table 1. *Composition of the dose. The placebo cigarette consisted of placebo material, tobacco filler, and mint leaves for masking flavor. The low dose was made up of marihuana, tobacco filler, and mint leaves. The high dose consisted of marihuana and mint leaves.*

Dose	Marihuana in each cigarette (g)	Total dose marihuana (2 cigarettes) (g)	Approximate dose THC
Placebo	—	—	—
Low	0.25	0.5	4.5 mg
High	1.0	2.0	18 mg

to subject. This second batch of marihuana was used in the experiments described below; the low dose was 0.5 gram, and the high dose was 2.0 grams.

All marihuana was administered in the form of cigarettes of standard size made with a hand-operated rolling machine. In any given experimental session, each person was required to smoke two cigarettes in succession (Table 1).

Placebo material consisted of the chopped outer covering of mature stalks of male hemp plants; it contained no THC. All cigarettes had a tiny plug of tobacco at one end and a plug of paper at the other end so that the contents were not visible. The length to which each cigarette was to be smoked was indicated by an ink line. Marihuana and placebos were administered to the naive subjects in double-blind fashion. Scented aerosols were sprayed in the laboratory before smoking, to mask the odor of marihuana. The protocol during an experimental session was as follows. The sessions began at approximately 5.30 p.m.

Time	Procedure
0:00	Physiological measurements; blood sample drawn
0:05	Psychological test battery No. 1 (base line)
0:35	Verbal sample No. 1
0:40	Cigarette smoking
1:00	Rest period
1:15	Physiological measurements; blood sample drawn
1:20	Psychological test battery No. 2
1:50	Verbal sample No. 2
1:55	Rest period (supper)
2:30	Physiological measurements
2:35	Psychological test battery No. 3
3:05	End of testing

Experimental Sessions

Chronic users were tested only on high doses of marihuana with no practice sessions. Each naive subject was required to come to four sessions, spaced about a week apart. The first was always a practice session, in which the subject learned the proper smoking technique and during which he became thoroughly acquainted with the tests and the protocol. In the practice session, each subject completed the entire protocol, smoking two hand-rolled tobacco cigarettes. He was instructed to take a long puff, to inhale deeply, and to maintain inspiration for 20 seconds, as timed by an experimenter with a stopwatch. Subjects were allowed 8 to 12 minutes to smoke each of the two cigarettes. One purpose of this practice smoking was to identify and eliminate individuals who were not tolerant to high doses of nicotine, thus reducing the effect of nicotine on the variables measured during subsequent drug sessions *(21)*. A surprising number (five) of volunteers who had described themselves in screening interviews as heavy cigarette smokers, "inhaling" up to two packs of cigarettes a day, developed acute nicotine reactions when they smoked two tobacco cigarettes by the required method. Occurrence of such a reaction disqualified a subject from participation in the experiments.

In subsequent sessions, when cigarettes contained either drug or placebo, all smoking was similarly supervised by an experimenter with a stopwatch. Subjects were not permitted to smoke tobacco cigarettes while the experiment was in progress. They were assigned to one of the three treatment groups listed in Table 2.

Table 2. *Order of treatment.*

Group	Drug session		
	1	2	3
I	High	Placebo	Low
II	Low	High	Placebo
III	Placebo	Low	High

PHYSIOLOGICAL AND PSYCHOLOGICAL MEASURES

The physiological parameters measured were heart rate, respiratory rate, pupil size, blood glucose level, and conjunctival vascular state. Pupil size was measured with a millimeter rule under constant illumination with eyes focused on an object at constant distance. Conjunctival appearance was rated by an experienced experimenter for dilation of blood vessels on a 0 to 4 scale with ratings of 3 and 4 indicating "significant" vasodilatation. Blood samples were collected for immediate determinations of serum glucose and for the serum to be frozen and stored for possible future biochemical studies. Subjects were asked not to eat and not to imbibe a beverage containing sugar or caffeine during the 4 hours preceding a session. They were given supper after the second blood sample was drawn.

The psychological test battery consisted of (i) the Continuous Performance Test (CPT)—5 minutes; (ii) the Digit Symbol Substitution Test (DSST)—90 seconds; (iii), CPT with strobe light distraction—5 minutes; (iv) self-rating bipolar mood scale—3 minutes; and (v) pursuit rotor—10 minutes.

The Continuous Performance Test was designed to measure a subject's capacity for sustained attention *(22)*. The subject was placed in a darkened room and directed to watch a small screen upon which six letters of the alphabet were flashed rapidly and in random order. The subject was instructed to press a button whenever a specified critical letter appeared. The number of letters presented, correct responses, and errors of commission and omission were counted over the 5-minute period. The test was also done with a strobe light flickering at 50 cycles per second. Normal subjects make no or nearly no errors on this test either with or without strobe distraction; but sleep deprivation, organic brain disease, and certain drugs like chlorpromazine adversely affect performance. Presence or absence of previous exposure to the task has no effect on performance.

The Digit Symbol Substitution Test is a simple test of cognitive function (see Fig. 1). A subject's score was the number of correct answers in a 90-second period. As in the case of the CPT, practice should have little or no effect on performance.

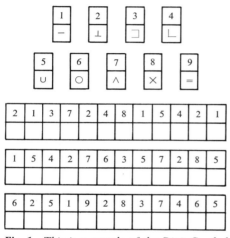

Fig. 1. *This is a sample of the Digit Symbol Substitution Test as used in these studies. On a signal from the examiner the subject was required to fill as many of the empty spaces as possible with the appropriate symbols. The code was always available to the subject during the 90-second administration of the test. [This figure appeared originally in* Psychopharmacologia, *5, 164 (1964).]*

The self-rating bipolar mood scale used in these experiments was one developed by Smith and Beecher *(23)* to evaluate subjective effects of morphine. By allowing subjects to rate themselves within a given category of moods, on an arbitrary scale from +3 to −3, it minimizes suggestion and is thus more neutral than the checklists often employed in drug testing.

The pursuit rotor measures muscular coordination and attention. The subject's task was to keep a stylus in contact with a small spot on a moving turntable. In these experiments, subjects were given ten 30-second trials in each battery. The score for each trial was total time in contact with the spot. There is a marked practice effect on this test, but naive subjects were brought to high levels of performance during their practice session, so that the changes due to practice were reduced during the actual drug sessions. In addition, since there was a different order of treatments for each of the three groups of naive subjects, any session-to-session practice effects were minimized in the statistical analysis of the pooled data.

At the end of the psychological test battery, a verbal sample was collected from each subject. The subject was left alone in a room with a tape recorder and instructions to describe "an interesting or dramatic experience" in his life until he was stopped. After exactly 5 minutes he was interrupted and asked how long he had been in the recording room. In this way, an estimate of the subject's ability to judge time was also obtained.

RESULTS

1. *Safety of marihuana in human volunteers.* In view of the apprehension expressed by many persons over the safety of administering marihuana to research subjects, we wish to emphasize that no adverse marihuana reactions occurred in any of our subjects. In fact, the five acute nicotine reactions mentioned earlier were far more spectacular than any effects produced by marihuana.

In these experiments, observable effects of marihuana were maximum at 15 minutes after smoking. They were diminished between 30 minutes and 1 hour, and they were largely dissipated 3 hours after the end of smoking. No delayed or persistent effects beyond 3 hours were observed or reported.

2. *Intoxicating properties of marihuana in a neutral setting.* With the high dose of marihuana (2.0 grams), all chronic users became "high" *(24)* by their own accounts and in the judgment of experimenters who had observed many persons under the influence of marihuana. The effect was consistent even though prior to the session some of these subjects expressed anxiety about smoking marihuana and submitting to tests in a laboratory.

On the other hand, only one of the nine naive subjects (No. 3) had a definite "marihuana reaction" on the same high dose. He became markedly euphoric and laughed continuously during his first battery of tests after taking the drug. Interestingly, he was the one subject who had expressed his desire to get high.

3. *Comparison of naive and chronic user subjects.* Throughout the experiments it was apparent that the two groups of subjects reacted differently to identical doses of marihuana. We must caution, however, that our study was designed to allow rigorous statistical analysis of data from the naive group—it was not designed to permit formal comparison between chronic users and naive subjects. The conditions of the experiment were not the same for both groups: the chronic users were tested with the drug on their first visit to the laboratory with no practice and were informed that they were to receive high doses of marihuana. Therefore, differences between the chronic and naive groups reported below—although statistically valid—must be regarded as trends to be confirmed or rejected by additional experiments.

4. *Recognition of marihuana versus placebo.* All nine naive subjects reported that they had not been able to identify the taste or smell of marihuana in the

experimental cigarettes. A few subjects remarked that they noticed differences in the taste of the three sets of cigarettes but could not interpret the differences. Most subjects found the pure marihuana cigarettes (high dose) more mild than the low dose or placebo cigarettes, both of which contained tobacco.

The subjects' guesses of the contents of cigarettes for their three sessions are presented in Table 3. It is noteworthy that one of the two subjects who called the high dose a placebo was the subject (No. 4) who had told us he wanted to prove that marihuana really did nothing. There were three outstanding findings: (i) most subjects receiving marihuana in either high or low dose recognized that they were getting a drug; (ii) most subjects receiving placebos recognized that they were receiving placebos; (iii) most subjects called their high dose a low dose, but none called his low dose a high dose, emphasizing the unimpressiveness of their subjective reactions.

Table 3. *Subjects' appraisal of the dose.*

Actual dose	Guessed dose			Fraction correct
	Placebo	Low	High	
Placebo	8	1	—	$\frac{8}{9}$
Low	3	6	—	$\frac{6}{9}$
High	2	6	1	$\frac{1}{9}$

5. *Effect of marihuana on heart rate.* The mean changes in heart rate from base-line rates before smoking the drug to rates at 15 and 90 minutes after smoking marihuana and placebo (Table 4) were tested for significance at the .05 level by an analysis of variance; Tukey's method was applied for all possible comparisons (Table 5). In the naive subjects, marihuana in low dose or high dose was followed by increased heart rate 15 minutes after smoking, but the effect was not demonstrated to be dose-dependent. The high dose caused a statistically greater increase in the heart rates of chronic users than in those of the naive subjects 15 minutes after smoking.

Two of the chronic users had unusually low resting pulse rates (56 and 42), but deletion of these two subjects (No. 11 and No. 15) still gave a significant difference in mean pulse rise of chronic users compared to naives. Because the conditions of the sessions and experimental design were not identical for the two groups, we prefer to report this difference as a trend that must be confirmed by further studies.

6. *Effect of marihuana on respiratory rate.* In the naive group, there was no change in respiratory rate before and after smoking marihuana. Chronic users showed a small but statistically significant increase in respiratory rate after smoking, but we do not regard the change as clinically significant.

Table 4. *Change in heart rate (beat/min) after smoking the test material. Results are recorded as a change from the base line 15 minutes and 90 minutes after the smoking session.*

Subject	15 Minutes			90 Minutes		
	Placebo	Low	High	Placebo	Low	High
Naive subjects						
1	+16	+20	+16	+20	− 6	− 4
2	+12	+24	+12	− 6	+ 4	− 8
3	+ 8	+ 8	+26	− 4	+ 4	+ 8
4	+20	+ 8			+20	− 4
5	+ 8	+ 4	− 8		+22	− 8
6	+10	+20	+28	−20	− 4	− 4
7	+ 4	+28	+24	+12	+ 8	+18
8	− 8	+20	+24	− 3	+ 8	−24
9		+20	+24	+ 8	+12	
Mean	+ 7.8	+16.9	+16.2	+ 0.8	+ 7.6	− 2.9
S.E.	2.8	2.7	4.2	3.8	3.2	3.8
Chronic subjects						
10		+32			+ 4	
11		+36			+36	
12		+20			+12	
13		+ 8			+ 4	
14		+32			+12	
15		+54			+22	
16		+24				
17		+60				
Mean		+33.2			+15.0	
S.E.		6.0			5.0	

Table 5 *Significance of differences (at the .05 level) in heart rate. Results of Tukey's test for all possible comparisons.*

Comparison	15 Minutes	90 Minutes
Low dose versus placebo	Significant	Significant
High dose versus placebo	Significant	Not significant
Low dose versus high dose	Not significant	Significant
Chronic users versus high dose	Significant	Significant

Table 6. *Significance of differences (at the .05 level) for the Digit Symbol Substitution Test. Results of Tukey's test for all possible comparisons.*

Comparison	15 Minutes	90 Minutes
Low dose versus placebo	Significant	Significant
High dose versus placebo	Significant	Significant
Low dose versus high dose	Significant	Not significant
Chronic users versus high dose	Significant	Significant

7. *Effect of marihuana on pupil size.* There was no change in pupil size before and after smoking marihuana in either group.

8. *Effect of marihuana on conjunctival appearance.* Significant reddening of conjunctivae due to dilatation of blood vessels occurred in one of nine subjects receiving placebo, three of nine receiving the low dose of marihuana, and eight of nine receiving the high dose. It occurred in all eight of the chronic users receiving the high dose and was rated as more prominent in them. The effect was more pronounced 15 minutes after the smoking period than 90 minutes after it.

9 . *Effect of marihuana on blood sugar.* There was no significant change in blood sugar levels after smoking marihuana in either group.

10. *Effect of marihuana on the Continuous Performance Test.* Performance on the CPT and on the CPT with strobe distraction was unaffected by marihuana for both groups of subjects.

11. *Effect of marihuana on the Digit Symbol Substitution Test.* The significance of the differences in mean changes of scores at the .05 level was determined by an analysis of variance by means of Tukey's method for all possible comparisons. Results of these tests are summarized in Tables 6 and 7.

The results indicate that: (i) Decrements in performance of naive subjects following low and high doses of marihuana were significant at 15 and 90 minutes after smoking. (ii) The decrement following marihuana was greater after high dose than after low dose at 15 minutes after taking the drug, giving preliminary evidence of a dose-response relationship. (iii) Chronic users started with good base-line performance and improved slightly on the DSST after smoking 2.0 grams of marihuana, whereas performance of the naive subjects was grossly impaired. Experience with the DSST suggests that absence of impairment in chronic users cannot be accounted for solely by a practice effect. Still, because of the different procedures employed, we prefer to report this difference as a trend.

12. *Effect of marihuana on pursuit rotor performance.* This result is presented in Table 8. Again applying Tukey's method in an analysis of variance, we tested differences in mean changes in scores (Table 9). Decrements in performance of naive subjects after both low and high doses of marihuana were significant at 15 and 90 minutes. This effect on performance followed a dose-response relation

Table 7. *Digit Symbol Substitution Test. Change in scores from base line (number correct) 15 and 90 minutes after the smoking session.*

Subject	15 Minutes			90 Minutes		
	Placebo	Low	High	Placebo	Low	High
	Naive subjects					
1	− 3	—	+ 5	− 7	+ 4	+ 8
2	+10	− 8	−17	− 1	−15	− 5
3	− 3	+ 6	− 7	−10	+ 2	− 1
4	+ 3	− 4	− 3		− 7	
5	+ 4	+ 1	− 7	+ 6		− 8
6	− 3	− 1	− 9	+ 3	− 5	−12
7	+ 2	− 4	− 6	+ 3	− 5	− 4
8	− 1	+ 3	+ 1	+ 4	+ 4	− 3
9	− 1	− 4	− 3	+ 6	− 1	−10
Mean	+ 0.9	− 1.2	− 5.1	+ 0.4	− 2.6	− 3.9
S.E.	1.4	1.4	2.1	1.9	2.0	2.0
	Chronic users					
10		− 4				−16
11		+ 1				+ 6
12		+11				+18
13		+ 3				+ 4
14		− 2				− 3
15		− 6				+ 8
16		− 4				
17		+ 3				
Mean		+ 0.25				+ 2.8
S.E.		1.9				4.7

on testing batteries conducted at both 15 minutes and 90 minutes after the drug was smoked.

All chronic users started from good baselines and improved on the pursuit rotor after smoking marihuana. These data are not presented, however, because it is probable that the improvement was largely a practice effect.

13. *Effect of marihuana on time estimation.* Before smoking, all nine naive subjects estimated the 5-minute verbal sample to be 5 ± 2 minutes. After placebo, no subject changed his guess. After the low dose, three subjects raised their estimates to 10 ± 2 minutes, and after the high dose, four raised their estimates.

14. *Subjective effects of marihuana.* When questioned at the end of their participation in the experiment, persons who had never taken marihuana previously reported minimum subjective effects after smoking the drug, or, more precisely, few effects like those commonly reported by chronic users. Nonusers reported

Table 8. *Pursuit rotor (naive subjects). Changes in scores (averages of ten trials) from base line (seconds).*

Subject	15 Minutes			90 Minutes		
	Placebo	Low	High	Placebo	Low	High
1	+1.20	−1.04	−4.01	+1.87	−1.54	−6.54
2	+0.89	−1.43	−0.12	+0.52	+0.44	−0.68
3	+0.50	−0.60	−6.56	+0.84	−0.96	−4.34
4	+0.18	−0.11	+0.11	+0.06	+1.95	−1.37
5	+3.20	+0.39	+0.13	+2.64	+3.33	+0.34
6	+3.45	−0.32	−3.46	+2.93	+0.22	−2.26
7	+0.81	+0.48	−0.79	+0.63	+0.16	−0.52
8	+1.75	−0.39	−0.92	+2.13	+0.40	+1.02
9	+3.90	−1.94	−2.60	+3.11	−0.97	−3.09
Mean	+1.8	−0.6	−2.0	+1.6	+0.3	−1.9
S.E.	0.5	0.3	0.8	0.4	0.5	0.8

Table 9. *Significance of differences (at the .05 level) for the pursuit rotor. Results of Tukey's test for all possible comparisons, 15 and 90 minutes after the smoking session.*

Comparison	15 Minutes	90 Minutes
Low dose versus placebo	Significant	Significant
High dose versus placebo	Significant	Significant
Low dose versus high dose	Significant	Significant

little euphoria, no distortion of visual or auditory perception, and no confusion. However, several subjects mentioned that "things seemed to take longer." Below are examples of comments by naive subjects after high doses.

Subject 1. "It was stronger than the previous time (low dose) but I really didn't think it could be marihuana. Things seemed to go slower."

Subject 2. "I think I realize why they took our watches. There was a sense of the past disappearing as happens when you're driving too long without sleeping. With a start you wake up to realize you were asleep for an instant; you discover yourself driving along the road. It was the same tonight with eating a sandwich. I'd look down to discover I'd just swallowed a bite but I hadn't noticed it at the time."

Subject 6. "I felt a combination of being almost-drunk and tired, with occasional fits of silliness—not my normal reaction to smoking tobacco."

Subject 8. "I felt faint briefly, but the dizziness went away, and I felt normal or slightly tired. I can't believe I had a high dose of marihuana."

Subject 9. "Time seemed very drawn out. I would keep forgetting what I was doing, especially on the continuous performance test, but somehow every time an "X" (the critical letter) came up, I found myself pushing the button."

After smoking their high dose, chronic users were asked to rate themselves on a scale of 1 to 10, 10 representing "the highest you've ever been." All subjects placed themselves between 7 and 10, most at 8 or 9. Many of these subjects expressed anxiety at the start of their first battery of tests after smoking the drug when they were feeling very high. Then they expressed surprise during and after the tests when they judged (correctly) that their performance was as good as or better than it had been before taking the drug.

15. The effect of marihuana on the self-rating mood scale, the effect of marihuana on a 5-minute verbal sample, and the correlation of personality type with subjective effects of marihuana will be reported separately.

DISCUSSION

Several results from this study raise important questions about the action of marihuana and suggest directions for future research. Our finding that subjects who were naive to marihuana did not become subjectively "high" after a high dose of marihuana in a neutral setting is interesting when contrasted with the response of regular users who consistently reported and exhibited highs. It agrees with the reports of chronic users that many, if not most, people do not become high on their first exposure to marihuana even if they smoke it correctly. This puzzling phenomenon can be discussed from either a physiological or psychosocial point of view. Neither interpretation is entirely satisfactory. The physiological hypothesis suggests that getting high on marihuana occurs only after some sort of pharmacological sensitization takes place. The psychosocial interpretation is that repeated exposure to marihuana reduces psychological inhibition, as part of, or as the result of a learning process.

Indirect evidence makes the psychological hypothesis attractive. Anxiety about drug use in this country is sufficiently great to make worthy of careful consideration the possibility of an unconscious psychological inhibition or block on the part of naive drug takers. The subjective responses of our subjects indicate that they had imagined a marihuana effect to be much more profoundly disorganizing than what they experienced. For example, subject No. 4, who started with a bias against the possibility of becoming high on marihuana, was able to control subjectively the effect of the drug and report that he had received a placebo when he had actually gotten a high dose. As anxiety about the drug is lessened with experience, the block may decrease, and the subject may permit himself to notice the drug's effects.

It is well known that marihuana users, in introducing friends to the drug, do actually "teach" them to notice subtle effects of the drug on consciousness *(25)*. The apparently enormous influence of set and setting on the form of the marihuana response is consistent with this hypothesis, as is the testimony of users that, as use becomes more frequent, the amount of drug required to produce intoxication decreases—a unique example of "reverse tolerance." (Regular use of many intoxicants is accompanied by the need for increasing doses to achieve the same effects.)

On the other hand, the suggestion arising from this study that users and nonusers react differently to the drug, not only subjectively but also physiologically, increases the plausibility of the pharmacological-sensitization hypothesis. Of course, reverse tolerance could equally well be a manifestation of this sensitization.

It would be useful to confirm the suggested differences between users and nonusers and then to test in a systematic manner the hypothetical explanations of the phenomenon. One possible approach would be to continue to administer high doses of marihuana to the naive subjects according to the protocol described. If subjects begin reporting high responses to the drug only after several exposures, in the absence of psychedelic settings, suggestions, or manipulations of mood, then the likelihood that marihuana induces a true psysiological sensitization or that experience reduces psychological inhibitions, permitting real drug effects to appear, would be increased. If subjects fail to become high, we could conclude that learning to respond to marihuana requires some sort of teaching or suggestion.

An investigation of the literature of countries where anxieties over drug use are less prominent would be useful. If this difference between responses of users and nonusers is a uniquely American phenomenon, a psychological explanation would be indicated, although it would not account for greater effects with smaller doses after the initial, anxiety-reducing stage.

One impetus for reporting the finding of differences between chronic and naive subjects on some of the tests, despite the fact that the experimental designs were not the same, is that this finding agrees with the statements of many users. They say that the effects of marihuana are easily suppressed—much more so than those of alcohol. Our observation, that the chronic users after smoking marihuana performed on some tests as well as or better than they did before taking the drug, reinforced the argument advanced by chronic users that maintaining effective levels of performance for many tasks—driving, for example *(26)* —is much easier under the influence of marihuana than under that of other psychoactive drugs. Certainly the surprise that the chronic users expressed when they found they were performing more effectively on the CPT, DSST, and pursuit rotor tests than they thought they would is remarkable. It is quite the opposite of the false sense of improvement subjects have under some psychoactive drugs that actually impair performance.

What might be the basis of this suppressibility? Possibly, the actions of marihuana are confined to higher cortical functions without any general stimulatory or depressive effect on lower brain centers. The relative absence of neurological—as opposed to psychiatric—symptoms in marihuana intoxication suggests this possibility *(7)*.

Our failure to detect any changes in blood sugar levels of subjects after they had smoked marihuana forces us to look elsewhere for an explanation of the hunger and hyperphagia commonly reported by users. A first step would be careful interviewing of users to determine whether they really become hungry after smoking marihuana or whether they simply find eating more pleasurable. Possibly, the basis of this effect is also central rather than due to some peripheral physiological change.

Lack of any change in pupil size of subjects after they had smoked marihuana is an enlightening finding especially because so many users and law-enforcement agents firmly believe that marihuana dilates pupils. (Since users generally observe each other in dim surroundings, it is not surprising that they see large pupils.) This negative finding emphasizes the need for data from carefully controlled investigations rather than from casual observation or anecdotal reports in the evaluation of marihuana. It also agrees with the findings of others that synthetic THC does not alter pupil size *(8, 27)*.

Finally, we would like to comment on the fact that marihuana appears to be a relatively mild intoxicant in our studies. If these results seem to differ from those of earlier experiments, it must be remembered that other experimenters have given marihuana orally, have given doses much higher than those commonly smoked by users, have administered potent synthetics, and have not strictly controlled the laboratory setting. As noted in our introduction, more powerful effects are often reported by users who ingest preparations of marihuana. This may mean that some active constituents which enter the body when the drug is ingested are destroyed by combustion, a suggestion that must be investigated in man. Another priority consideration is the extent to which synthetic THC reproduces marihuana intoxication—a problem that must be resolved before marihuana research proceeds with THC instead of the natural resin of the whole plant.

The set, both of subjects and experimenters, and the setting must be recognized as critical variables in studies of marihuana. Drug, set, and setting interact to shape the form of a marihuana reaction. The researcher who sets out with prior conviction that hemp is psychotomimetic or a "mild hallucinogen" is likely to confirm his conviction experimentally *(10)*, but he would probably confirm the opposite hypothesis if his bias were in the opposite direction. Precautions to insure neutrality of set and setting, including use of a double-blind procedure as an absolute minimum, are vitally important if the object of investigation is to measure real marihuana-induced responses.

CONCLUSIONS

1. It is feasible and safe to study the effects of marihuana on human volunteers who smoke it in a laboratory.

2. In a neutral setting persons who are naive to marihuana do not have strong subjective experiences after smoking low or high doses of the drug, and the

effects they do report are not the same as those described by regular users of marihuana who take the drug in the same neutral setting.

3. Marihuana-naive persons do demonstrate impaired performance on simple intellectual and psychomotor tests after smoking marihuana; the impairment is dose-related in some cases.

4. Regular users of marihuana do get high after smoking marihuana in a neutral setting but do not show the same degree of impairment of performance on the tests as do naive subjects. In some cases, their performance even appears to improve slightly after smoking marihuana.

5. Marihuana increases heart rate moderately.

6. No change in respiratory rate follows administration of marihuana by inhalation.

7. No change in pupil size occurs in short term exposure to marihuana.

8. Marihuana administration causes dilatation of conjunctival blood vessels.

9. Marihuana treatment produces no change in blood sugar levels.

10. In a neutral setting the physiological and psychological effects of a single, inhaled dose of marihuana appear to reach maximum intensity within one-half hour of inhalation, to be diminished after 1 hour, and to be completely dissipated by 3 hours.

REFERENCES AND NOTES

1. R. J. Bouquet, *Bull. Narcotics* **2**, 14 (1950).

2. F. Korte and H. Sieper, in *Hashish: Its Chemistry and Pharmacology*, G. E. W. Wolstenholme and J. Knight, Eds. (Little, Brown, Boston, 1965), pp. 15–30.

3. Task Force on Narcotics and Drug Abuse, the President's Commission on Law Enforcement and the Administration of Justice, *Task Force Report: Narcotics and Drug Abuse* (1967), p. 14.

4. R. Mechoulam, and Y. Gaoni, *J. Amer. Chem. Soc.* **67**, 3273 (1965).

5. J. F. Siler, W. L. Sheep, L. B. Bates, G. F. Clark, G. W. Cook, W. A. Smith, *Mil. Surg.* (November 1933), pp. 269–280.

6. Mayor's Committee on Marihuana, *The Marihuana Problem in the City of New York*, 1944.

7. E. G. Williams, C. K. Himmelsbach, A. Winkler, D. C. Ruble, B. J. Lloyd, *Public Health Rep.* **61**, 1059 (1946).

8. H. Isbell, *Psychopharmacologia* **11**, 184 (1967).

9. I. C. Chopra and R. N. Chopra, *Bull. Narcotics* **9**, 4 (1957).

10. F. Ames, *J. Ment. Sci.* **104**, 972 (1958).

11. C. J. Miras, in *Hashish: Its Chemistry and Pharmacology*, G. E. W. Wolstenholme and J. Knight, Eds. (Little, Brown, Boston, 1965), pp. 37–47.

12. J. M. Watt, in *Hashish: Its Chemistry and Pharmacology*, G. E. W. Wolstenholme and J. Knight, Eds. (Little, Brown, Boston, 1965), pp. 54–66.

13. AMA Council on Mental Health, *J. Amer. Med. Ass.* **204**, 1181 (1968).

14. G. Joachimoglu, in *Hashish: Its Chemistry and Pharmacology*, G. E. W. Wolstenholme and J. Knight, Eds. (Little, Brown, Boston, 1965), pp. 2–10.

15. We thank M. Lerner and A. Bober of the U.S. Customs Laboratory, Baltimore, for performing this assay.

16. We thank R. H. Pace and E. H. Hall of the Peter J. Schweitzer Division of the Kimberly-Clark Corp. for supplying placebo material.

17. S. Garattini, in *Hashish: Its Chemistry and Pharmacology*, G. E. W. Wolstenholme and J. Knight, Eds. (Little, Brown, Boston, 1965), pp. 70–78.

18. J. H. Jaffee, in *The Pharmacological Basis of Therapeutics*, L. S. Goodman and A. Gilman, Eds. (Macmillan, New York, ed. 3, 1965), pp. 299–301.

19. We thank E. L. Richardson, Attorney General of the Commonwealth of Massachusetts for permitting these experiments to proceed and N. L. Chayet for legal assistance. We do not consider it appropriate to describe here the opposition we encountered from governmental agents and agencies and from university bureaucracies.

20. We thank D. Miller and M. Seifer of the Federal Bureau of Narcotics (now part of the Bureau of Narcotics and Dangerous Drugs, under the Department of Justice) for help in obtaining marihuana for this research.

21. The doses of tobacco in placebo and low-dose cigarettes were too small to cause physiological changes in subjects who qualified in the practice session.

22. K. E. Rosvold, A. F. Mirsky, I. Sarason, E. D. Bransome, L. H. Beck, *J. Consult. Psychol.* **20**, 343 (1956); A. F. Mirsky and P. V. Cardon, *Electroencephalogr. Clin. Neurophysiol.* **14**, 1 (1962); C. Kornetsky and G. Bain, *Psychopharmacologia* **8**, 277 (1965).

23. G. M. Smith and H. K. Beecher, *J. Pharmacol.* **126**, 50 (1959).

24. We will attempt to define the complex nature of a marihuana high in a subsequent paper discussing the speech samples and interviews.

25. H. S. Becker, *Outsiders: Studies in the Sociology of Deviance* (Macmillan, New York, 1963), chap. 3.

26. Although the motor skills measured by the pursuit rotor are represented in driving ability, they are only components of that ability. The influence of marihuana on driving skill remains an open question of high medico-legal priority.

27. L. E. Hollister, R. K. Richards, H. K. Gillespie, in preparation.

28. Sponsored and supported by Boston University's division of psychiatry, in part through PHS grants MH12568, MH06795-06, MH7753-06, and MH33319, and the Boston University Medical Center. The authors thank Dr. P. H. Knapp and Dr. C. Kornetsky of the Boston University School of Medicine, Department of Psychiatry and Pharmacology, for consistent support and excellent advice, and J. Finkelstein of 650 Madison Avenue, New York City, for his support at a crucial time.

Section II
The Cell and
General Physiology

Introduction

The papers in this section are concerned with two seemingly different, but actually closely related, topics: (1) cell structure and function, and (2) general organ physiology.

In the middle of the nineteenth century it became increasingly clear that organisms were composed of specific building blocks, or units, which came to be called *cells*. In the famous "cell theory" of Schleiden and Schwann of 1839, the generalization was advanced that the cells of all organisms represent modifications of the same basic unit structure. Schwann, in his book, a portion of which is given here, compared his own careful observations on animal cells with the equally detailed studies of plant cells by Schleiden. Schwann went on to develop a theory of how cells reproduce by a process similar to the formation of inorganic crystals.

Approximately twenty years later Rudolf Virchow showed that the cell was not only a structural unit (as Schleiden and Schwann had emphasized), but was also a functional, physiological unit (a point at which the earlier authors had only hinted). A physician, and most particularly a pathologist, Virchow showed that the cell was more than the unit of normal function; it was also the unit of malfunction, or, in other words, disease. Believing that cells were highly organized collections of molecules which functioned in a specific manner, Virchow saw disease as an interruption in normal molecular interactions. Physicians and physiologists must look to the cell, he claimed, for an understanding of disease, even though the visible effects of the disease seem to be widespread throughout various organs and tissues. Virchow added to the largely structural concepts of Schwann (and Schleiden) a strong emphasis on the cell as a functional (physiological) unit.

The cell theory pointed out to physiologists during the latter half of the nineteenth century that the function of the whole organism can best be under-stood in terms of the function of the cells of which it is composed. The remaining papers in this section deal with particular aspects of physiology—gastric digestion, muscle contractility, and nerve reflexes—which in themselves do not relate specifically to the cell theory. Yet one can more thoroughly understand the conclusions reached by recognizing that at the basis of each phenomenon lie chemical and physical reactions which occur ultimately within living cells. Although working at different levels of organization, the authors of all the papers in this section are asking the same kinds of questions. They are concerned with how specifically defined biological units (cells, individual organs such as the stomach, or groups of tissues such as a reflex pathway) function in a physical and chemical manner. Beaumont's study on the stomach is the least overt in this regard; Galvani's and Pavlov's experiments are the most.

Attempts to understand the function of various organs of digestion, particularly the stomach, have been common since the early Greeks. However, most of the early results were based on anatomical studies of the structure of the stomach (or other organs) and deductions from this about function. It is obvious that such a method has its limitations, since the structure of many organs is not in any *a priori* way related to their function. Therefore, the work of Réaumur is particularly interesting, not only as a means of understanding how, in live organisms, the stomach affects various kinds of food, but also because of the ingenious, if bizarre, experimental techniques he chose. His work represents one of the first attempts to perform systematically a set of experiments on digestion in a living animal. Réaumur's studies on the buzzard are complemented by Beaumont's later studies, with his equally dramatic observations on his patient, Alexis St. Martin. The victim of a nearly fatal gun shot wound in the abdomen, St. Martin was left with a direct opening through the abdominal and stomach walls. By removing the bandage which covered the wound and which therefore prevented the food from spilling out, Beaumont could insert samples of various types of food into the stomach and observe *in vivo* the effects of gastric juice on each. His experiments extended earlier conclusions on animals to man himself.

The middle and late eighteenth century was a time of increasing enthusiasm for the study of electrical phenomena. In the 1750's and 1760's Benjamin Franklin had developed his electrical theory, and in many sophisticated circles the famous Leyden jar, or what we today would call an electrical condenser (see the description in the footnote on page 83), had become a popular plaything. Slightly later, in the 1790's, Luigi Galvani came to recognize accidentally that discharges from an electrical machine (i.e., a machine for generating static electricity) would cause a living nerve-muscle preparation to react; i.e., the muscles would contract. From this simple and marvelous occurrence, Galvani began to study the phenomenon known as "animal electricity." The much-feared electrical activity of the torpedo fish and the electrical eel was known to Galvani, and he was curious to know whether all living tissue showed an inherent electrical activity. Did the nerve-muscle preparation respond only to machine-generated electricity, or would atmospheric electricity (lightning) stimulate it as well? Why did the muscle respond to machine-generated electricity at some times and not at others? Was the electricity generated by the torpedo the same as that generated by lightning or by the electrical machine? Running throughout Galvani's experiments was his desire to show the relationship between these phenomena. This is nowhere more apparent than in his comparison of the frog muscle, or the torpedo, to a Leyden jar. For Galvani, the comparison was more than illustrative. He was seeking the operation of universal principles which carried from the physical to the biological world. Yet his experimental results did not lead him to firm conclusions on some of these questions, and he judiciously refrained from sheer speculation. Galvani's approach, like that of Ivan Pavlov in the next paper, was based on the attempt to understand biological phenomena in mechanistic and physical terms.

The final article in this section is from Pavlov's lectures on the nature and function of nerve reflex arcs. Though based on less simplistic physical analogies than the work of Galvani, Pavlov's approach was also highly mechanistic in both conception and execution. Pavlov was one of the outstanding physiologists of the late nineteenth and early twentieth centuries. For his studies on the nervous control of salivary secretion he was awarded the Nobel prize in medicine for 1904. From this work eventually came his equally significant studies on the conditioned reflex, described in detail in the paper reprinted here. The concept of reflex conditioning became a cornerstone not only for later studies in neural physiology, but also for the study of psychology.

These papers can be used principally with Chapters 6, 7, 10, and 11 of *The Study of Biology*.

Microscopical Researches into the Accordance in the Structure and Growth of Animals and Plants

by THEODOR SCHWANN

GENERAL RETROSPECT

When organic nature, animals and plants, is regarded as a Whole, in contradistinction to the inorganic kingdom, we do not find that all organisms and all their separate organs are compact masses, but that they are composed of innumerable small particles of a definite form. These elementary particles, however, are subject to the most extraordinary diversity of figure, especially in animals; in plants they are, for the most part or exclusively, cells. This variety in the elementary parts seemed to hold some relation to their more diversified physiological function in animals, so that it might be established as a principle, that every diversity in the physiological signification of an organ requires a difference in its elementary particles; and, on the contrary, the similarity of two elementary particles seemed to justify the conclusion that they were physiologically similar. It was natural that among the very different forms presented by the elementary particles, there should be some more or less alike, and that they might be divided, according to their similarity of figure, into fibres, which compose the great mass of the bodies of animals, into cells, tubes, globules, &c. The division was, of course, only one of natural history, not expressive of any physiological idea, and just as a primitive muscular fibre, for example, might seem to differ from one of areolar tissue, or all fibres from cells, so would there be in like manner a difference, however gradually marked between the different kinds of cells. It seemed as if the organism arranged the molecules in the definite forms exhibited by its different elementary particles, in the way required by its physiological function. It might be expected that there would be a definite mode of development for each separate kind of elementary structure, and that it would be similar in those structures which were physiologically identical, and such a mode of development was, indeed, already more or less perfectly known with regard to muscular fibres, blood-corpuscles, the ovum (see the Supplement), and epithelium-cells. The only

Abridged from Theodor Schwann, *Microscopical Researches into the Accordance in the Structure and Growth of Animals and Plants,* trans. Henry Smith (London: The Sydenham Society, 1847), Section III.

process common to all of them, however, seemed to be the expansion of their elementary particles after they had once assumed their proper form. The manner in which their different elementary particles were first formed appeared to vary very much. In muscular fibres they were globules, which were placed together in rows, and coalesced to form a fibre, whose growth proceeded in the direction of its length. In the blood-corpuscles it was a globule, around which a vesicle was formed, and continued to grow; in the case of the ovum, it was a globule, around which a vesicle was developed and continued to grow, and around this again a second vesicle was formed.

The formative process of the cells of plants was clearly explained by the researches of Schleiden, and appeared to be the same in all vegetable cells. So that when plants were regarded as something special, as quite distinct from the animal kingdom, one universal principle of development was observed in all the elementary particles of the vegetable organism, and physiological deductions might be drawn from it with regard to the independent vitality of the individual cells of plants, &c. But when the elementary particles of animals and plants were considered from a common point, the vegetable cells seemed to be merely a separate species, co-ordinate with the different species of animal cells, just as the entire class of cells was co-ordinate with the fibres, &c., and the uniform principle of development in vegetable cells might be explained by the slight physiological difference of their elementary particles.

The object, then, of the present investigation was to show that the mode in which the molecules composing the elementary particles of organisms are combined does not vary according to the physiological signification of those particles, but that they are everywhere arranged according to the same laws; so that whether a muscular fibre, a nerve-tube, an ovum, or a blood-corpuscle is to be formed, a corpuscle of a certain form, subject only to some modifications, a cell-nucleus, is universally generated in the first instance; around this corpuscle a cell is developed, and it is the changes which one or more of these cells undergo that determine the subsequent forms of the elementary particles; in short, that there is one common principle of development for all the elementary particles of organisms.

In order to establish this point it was necessary to trace the progress of development in two given elementary parts, physiologically dissimilar, and to compare them with one another. If these not only completely agreed in growth, but in their mode of generation also, the principle was established that elementary parts, quite distinct in a physiological sense, may be developed according to the same laws. This was the theme of the first section of this work. The course of development of the cells of cartilage and of the cells of the chorda dorsalis was compared with that of vegetable cells. Were the cells of plants developed merely as infinitely minute vesicles which progressively expand, were the circumstances of their development less characteristic than those pointed out by Schleiden, a comparison, in the sense here required, would scarcely have been possible. We endeavoured to prove in the first section that the complicated process of development in the cells of plants recurs in those of cartilage and of the chorda dorsalis. We remarked the similarity in the formation of the cell-nucleus, and of its nucleolus in all its modifications, with the nucleus of vegetable cells, the pre-existence of the cell-nucleus and the development of the cell around it, the similar situation of the nucleus in relation to the cell, the growth of the cells, and the thickening of their wall during growth, the formation of cells within cells, and the transformation of the cell-contents just as in the cells of plants. Here, then, was a complete accordance in every known stage in the progress of development of two elementary parts which are quite distinct, in a physiological sense, and it was established that the principle of development in two such parts may be the same, and so far as could be ascertained in the cases here compared, it is really the same.

But regarding the subject from this point of view we are compelled to prove the universality of this principle of development, and such was the object of the second section. For so long as we admit that there are elementary parts which originate according to entirely different laws, and between which and the cells which have just been compared as to the principle of their development there is no connexion, we must presume that there may still be some unknown difference in the laws of the formation of the parts just compared, even though they agree in many points. But, on the contrary, the greater the number of physiologically different elementary parts, which, so far as can be known, originate in a similar manner, and the greater the difference of these parts in form and physiological signification, while they agree in the perceptible phenomena of their mode of formation, the more safely may we assume that all elementary parts have one and the same fundamental principle of development. It was, in fact, shown that the elementary parts of most tissues, when traced backwards from their state of complete development to their primary condition are only developments of cells, which so far as our observations, still incomplete, extend, seemed to be formed in a similar manner to the cells compared in the first section. As might be expected, according to this principle the cells, in their earliest stage, were almost always furnished with the characteristic nuclei, in some the pre-existence of this nucleus, and the formation of the cell around it was proved, and it was then that the cells began to undergo the various modifications, from which the diverse forms of the elementary parts of animals resulted. Thus the apparent difference in the mode of development of muscular fibres and blood-corpuscles, the former originating by the arrangement of globules in rows, the latter by the formation of a vesicle around a globule, was reconciled in the fact that muscular fibres are not elementary parts co-ordinate with blood-corpuscles, but that the globules composing muscular fibres at first correspond to the blood-corpuscles, and are like them, vesicles or cells, containing the characteristic cell-nucleus, which, like the nucleus of the blood-corpuscles, is probably formed before the cell. The elementary parts of all tissues are formed of cells in an analogous, though very diversified manner, so that it may be asserted, *that there is one universal principle of development for the elementary parts of organisms, however different, and that this principle is the formation of cells.* This is the chief result of the foregoing observations.

The same process of development and transformation of cells within a structureless substance is repeated in the formation of all the organs of an organism, as well as in the formation of new organisms; and the fundamental phenomenon attending the exertion of productive power in organic nature is accordingly as follows: *a structureless substance is present in the first instance, which lies either around or in the interior of cells already existing; and cells are formed in it in accordance with certain laws, which cells become developed in various ways into the elementary parts of organisms.*

The development of the proposition, that there exists one general principle for the formation of all organic productions, and that this principle is the formation of cells, as well as the conclusions which may be drawn from this proposition, may be comprised under the term *cell-theory*, using it in its more extended signification, whilst in a more limited sense, by theory of the cells we understand whatever may be inferred from this proposition with respect to the powers from which these phenomena result.

But though this principle, regarded as the direct result of these more or less complete observations, may be stated to be generally correct, it must not be concealed that there are some exceptions, or at least differences, which as yet remain unexplained. Such, for instance, is the splitting into fibres of the walls of the cells in the interior of the chorda dorsalis of osseous[1] fishes. . . . Several observers have also drawn attention to the fibrous structure of the firm substance of some cartilages. In the costal cartilages of old persons for example, these fibres are very distinct. They do not, however, seem to be uniformly diffused throughout the cartilage, but to be scattered merely here and there. I have not observed them at all in new-born children. It appears as if the previously structureless cytoblastema in this instance became split into fibres; I have not, however, investigated the point accurately. Our observations also fail to supply us with any explanation of the formation of the medullary canaliculi in bones, and an analogy between their mode of origin and that of capillary vessels, was merely suggested hypothetically. The formation of bony lamellae around these canaliculi is also an instance of the cytoblastema assuming a distinct form. But we will return presently to an explanation of this phenomenon that is not altogether improbable. In many glands, as for instance, the kidneys of a young mammalian fœtus, the stratum of cells surrounding the cavity of the duct, is enclosed by an exceedingly delicate membrane, which appears to be an elementary structure, and not to be composed of areolar tissue. The origin of this membrane is not at all clear, although we may imagine various ways of reconciling it with the formative process of cells. (These gland-cylinders seem at first to have no free cavity, but to be quite filled with cells. In the kidneys of the embryos of pigs, I found many cells in the cylinders, which were so large as to occupy almost the entire thickness of the canal. In other cylinders, the cellular layer, which was subsequently to line their walls, was formed, but the cavity was filled with very pale transparent cells, which could be pressed out from the free end of the tube.)

---

[1] Osseous means bony. Chorda dorsalis refers to the spinal cord of vertebrates. [*Eds.*]

These and similar phenomena may remain for a time unexplained. Although they merit the greatest attention and require further investigations, we may be allowed to leave them for a moment, for history shows that in the laying down of every general principle, there are almost always anomalies at first, which are subsequently cleared up.

The elementary particles of organisms, then, no longer lie side by side unconnectedly, like productions which are merely capable of classification in natural history, according to similarity of form; they are united by a common bond, the similarity of their formative principle, and they may be compared together and physiologically arranged in accordance with the various modifications under which that principle is exhibited. . . .

SURVEY OF CELL-LIFE

The foregoing investigation has conducted us to the principle upon which the elementary parts of organized bodies are developed, by tracing these elementary parts, from their perfected condition, back to the earlier stages of development. Starting now from the principle of development, we will reconstruct the elementary parts as they appear in the matured state, so that we may be enabled to take a comprehensive view of the laws which regulate the formation of the elementary particles. We have, therefore, to consider—1, the cytoblastema; 2, the laws by which new cells are generated in the cytoblastema; 3, the formative process of the cells themselves; 4, the very various modes in which cells are developed into the elementary parts of organisms.

Cytoblastema. The cytoblastema, or the amorphous substance in which new cells are to be formed, is found either contained within cells already existing, or else between them in the form of intercellular substance. The cytoblastema, which lies on the outside of existing cells, is the only form of which we have to treat at present, as the cell-contents form matter for subsequent consideration. Its quantity varies exceedingly, sometimes there is so little that it cannot be recognized with certainty between the fully-developed cells, and can only be observed between those most recently formed; for instance, in the second class of tissues; at other times there is so large a quantity present, that the cells contained in it do not come into contact, as is the case in most cartilages. The chemical and physical properties of the cytoblastema are not the same in all parts. In cartilages it is very consistent, and ranks among the most solid parts of the body; in areolar[2] tissue it is gelatinous; in blood quite fluid. These physical distinctions imply also a chemical difference. The cytoblastema of cartilage becomes converted by boiling into gelatine, which is not the case with the blood; and the mucus in which the mucus-cells are formed differs from the cytoblastema of the cells of blood and cartilage. The cytoblastema, external to the existing cells, appears to be subject to the same changes as the cell-contents; in general it is a homogeneous substance; yet it may become minutely granulous as the result of a chemical

---

[2] Aerolar means lung. [*Eds.*]

transformation, for instance, in areolar tissue and the cells of the shaft of the feather, &c. As a general rule, it diminishes in quantity, relatively with the development of the cells, though it seems that in cartilages there may be even a relative increase of the cytoblastema proportionate to the growth of the tissue. The physiological relation which the cytoblastema holds to the cells may be twofold: first, it must contain the material for the nutrition of the cells; secondly, it must contain at least a part of what remains of this nutritive material after the cells have withdrawn from it what they required for their growth. . . .

Laws of the generation of new cells in the cytoblastema. In every tissue, composed of a definite kind of cells, new cells of the same kind are formed at those parts only where the fresh nutrient material immediately penetrates the tissue. On this depends the distinction between organized or vascular, and unorganized or non-vascular tissues. In the former, the nutritive fluid, the liquor sanguinis, permeates by means of the vessels the whole tissue, and therefore new cells originate throughout its entire thickness. Non-vascular tissues, on the contrary, such as the epidermis, receive the nutritive fluid only from the tissue beneath; and new cells therefore originate only on their under surface, that is, at the part where the tissue is in connexion with organized substance. So also in the earlier period of growth of cartilage, while it is yet without vessels new cartilage-cells are formed around its surface only, or at least in the neighbourhood of it, because the cartilage is connected with the organized substance at that part, and the cytoblastema penetrates from without. We can readily conceive this to be the case, if we assume that a more concentrated cytoblastema is requisite for the formation of new cells than for the growth of those already formed. In the epidermis, for instance, the cytoblastema below must contain a more concentrated nutritive material. When young cells are formed in that situation, the cytoblastema, which penetrates into the upper layers, is less concentrated, and may therefore serve very well for the growth of cells already formed, but not be capable of generating new ones. . . .

THEORY OF THE CELLS

The whole of the foregoing investigation has been conducted with the object of exhibiting from observation alone the mode in which the elementary parts of organized bodies are formed. Theoretical views have been either entirely excluded, or where they were required (as in the foregoing retrospect of the cell-life), for the purpose of rendering facts more clear, or preventing subsequent repetitions, they have been so presented that it can be easily seen how much is observation and how much argument. But a question inevitably arises as to the basis of all these phenomena; and an attempt to solve it will be more readily permitted us, since by making a marked separation between theory and observation the hypothetical may be clearly distinguished from that which is positive. An hypothesis is never prejudicial so long as we are conscious of the degree of reliance which may be placed upon it, and of the grounds on which it rests. Indeed it is advantageous, if not necessary for science, that when a certain series of phenomena is proved by observation, some provisional explanation should be conceived that will suit them as nearly as possible, even though it be in danger of being overthrown by subsequent observations; for it is only in this manner that we are rationally led to new discoveries, which either establish or refute the explanation. It is from this point of view I would beg that the following theory of organization may be regarded; for the inquiry into the source of development of the elementary parts of organisms is, in fact, identical with the theory of organized bodies.

The various opinions entertained with respect to the fundamental powers of an organized body may be reduced to two, which are essentially different from one another. The first is, that every organism originates with an inherent power, which models it into conformity with a predominant idea, arranging the molecules in the relation necessary for accomplishing certain purposes held forth by this idea. Here, therefore, that which arranges and combines the molecules is a power acting with a definite purpose. A power of this kind would be essentially different from all the powers of inorganic nature, because action goes on in the latter quite blindly. A certain impression is followed of necessity by a certain change of quality and quantity, without regard to any purpose. In this view, however, the fundamental power of the organism (or the soul, in the sense employed by Stahl) would, inasmuch as it works with a definite individual purpose, be much more nearly allied to the immaterial principle, endued with consciousness which we must admit operates in man.

The other view is, that the fundamental powers of organized bodies agree essentially with those of inorganic nature, that they work together blindly according to laws of necessity and irrespective of any purpose, that they are powers which are as much established with the existence of matter as the physical powers are. It might be assumed that the powers which form organized bodies do not appear at all in inorganic nature, because this or that particular combination of molecules, by which the powers are elicited, does not occur in inorganic nature, and yet they might not be essentially distinct from physical and chemical powers. It cannot, indeed, be denied that adaptation to a particular purpose, in some individuals even in a high degree, is characteristic of every organism; but, according to this view, the source of this adaptation does not depend upon each organism being developed by the operation of its own power in obedience to that purpose, but it originates as in inorganic nature, in the creation of the matter with its blind powers by a rational Being. We know, for instance, the powers which operate in our planetary system. They operate, like all physical powers, in accordance with blind laws of necessity, and yet is the planetary system remarkable for its adaptation to a purpose. The ground of this adaptation does not lie in the powers, but in Him, who has so constituted matter with its powers, that in blindly obeying its laws it produces a whole suited to fulfil an intended purpose. We may even assume that the planetary system has an individual adaptation to a purpose. Some external influence, such as a comet, may occasion disturbances of motion, without thereby bringing the whole into collision;

derangements may occur on single planets, such as a high tide, &c., which are yet balanced entirely by physical laws. As respects their adaptation to a purpose, organized bodies differ from these in degree only; and by this second view we are just as little compelled to conclude that the fundamental powers of organization operate according to laws of adaptation to a purpose, as we are in inorganic nature. . . .

We set out, therefore, with the supposition that an organized body is not produced by a fundamental power which is guided in its operation by a definite idea,[3] but is developed, according to blind laws of necessity, by powers which, like those of inorganic nature, are established by the very existence of matter. As the elementary materials of organic nature are not different from those of the inorganic kingdom, the source of the organic phenomena can only reside in another combination of these materials, whether it be in a peculiar mode of union of the elementary atoms to form atoms of the second order, or in the arrangement of these conglomerate molecules when forming either the separate morphological elementary parts of organisms, or an entire organism. We have here to do with the latter question solely, whether the cause of organic phenomena lies in the whole organism, or in its separate elementary parts. If this question can be answered, a further inquiry still remains as to whether the organism or its elementary parts possess this power through the peculiar mode of combination of the conglomerate molecules, or through the mode in which the elementary atoms are united into conglomerate molecules.

We may, then, form the two following ideas of the cause of organic phenomena, such as growth, &c. First, that the cause resides in the totality of the organism. By the combination of the molecules into a systematic whole, such as the organism is in every stage of its development, a power is engendered, which enables such an organism to take up fresh material from without, and appropriate it either to the formation of new elementary parts, or to the growth of those already present. Here, therefore, the cause of the growth of the elementary parts resides in the totality of the organism. The other mode of explanation is, that growth does not ensue from a power resident in the entire organism, but that each separate elementary part is possessed of an independent power, an independent life, so to speak; in other words, the molecules in each separate elementary part are so combined as to set free a power by which it is capable of attracting new molecules, and so increasing, and the whole organism subsists only by means of the reciprocal[4] action of the single elementary parts. So that here the single elementary parts only exert an active influence on nutrition, and totality of the organism may indeed be a condition, but is not in this view a cause.

In order to determine which of these two views is the correct one, we must summon to our aid the results of the previous investigation. We have seen that

---

[3] That is, purpose. The idea that organisms develop according to specific purposes, as in the mind of a creator of some sort is called a "teleological approach." [*Eds.*]

[4] The word "reciprocal action" must here be taken in its widest sense, as implying the preparation of material by one elementary part, which another requires for its own nutrition.

all organized bodies are composed of essentially similar parts, namely, of cells; that these cells are formed and grow in accordance with the essentially similar laws; and, therefore, that these processes must, in every instance, be produced by the same powers. Now, if we find that some of these elementary parts, not differing from the others, are capable of separating themselves from the organism, and pursuing an independent growth, we may thence conclude that each of the other elementary parts, each cell, is already possessed of power to take up fresh molecules and grow; and that, therefore, every elementary part possesses a power of its own, an independent life, by means of which it would be enabled to develop itself independently, if the relations which it bore to external parts were but similar to those in which it stands in the organism. ... Now, as all cells grow according to the same laws, and consequently the cause of growth cannot in one case lie in the cell, and in another in the whole organism; and since it may be further proved that some cells, which do not differ from the rest in their mode of growth, are developed independently, we must ascribe to all cells an independent vitality, that is, such combinations of molecules as occur in any single cell, are capable of setting free the power by which it is enabled to take up fresh molecules. The cause of nutrition and growth resides not in the organism as a whole, but in the separate elementary parts—the cells. The failure of growth in the case of any particular cell, when separated from an organized body, is as slight an objection to this theory, as it is an objection against the independent vitality of a bee, that it cannot continue long in existence after being separated from its swarm. The manifestation of the power which resides in the cell depends upon conditions to which it is subject only when in connexion with the whole (organism).

The question, then, as to the fundamental power of organized bodies resolves itself into that of the fundamental powers of the individual cells. We must now consider the general phenomena attending the formation of cells, in order to discover what powers may be presumed to exist in the cells to explain them. These phenomena may be arranged in two natural groups: first, those which relate to the combination of the molecules to form a cell, and which may be denominated the *plastic* phenomena of the cells; secondly, those which result from chemical changes either in the component particles of the cell itself, or in the surrounding cytoblastema, and which may be called *metabolic* phenomena (τὸ μεταβολικὸν, implying that which is liable to occasion or to suffer change).

The general plastic appearances in the cells are, as we have seen, the following: at first a minute corpuscle is formed, (the nucleolus); a layer of substance (the nucleus) is then precipitated around it, which becomes more thickened and expanded by the continual deposition of fresh molecules between those already present. Deposition goes on more vigorously at the outer part of this layer than at the inner. Frequently the entire layer, or in other instances the outer part of it only, becomes condensed to a membrane, which may continue to take up new molecules in such a manner that it increases more rapidly in superficial extent than in thickness, and thus an intervening cavity is necessarily formed between it and the nucleolus. A second layer (cell) is next precipitated around this first, in which precisely the same phenomena are repeated, with merely the difference that in this case the processes, especially the growth of the layer, and the formation of the space intervening between it and the first layer (the cell-cavity), go on more rapidly and more completely. Such were the phenomena in the formation of most cells; in some, however, there appeared to be only a single layer formed, while in others (those especially in which the nucleolus was hollow) there were three. The other varieties in the development of the elementary parts were (as we saw) reduced to these—that if two neighbouring cells commence their formation so near to one another that the boundaries of the layers forming around each of them meet at any spot, a common layer may be formed enclosing the two incipient cells. So at least the origin of nuclei, with two or more nucleoli, seemed explicable, by a coalescence of the first layers (corresponding to the nucleus), and the union of many primary cells into one secondary cell by a similar coalescence of the second layers (which correspond to the cell). But the further development of these common layers proceeds as though they were only an ordinary single layer. Lastly, there were some varieties in the progressive development of the cells, which were referable to an unequal deposition of the new molecules between those already present in the separate layers. In this way modifications of form and division of the cells were explained. And among the number of the plastic phenomena in the cells we may mention, lastly, the formation of secondary deposits; for instances occur in which one or more new layers, each on the inner surface of the previous one, are deposited on the inner surface of a simple or of a secondary cell.

These are the most important phenomena observed in the formation and development of cells. The unknown cause, presumed to be capable of explaining these processes in the cells, may be called the plastic power of the cells. We will, in the next place, proceed to determine how far a more accurate definition of this power may be deduced from these phenomena.

In the first place, there is a power of attraction exerted in the very commencement of the cell, in the nucleolus, which occasions the addition of new molecules to those already present. We may imagine the nucleolus itself to be first formed by a sort of crystallization from out of a concentrated fluid. For if a fluid be so concentrated that the molecules of the substance in solution exert a more powerful mutual attraction than is exerted between them and the molecules of the fluid in which they are dissolved, a part of the solid substance must be precipitated. One can readily understand that the fluid must be more concentrated when new cells are being formed in it than when those already present have merely to grow. For if the cell is already partly formed, it exerts an attractive force upon the substance still in solution. There is then a cause for the deposition of this substance, which does not co-operate when no part of the cell is yet formed. Therefore, the greater the attractive force of the cell is, the less concentration of the fluid is required; while, at the commencement of the formation of a cell, the fluid must be more than concentrated. But the conclusion which may be thus directly drawn, as to the attractive power of the cell, may also be verified by observation. Wherever the nutrient fluid is not equally distributed in a tissue, the new cells are formed in that part into which the fluid penetrates first, and where, consequently, it is most concentrated. Upon this fact, as we have seen, depended the difference between the growth of organized and unorganized tissues. . . . And this confirmation of the foregoing conclusion by experience speaks also for the correctness of the reasoning itself.

The attractive power of the cells operates so as to effect the addition of new molecules in two ways,—first, in layers, and secondly, in such a manner in each layer that the new molecules are deposited between those already present. This is only an expression of the fact; the more simple law, by which several layers are formed and the molecules are not all deposited between those already present, cannot yet be explained. The formation of layers may be repeated once, twice, or thrice. The growth of the separate layers is regulated by a law, that the deposition of new molecules should be greatest at the part where the nutrient fluid is most concentrated. Hence the outer part particularly becomes condensed into a membrane both in the layer corresponding to the nucleus and in that answering to the cell, because the nutrient fluid penetrates from without, and consequently is more concentrated at the outer than at the inner part of each layer. For the same reason the nucleus grows rapidly, so long as the layer of the cell is not formed around it, but it either stops growing altogether, or at least grows much more slowly so soon as the cell-layer has surrounded it; because then the latter receives the nutrient matter first, and, therefore, in a more concentrated form. And hence the cell becomes, in a general sense, much more completely developed, while the nucleus-layer usually remains at a stage of development, in which the cell-layer had been in its earlier period. The addition of new molecules is so arranged that the layers increase more considerably in superficial extent than in thickness; and thus an intervening space is formed between each layer and the one preceding it, by which cells and nuclei are formed into actual hollow vesicles. From this it may be inferred that the deposition of new molecules is more active between those which lie side by side along the surface of the membrane, than between those which lie one upon the other in its thickness. Were it otherwise, each layer would increase in thickness, but there would be no intervening cavity between it and the previous one, there would be no vesicles, but a solid body composed of layers.

Attractive power is exerted in all the solid parts of the cell. This follows, not only from the fact that new molecules may be deposited everywhere between those already present, but also from the formation of secondary deposits. When the cavity of a cell is once formed, material may be also attracted from its contents and deposited in layers; and as this deposition takes place upon the inner surface of the membrane of the cell, it is probably that which exerts the attractive influence. This formation of layers on the inner surface of the cell-membrane is, perhaps, merely a repetition of the same process by which, at an earlier period, nucleus and cell were precipitated as layers around the nucleolus. It must, however, be remarked that the identity of these two processes cannot be so clearly proved as that of the processes by which nucleus and cell are formed; more especially as there is a variety in the phenomena, for the secondary deposits in plants occur in spiral forms, while this has at least not yet been demonstrated in the formation of the cell-membrane and the nucleus, although by some botanical writers the cell-membrane itself is supposed to consist of spirals.

The power of attraction may be uniform throughout the whole cell, but it may also be confined to single spots; the deposition of new molecules is then more vigorous at these spots, and the consequence of this uneven growth of the cell-membrane is a change in the form of the cell.

The attractive power of the cells manifests a certain form of election in its operation. It does not take up all the substances contained in the surrounding cytoblastema, but only particular ones, either those which are analogous with the substance already present in the cell (assimilation), or such as differ from it in chemical properties. The several layers grow by assimilation, but when a new layer is being formed, different material from that of the previously-formed layer is attracted: for the nucleolus, the nucleus and cell-membrane are composed of materials which differ in their chemical properties.

Such are the peculiarities of the plastic power of the cells, so far as they can as yet be drawn from observation. But the manifestations of this power presuppose another faculty of the cells. The cytoblastema, in which the cells are formed, contains the elements of the materials of which the cell is composed, but in other combinations: it is not a mere solution of cell-material, but it contains only certain organic substances in solution. The cells, therefore, not only attract materials from out of the cytoblastema, but they must have the faculty of producing chemical changes in its constituent particles. Besides which, all the parts of the cell itself may be chemically altered during the process of its vegetation. The unknown cause of all these phenomena, which we comprise under the term metabolic phenomena of the cells, we will denominate the *metabolic power*.

The next point which can be proved is, that this power is an attribute of the cells themselves, and that the cytoblastema is passive under it. We may mention vinous fermentation as an instance of this. A decoction of malt will remain for a long time unchanged; but as soon as some yeast is added to it, which consists partly of entire fungi and partly of a number of single cells, the chemical change immediately ensues. Here the decoction of malt is the cytoblastema; the cells clearly exhibit activity, the cytoblastema, in this instance even a boiled fluid, being quite passive during the change. The same occurs when any simple cells, as the spores of the lower plants, are sown in boiled substances.

In the cells themselves again, it appears to be the solid parts, the cell-membrane and the nucleus, which produce the change. The contents of the cell undergo similar and even more various changes than the external cytoblastema, and it is at least probable that these changes originate with the solid parts composing the cells, especially the cell-membrane, because the secondary deposits are formed on the inner surface of the cell-membrane, and other precipitates are generally formed in the first instance around the nucleus. It may therefore, on the whole, be said that the solid component particles of the cells possess the power of chemically altering the substances in contact with them. . . . .

Each cell is not capable of producing chemical changes in every organic substance contained in solution, but only in particular ones. The fungi of fermentation, for instance, effect no changes in any other solutions than sugar; and the spores of certain plants do not become developed in all substances. In the same manner it is probable that each cell in the animal body converts only particular constituents of the blood.

The metabolic power of the cells is arrested not only by powerful chemical actions, such as destroy organic substances in general, but also by matters which chemically are less uncongenial; for instance, concentrated solutions of neutral salts. Other substances, as arsenic, do so in less quantity. The metabolic phenomena may be altered in quality by other substances, both organic and inorganic, and a change of this kind may result even from mechanical impressions on the cells.

Such are the most essential characteristics of the fundamental powers of the cells, so far as they can as yet be deduced from the phenomena. And now, in order to comprehend distinctly in what the peculiarity of the formative process of a cell, and therefore in what the peculiarity of the essential phenomenon in the formation of organized bodies consists, we will compare this process with a phenomenon of inorganic nature as nearly as possible similar to it. Disregarding all that is specially peculiar to the formation of cells, in order to find a more general definition in which it may be included with a process occurring in inorganic nature, we may view it as a process in which a solid body of definite and regular shape is formed in a fluid at the expense of a substance held in solution by that fluid. The process of crystallization in inorganic nature comes also within this definition, and is, therefore, the nearest analogue to the formation of cells.

Let us now compare the two processes, that the difference of the organic process may be clearly manifest. First, with reference to the plastic phenomena, the forms of cells and crystals are very different. The primary forms of crystals are simple, always angular, and bounded by plane surfaces; they are regular, or at least symmetrical, and even the very varied secondary forms of crystals are almost, without exception, bounded by plane surfaces. But manifold as is the form of cells, they have very little resemblance to crystals: round surfaces predominate, and where angles occur, they are never quite sharp, and the polyhedral crystal-like form of many cells results only from mechanical causes. The structure too of cells and of crystals is different. Crystals are solid bodies, composed merely of layers placed one upon another; cells are hollow vesicles, either single, or several inclosed one within another. And if we regard the membranes of these vesicles as layers, there will still remain marks of difference between them and crystals; these layers are not in contact, but contain fluid between them, which is not the case with crystals; the layers in the cells are few, from one to three only; and they differ from each other in chemical properties, while those of crystals consist of the same chemical substance. Lastly, there is also a great difference between crystals and cells in their mode of growth. Crystals grow by apposition, the new molecules are set only upon the surface of those already deposited, but cells increase also by intussusception, that is to say, the new molecules are deposited also between those already present.

But greatly as these plastic phenomena differ in cells and in crystals, the metabolic are yet more different, or rather they are quite peculiar to cells. For a crystal to grow, it must be already present as such in the solution, and some extraneous cause must interpose to diminish its solubility. Cells, on the contrary, are capable of producing a chemical change in the surrounding fluid, of generating matters which had not previously existed in it as such, but of which only the elements were present in another combination. They therefore require no extraneous influence to effect a change of solubility; for if they can produce chemical changes in the surrounding fluid, they may also produce such substances as could not be held in solution under the existing circumstances, and therefore need no external cause of growth. If a crystal be laid in a pretty strong solution, of a substance similar even to itself, nothing ensues without our interference, or the crystal dissolves completely: the fluid must be evaporated for the crystal to increase. If a cell be laid in a solution of a substance, even different from itself, it grows and converts this substance without our aid. And this it is from which the process going on in the cells (so long as we do not separate it into its several acts) obtains that magical character, to which attaches the idea of Life.

From this we perceive how very different are the phenomena in the formation of cells and of crystals. Meanwhile, however, the points of resemblance between them should not be overlooked. They agree in this important point, that solid bodies of a certain regular shape are formed in obedience to definite laws at the expense of a substance contained in solution in a fluid; and the crystal, like the cell, is so far an active and positive agent as to cause the substances which are precipitated to be deposited on itself, and nowhere else. We must, therefore, attribute to it as well as to the cell a power to attract the substance held in solution in the surrounding fluid. It does not indeed follow that these two attractive powers, the power of crystallization—to give it a brief title—and the plastic power of the cells are essentially the same. This could only be admitted, if it were proved that both powers acted according to the same laws. But this is seen at the first glance to be by no means the case: the phenomena in the formation of cells and crystals, are, as we have observed, very different, even if we regard merely the plastic phenomena of the cells, and leave their metabolic power (which may possibly arise from some other peculiarity of organic substance) for a time entirely out of the question.

Is it, however, possible that these distinctions are only secondary, that the power of crystallization and the plastic power of the cells are identical, and that an original difference can be demonstrated between the substance of cells and that of crystals, by which we may perceive that the substance of cells must crystallize as cells according to the laws by which crystals are formed, rather than in the shape of the ordinary crystals? It may be worth while to institute such an inquiry.

In seeking such a distinction between the substance of cells and that of crystals, we may say at once that it cannot consist in anything which the substance of cells has in common with those organic substances which crystallize in the ordinary form. Accordingly, the more complicated arrangement of the atoms of the second order in organic bodies cannot give rise to this difference; for we see in sugar, for instance, that the mode of crystallization is not altered by this chemical composition.

Another point of difference by which inorganic bodies are distinguished from at least some of the organic bodies, is the faculty of imbibition. Most organic bodies are capable of being infiltrated by water, and in such a manner that it penetrates not so much into the interspaces between the elementary tissues of the body, as into the simple structureless tissues, such as areolar tissue, &c.; so that they form an homogeneous mixture, and we can neither distinguish particles of organic matter, nor interspaces filled with water. The water occupies the infiltrated organic substances, just as it is present in a solution, and there is as much difference between the capacity for imbibition and capillary permeation, as there is between a solution and the phenomena of capillary permeation. When water soaks through a layer of glue, we do not imagine it to pass through pores, in the common sense of the term; and this is just the condition of all substances capable of imbibition. They possess, therefore, a double nature, they have a definite form like solid bodies; but like fluids, on the other hand, they are also permeable by anything held in solution. As a specifically lighter fluid poured on one specifically heavier so carefully as not to mix with it, yet gradually penetrates it, so also, every solution, when brought into contact with a membrane already infiltrated with water, bears the same relations to the membrane, as though it were a solution. And crystallization being the transition from the fluid to the solid state, we may conceive it possible, or even probable, that if bodies, capable of existing in an intermediate state between solid and fluid could be made to crystallize, a considerable difference would be exhibited from the ordinary mode of crystallization. In fact, there is nothing, which we call a crystal, composed of substance capable of imbibition; and even among organized substances, crystallization takes place only in those which are capable of imbibition, as fat, sugar, tartaric acid, &c. The bodies capable of imbibition, therefore, either do not crystallize at all, or they do so under a form so different from the crystal, that they are not recognized as such.

Let us inquire what would most probably ensue, if material capable of imbibition crystallized according to the ordinary laws, what varieties from the common crystals would be most likely to show themselves, assuming only that the solution has permeated through the parts of the crystal already formed, and that new molecules can therefore be deposited between them. The ordinary crystals increase only by apposition; but there may be an important difference in the mode of this apposition. If the molecules were all deposited symmetrically one upon another, we might indeed have a body of a certain external form like a crystal; but it would not have the structure of one, it would not consist of layers. The existence of this laminated structure in crystals presupposes a double kind of apposition of their molecules; for in each layer the newly-deposited molecules coalesce, and become continuous with those of the same layer already present; but those molecules which form the adjacent surfaces of two layers do not coalesce. This is a remarkable peculiarity in the formation of crystals, and we are quite ignorant of its cause. We cannot yet perceive why the new molecules, which are being deposited on the surface of a crystal (already formed up to a certain point), do not coalesce and become continuous with those already deposited, like the molecules in each separate layer, instead of forming, as they do, a new layer; and why this new layer does not constantly increase in thickness, instead of producing a second layer around the crystal, and so on. In the meantime we can do no more than express the fact in the form of a law, that the coalescing molecules are deposited rather along the surface beside each other, than in the thickness upon one another, and thus, as the breadth of the layer depends upon the size of the crystal, so also the layer can attain only a certain thickness, and beyond this, the molecules which are being deposited cannot coalesce with it, but must form a new layer.

If we now assume that bodies capable of imbibition could also crystallize, the two modes of junction of the molecules should be shown also by them. Their structure should also be laminated, at least there is no perceptible reason for a difference in this particular, as the very fact of layers being formed in common crystals shows that the molecules need not be all joined together in the most exact manner possible. The closest possible conjunction of the molecules takes place only in the separate layers. In the common crystals this occurs by apposition of the new molecules on the surface of those present and coalescence with them. In bodies capable of imbibition, a much closer union is possible, because in them the new molecules may be deposited by intussusception between those already present. It is scarcely, therefore, too bold an hypothesis to assume, that when bodies capable of imbibition crystallize, their separate layers would increase by intussusception; and that this does not happen in ordinary crystals, simply because it is impossible.

Let us then imagine a portion of the crystal to be formed: new molecules continue to be deposited, but do not coalesce with the portion of the crystal already formed; they unite with one another only, and form a new layer, which, according to analogy with the common crystals, may invest either the whole or a part of the crystal. We will assume that it invests the entire crystal. Now, although this layer be formed by the deposition of new molecules between those already present instead of by apposition, yet this does not involve any change in the law, in obedience to which the deposition of the coalescing molecules goes on more vigorously in two directions, that is, along the surface, than it does in the third direction corresponding to the thickness of the layer; that is to say, the molecules which are deposited by intussusception between those already present, must be deposited much more vigorously between those lying together along the surface of the layer than between those which lie over one another in its thickness. This deposition of molecules side by side is limited in common crystals by the size of the crystal, or by that of the surface on which the layer is formed; the coalescence of molecules therefore ceases as regards that layer, and a new one begins. But if the layers grow by intussusception in crystals capable of imbibition, there is nothing to prevent the deposition of more molecules between those which lie side by side upon the surface, even after the lamina has invested the whole crystal; it may continue to grow without the law by which the new molecules coalesce requiring to be altered. But the consequence is, that the layer becomes, in the first instance more condensed, that is, more solid substance is taken into the same space; and afterwards it will expand and separate from the completed part of the crystal so as to leave a hollow space between itself and the crystal; this space fills with fluid by imbibition,[5] and the first-formed portion of the crystal adheres to a spot on its inner surface. Thus, in bodies capable of imbibition, instead of a new layer attached to the part of the crystal already formed, we obtain a hollow vesicle. At first this must have the shape of the body of the crystal around which it is formed, and must, therefore, be angular, if the crystal is angular. If, however, we imagine this layer to be composed of soft substance capable of imbibition, we may readily comprehend how such a vesicle must very soon become round or oval. But the first formed part of the crystal also consists of substance capable of imbibition, so that it is very doubtful whether it must have an angular form at all. . . . The quantity of the solid substance that must crystallize in a given time, depends upon the concentration of the fluid; the number of molecules that may, in accordance with the law already mentioned, be deposited in the layer in a given time depends upon the quantity of the solution which can penetrate the membrane by imbibition during that time. If in consequence of the concentration of the fluid there must be more precipitated in the time than can penetrate the membrane, it can only be deposited as a new layer on the outer surface of the vesicle. When this second layer is formed, the new molecules are deposited in it, and it rapidly becomes expanded into a vesicle, on the inner surface of which the first vesicle lies with its primitive corpuscle. The first vesicle now either does not grow at all, or at any rate much more slowly, and then only when the endosmosis into the cavity of the second vesicle proceeds so rapidly that all that might be precipitated while passing through it, is not deposited. The second vesicle, when it is developed at all, must needs be developed relatively with more rapidity than the first; for as the solution is in the most concentrated state at the beginning, the necessity for the formation of a second layer then occurs sooner; but when it is formed, the concentration of the fluid is diminished, and this necessity occurs either later or not at all. It is possible, however, that even a third, or fourth, and more, may be formed; but the outermost layer must always be relatively the most vigorously developed; for when the concentration of the solution is only so strong, that all that *must* be deposited in a certain time, *can* be deposited in the outermost layer, it is all applied to the increase of this layer.

Such, then, would be the phenomena under which substances capable of

---

[5] The taking in of liquid (water, in this case), by absorption into spaces between existing molecules. [*Eds.*]

imbibition would probably crystallize, if they did so at all. I say probably, for our incomplete knowledge of crystallization and the faculty of imbibition, does not as yet admit of our saying anything positively *a priori*. It is, however, obvious that these are the principal phenomena attending the formation of cells. They consist always of substance capable of imbibition; the first part formed is a small corpuscle, not angular (nucleolus), around this a lamina is deposited (nucleus), which advances rapidly in its growth, until a second lamina (cell) is formed around it. This second now grows more quickly and expands into a vesicle, as indeed often happens with the first layer. In some rarer instances only one layer is formed; in others, again, there are three. The only other difference in the formation of cells is, that the separate layers do not consist of the same chemical substance, while a common crystal is always composed of one material. In instituting a comparison, therefore, between the formation of cells and crystal-lization, the above-mentioned differences in form, structure, and mode of growth fall altogether to the ground. If crystals were formed from the same substance as cells, they would probably, in *these* respects, be subject to the same conditions as the cells. Meanwhile the metabolic phenomena, which are entirely absent in crystals, still indicate essential distinctions.

Should this important difference between the mode of formation of cells and crystals lead us to deny all intimate connexion of the two processes, the com-parison of the two may serve at least to give a clear representation of the cell-life. The following may be conceived to be the state of the matter: the material of which the cells are composed is capable of producing chemical changes in the substance with which it is in contact, just as the well-known preparation of platinum converts alcohol into acetic acid. This power is possessed by every part of the cell. Now, if the cytoblastema be so changed by a cell already formed, that a substance is produced which cannot become attached to that cell, it immediately crystallizes as the central nucleolus of a new cell. And then this converts the cytoblastema in the same manner. A portion of that which is converted may remain in the cytoblastema in solution, or may crystallize as the commencement of new cells; another portion, the cell-substance, crystallizes around the central corpuscle. The cell-substance is either soluble in the cyto-blastema, and crystallizes from it, so soon as the latter becomes saturated with it; or else it is insoluble, and crystallizes at the time of its formation, according to the laws of crystallization of bodies capable of imbibition mentioned above, forming in this manner one or more layers around the central corpuscle, and so on. If we conceive the above to represent the mode of the formation of cells, we regard the plastic power of the cells as identical with the power by which crystals grow. According to the foregoing description of the crystallization of bodies capable of imbibition, the most important plastic phenomena of the cells are certainly satisfactorily explained. But let us see if this comparison agrees with all the characteristics of the plastic power of the cells. . . .

We come now, however, to some peculiarities in the plastic power of cells, to which we might, at first sight, scarcely expect to find anything analogous in crystals. The attractive power of the cells manifests a certain degree of election in its operation; it does not attract every substance present in the cytoblastema, but only particular ones; and here a muscle-cell, there a fat-cell, is generated from the same fluid, the blood. Yet crystals afford us an example of a precisely similar phenomenon, and one which has already been frequently adduced as analogous to assimilation. If a crystal of nitre be placed in a solution of nitre and sulphate of soda, only the nitre crystallizes; when a crystal of sulphate of soda is put in, only the sulphate of soda crystallizes. Here, therefore, there occurs just the same selection of the substance to be attracted. . . .

We see then how all the plastic phenomena in the cells may be compared with phenomena which, in accordance with the ordinary laws of crystallization, would probably appear if bodies capable of imbibition could be brought to crystallize. So long as the object of such a comparison were merely to render the representation of the process by which cells are formed more clear, there could not be much urged against it; it involves nothing hypothetical, since it contains no explanation; no assertion is made that the fundamental power of the cells really has something in common with the power by which crystals are formed. We have, indeed, compared the growth of organisms with crystallization, in so far as in both cases solid substances are deposited from a fluid, but we have not therefore asserted the identity of the fundamental powers. So far we have not advanced beyond the data, beyond a certain simple mode of representing the facts.

The question is, however, whether the exact accordance of the phenomena would not authorize us to go further. If the formation and growth of the elementary particles of organisms have nothing more in common with crystallization than merely the deposition of solid substances from out of a fluid, there is certainly no reason for assuming any more intimate connexion of the two processes. But we have seen, first, that the laws which regulate the deposition of the molecules forming the elementary particles of organisms are the same for all elementary parts; that there is a common principle in the development of all elementary parts, namely, that of the formation of cells; it was then shown that the power which induced the attachment of the new molecules did not reside in the entire organism, but in the separate elementary particles (this we called the plastic power of the cells); lastly, it was shown that the laws, according to which the new molecules combine to form cells, are (so far as our incomplete knowledge of the laws of crystallization admits of our anticipating their probability) the same as those by which substances capable of imbibition would crystallize. Now the cells do, in fact, consist only of material capable of imbibition; should we not then be justified in putting forth the proposition, that the formation of the elementary parts of organisms is nothing but a crystallization of substance capable of imbibition, and the organism nothing but an aggregate of such crystals capable of imbibition?

To advance so important a point as absolutely true, would certainly need the clearest proof; but it cannot be said that even the premises which have been set forth have in all points the requisite force. For too little is still known of the cause of crystallization to predict with safety (as was attempted above) what would follow if a substance capable of imbibition were to crystallize. And if these premises were allowed, there are two other points which must be proved in order to establish the proposition in question : 1. That the metabolic phenomena of the cells, which have not been referred to in the foregoing argument, are as much the necessary consequence of the faculty of imbibition, or of some other peculiarity of the substance of cells, as the plastic phenomena are. 2. That if a number of crystals capable of imbibition are formed, they must combine according to certain laws so as to form a systematic whole, similar to an organism. Both these points must be clearly proved, in order to establish the truth of the foregoing view. But it is otherwise if this view be adduced merely as an hypothesis, which may serve as a guide for new investigations. In such case the inferences are sufficiently probable to justify such an hypothesis, if only the two points just mentioned can be shown to accord with it.

With reference to the first of these points, it would certainly be impossible, in our ignorance as to the cause of chemical phenomena in general, to prove that a crystal capable of imbibition must produce chemical changes in substances surrounding it; but then we could not infer, from the manner in which spongy platinum is formed, that it would act so peculiarly upon oxygen and hydrogen. But in order to render this view tenable as a possible hypothesis, it is only necessary to see that it *may* be a consequence. It cannot be denied that it may: there are several reasons for it, though they certainly are but weak. For instance, since all cells possess this metabolic power, it is more likely to depend on a certain position of the molecules, which in all probability is essentially the same in all cells, than on the chemical combination of the molecules, which is very different in different cells. The presence, too, of different substances on the inner and the outer surface of the cell-membrane . . . in some measure implies that a certain direction of the axes of the atoms may be essential to the metabolic phenomena of the cells. I think, therefore, that the cause of the metabolic phenomena resides in that definite mode of arrangement of the molecules which occurs in crystals, combined with the capacity which the solution has to penetrate between these regularly deposited molecules (by means of which, presuming the molecules to possess polarity, a sort of galvanic pile will be formed), and that the same phenomena would be observed in an ordinary crystal, if it would be rendered capable of imbibition. And then perhaps the differences of quality in the metabolic phenomena depend upon their chemical composition.

In order to render tenable the hypothesis contained in the second point, it is merely necessary to show that crystals capable of imbibition can unite with one another according to certain laws. If at their first formation all crystals were isolated, if they held no relation whatever to each other, the view would leave entirely unexplained how the elementary parts of organisms, that is, the crystals in question, become united to form a whole. It is therefore necessary to show that crystals do unite with each other according to certain laws, in order to perceive, at least, the possibility of their uniting also to form an organism, without the need of any further combining power. But there are many crystals in which a union of this kind, according to certain laws, is indisputable; indeed they often form a whole, so like an organism in its entire form, that groups of crystals are known in common life by the names of flowers, trees, &c. I need only refer to the ice-flowers on the windows, or to the lead-tree, &c. In such instances a number of crystals arrange themselves in groups around others, which form an axis. If we consider the contact of each crystal with the surrounding fluid to be an indispensable condition to the growth of crystals—which are not capable of imbibition, but that those which are capable of imbibition, in which the solution can penetrate whole layers of crystals, do not require this condition, we perceive that the similarity between organisms and these aggregations of crystals is as great as could be expected with such difference of substance. As most cells require for the production of their metabolic phenomena, not only their peculiar nutrient fluid, but also the access of oxygen and the power of exhaling carbonic acid, or *vice versa*; so, on the other hand, organisms in which there is no circulation of respiratory fluid, or in which at least it is not sufficient, must be developed in such a way as to present as extensive a surface as possible to the atmospheric air. This is the condition of plants, which require for their growth that the individual cells should come into contact with the surrounding medium in a similar manner, if not in the same degree as occurs in a crystal tree, and in them indeed the cells unite into a whole organism in a form much resembling a crystal tree. But in animals the circulation renders the contact of the individual cells with the surrounding medium superfluous, and they may have more compact forms, even though the laws by which the cells arrange themselves are essentially the same.

The view then that organisms are nothing but the form under which substances capable of imbibition crystallize, appears to be compatible with the most important phenomena of organic life, and may be so far admitted, that it is a possible hypothesis, or attempt towards an explanation of these phenomena. It involves very much that is uncertain and paradoxical, but I have developed it in detail, because it may serve as a guide for new investigations. For even if no relation between crystallization and the growth of organisms be admitted in principle, this view has the advantage of affording a distinct representation of the organic processes; an indispensable requisite for the institution of new inquiries in a systematic manner, or for testing by the discovery of new facts a mode of explanation which harmonizes with phenomena already known.

Cellular Pathology

by RUDOLF VIRCHOW

. . . With the tools of the biologist—and pathology is not the least branch of this beautiful science—everything that lives is dissolved into tiny elements, not all so small that their presence cannot be recognized with the naked eye, to be sure, but possessing a structure so fine that a clear understanding of it is completely impossible without microscopic study. In my article "Nutritional Units and Foci of Disease," I have shown that these tiny elements, the cells, are the actual loci of life and hence also of disease—the true bearers of vital function in plants and animals on whose existence life depends, and whose fine structure determines the vital expressions of living beings.

Life, therefore, does not reside in the fluids as such, but only in their cellular parts; it is necessary to exclude cell-free fluids (such as secretions and transudates) from the realm of the living, and intercellular material of cell-containing fluids (such as the *liquor sanguinis*, the much discussed blood plasma) as well. To the extent that cells, in contrast with pure fluids, still represent something solid, though in a very limited sense, we side with solidary pathology. But not everything that is solid can be looked on as a seat of life. Solid intercellular substances behave like the fluid intercellular substance of blood. It may be admitted that a trace of life-activity (left over from the cells from which and through which they originated) inheres in them, but no well-established fact indicates that this remainder is sufficient to maintain itself intact, or to carry on and transmit the life-process without the continual influence of cells. At most they can stimulate life-reactions in other tissues. My solidary pathology is, therefore, very restricted in comparison with that of the older school, and in no way does it exclude a refined form of humoral pathology, as Herr Seyfert fears.

May we really hope to attract the present generation to such a biological conception? Does this new kind of vitalism not stand in irreconcilable opposition to the dominant tendencies of modern science? The condescension with which the proponents of chemical and physical viewpoints—even those who have only a very imperfect understanding of microscopic anatomy—look down on morphology is well known. And indeed, when one considers the great successes that have been achieved by the chemical and physical investigations of our contemporaries, one might well come to believe that nothing more can be done with the cell idea.

Such a thought is easily countered. Should it be possible to present life as a whole in terms of a mechanical result of known molecular forces—and this has

Abridged from Rudolf Virchow, "Cellular Pathology," trans. L. J. Rather, in *Disease, Life and Man,* ed. and trans. L. J. Rather (New York: Collier Books, 1962), pp. 97–115. Reprinted by permission of the Stanford University Press. Originally published in the *Archiv für pathologische Anatomie und Physiologie und für klinische Medizin* for 1855.

admittedly not been done up to the present—it would not be possible to avoid designating with a special name the peculiarity of form in which the molecular forces manifest themselves, thus differentiating them from other expressions of these forces. Life will always remain something apart, even if we should find out that it is mechanically aroused and propagated down to the minutest detail. To no mortal is it granted to understand life in a diffuse, if you will, a spiritual, form—after the destruction of physical or chemical substance—and if this were really to happen, it would certainly be the worst blow that could be struck against the present-day scientific world-view. All of our experience indicates that life can manifest itself only in a concrete form, and that it is bound to certain substantial loci. These loci are cells and cell formations. But we are far from seeking the last and highest level of understandings in the morphology of these loci of life. Anatomy does not exclude physiology, but physiology certainly presupposes anatomy. The phenomena that the physiologist investigates occur in special organs with quite characteristic anatomical arrangements; the various morphological parts disclosed by the anatomist are the bearers of properties or, if you will, of forces probed by the physiologist; when the physiologist has established a law, whether through physical or chemical investigation, the anatomist can still proudly state: This is the structure in which the law becomes manifest. To whatever conceivable degree the phenomena of human life may proceed in a mechanical manner, the existence of the living human individual can never on this account be overlooked.

What the individual is on a large scale, the cell is on a small scale—perhaps to an even greater degree. The cell is the locus to which the action of mechanical matter is bound, and only within its limits can that power of action justifying the name of life be maintained. *But within this locus it is mechanical matter that is active—active according to physical and chemical laws.* In order to comprehend the essentially cellular phenomena of life we must understand the composition, the mechanical characteristics, and the functional changes of cell substance; as far as the course of investigation is concerned, there can be no disagreement regarding the fact that chemical and physical investigation is primary, and anatomical or morphological investigation secondary. For my own part it is hardly necessary to go into the matter further, since I have had, rather, to defend myself, from the time of my earliest writings up to the present day, against the reproach of having sought out too minute chemical differences.

Too easily, however, the question of the concrete significance of the thing toward which an investigation is aimed is forgotten in a quarrel over the degree of difficulty or accuracy of the investigation. It may be more difficult to isolate the individual substances composing a cell, or a body formed by cells, than to depict a cell or cell-structure, but the cell will always be higher and more important in spite of this. As little as inositol and creatin are more important than the heart in whose muscle they are found are they more significant than the individual, primary, muscle bundles. *The significance of the constituent parts will at all times be found only in the Whole.* If we advance to the last boundaries within which there remain elements with the character of totality or, if you will, of unity, we can go no farther than the cell. It is the final and constantly present link in the great chain of mutually subordinated structures composing the human body. I can only say that the cells are the vital elements from which the tissues, organs, systems, and the whole individual are composed. Beyond them there is nothing but change. . . .

It arouses the concern of Herr Spiess that I have permitted myself the expression "life-force," which I formerly avoided. I have never assumed "special vital forces," as Herr Spiess claims. I do not deny that this has its risks, though not so much on my account as on that of others who think of something quite different from my conception in connection with this word. In the end, however, a term is needed, and it would be impossible to find one that could not be misunderstood or misinterpreted. Nowhere have I even hinted that life-force is primary, or specifically different from the other natural forces; on the contrary, I have repeatedly and emphatically stated the likelihood of its mechanical origin. But it is high time that we give up the scientific prudery of regarding living processes as nothing more than the mechanical resultant of molecular forces inherent in the constitutive particles.

As little as a cannon ball is moved by a force from within, as little as the force with which it strikes other bodies is a simple resultant of properties of its own substance, as little as the celestial bodies move of their own accord, or as the power of their movements can be derived simply from their form and composition, so little are the phenomena of life to be fully explained from the properties of the substances making up the individual parts. That this is still done today is the last fruit of that obscure side of Hegel's philosophy (converted into orthodoxy by C. H. Schultz) in which self-arousal of life was the supreme dogma. It is most peculiar that we have to combat just this dogma, which harmonizes so little with Church dogma. For *generatio equivoca,* particularly when it is conceived of as self-arousal, is downright heresy or devil's work, and when we, of all people, are the ones to defend an inheritance of generations in macroscopic forms, as well as the legitimate succession of cell forms, this is truly trustworthy testimony. I formulate the doctrine of pathological generation, and of neoplasia in the cellular pathological sense, in simple terms: *omnis cellula a cellula.*

I do not recognize any kind of life with respect to which a matrix or a mother-structure must not be sought for. One cell transmits the life-movement to another, and the force of this movement (possibly, or even probably, a very composite one) I call the life-force. That I am in no way inclined to personify this force, or to make it simple and isolable, I have already stated clearly enough. Here I may be permitted to refer again to my statement: "Since we seek life in the individual parts and attribute an essential independence to them (in spite of every dependency they have on each other), we can also seek only in these parts for the immediate basis of the activity through which they remain intact. This activity pertains to the molecular particles, with the properties or forces immanent in them, set in motion by the life-force, although we are not in a position either to recognize some additional interior or exterior power as effective, whether this is called a formative or a natural healing power, or to ascribe to the transmitted life-force some special activity *(spiritus rector)* other than the general stimulation of formative and nutritive movements."

This quite sober viewpoint is far from being merely speculative; on the contrary it is so very empirical that I first broke through to it when I was able, by demonstrating the connective tissue cells and the cellular character of cartilage and bone, to divide the body of the adult vertebrate into cell territories such as were until then known only in the embryo and in many lower plants and animals. A unified view of the whole field of biology thereby became possible for the first time; moreover, a general principle—for which neural pathology has, up to the present, sought in vain—was found by combining different facts (therefore, by the speculative path). As far as the nerves are concerned, empirical proof that they possess an essentially trophic influence is lacking up to the present, but we can demonstrate empirically that cells possess both trophic and functional activity even in the absence of innervation. We must protest, however, when our remarks with respect to cells are interpreted as if they did not apply to the nerves. We have constantly emphasized that cells, whether isolated or growing together and developing into larger formations including nerves and muscles, are living and irritable. Nerves and muscles, however, even if more highly organized, nobler, and more important parts, are still only parts among other coordinated parts, each one of which can perform its peculiar task and can stimulate others to their own tasks. For not only do the nerves stimulate the characteristic functions of muscles and other parts, but in turn these other parts stimulate the function of the nerves. . . .

The nucleus and cell membranes show themselves to be the relatively permanent part of the cells; the cell contents are the more variable. When the former undergo essential changes the composition of the latter does not remain undisturbed. Growing parts sacrifice their functional capability to the degree that phenomena of division more clearly manifest themselves among the nuclei; a state of fatigue or weakness, necessarily indicating a change in the molecular state of the functional component of the cellular contents, then occurs. It follows, on the other hand, that the cell membrane is at different times more or less open to the passage of materials, that it permits various substances to pass through in a different fashion and is variably permeable to the same substances at different times. In a viable condition the red cell does not allow hematin to escape; when it remains in the same place, however, whether within or without a vessel, its membrane gradually becomes permeable to hematin even when the persistence of its elasticity cannot be doubted. As I have previously shown, one then observes a decolorization of the blood cell—the membrane becoming even more distinct and at the same time the surrounding fluids becoming colored. Just as little do external substances penetrate into the parts, as we best see in the case of the colored substances (madder, bile, pigment, etc.); specific parts have definite degrees of attraction for them.

At various places in my Handbook I have emphasized a matter which to me appears of very great significance for the understanding of these phenomena; I refer to the relation between function and nutrition. The best physiologists of the present day are much inclined to group both together, since it appears that function both determines and is dependent on nutrition, and conversely that function and nutrition lead to intrinsic changes in the molecular state of the parts. Correct as this is, nevertheless it seems to me that the essential difference lies in the fact that nutritive processes rest on the continued exchange of internal and external substances, while functional processes rest on alterations periodically taking place in the ordering and combination of substances already available within the cell. The functional processes cause new groupings of the constituent parts; the nutritive processes maintain the original groupings by exchanging the altered parts for new ones drawn in from the outside. . . .

When we require *cellular pathology to be the basis of the medical viewpoint*, a most concrete and quite empirical task is at stake, in which no *a priori* or arbitrary speculation is involved. All diseases are in the last analysis reducible to disturbances, either active or passive, of large or small groups of living units, whose functional capacity is altered in accordance with the state of their molecular composition and is thus dependent on physical and chemical changes of their contents. Physical and chemical investigation has a very great significance in this respect, and we can do no more than wish a prosperous development to the school which is striving to form itself. But we should not conceal from ourselves that the story of metabolic interchange will be brought to a satisfactory conclusion only when it is carried back to the primary active parts; in other words, when it becomes possible to describe the particular role every tissue, and every pathologically altered part of a tissue, plays in that story. Therefore, although one may begin with the outworks, the ultimate goal, beyond the urine and the sweat and the various waste products of organic activity, must never be lost from sight, nor should it be supposed that these waste products are themselves the goal. There would always be the danger of suffering shipwreck in a more or less exclusively humoral pathology, if this were to be the case.

The practicing physician, however, once he has convinced himself of the finer construction of the body through his own observations, will easily become accustomed to interpreting his experience in accordance with this point of view, and, as I have said, will accustom himself to thinking microscopically. If the physicist, in accordance with his basic viewpoints, is able to interpret events as movements of molecules (which he has never seen, and will never see), the medical man is in a much more fortunate position. He has already accustomed himself, even more than is necessary and justifiable, to think and speak of capillaries and nerve fibers which he, likewise, is unable to trace with the naked eye! The task of our time is to develop and win acceptance for a point of view based on an understanding of the special peculiarities and interrelations of the different tissue elements; a point of view, accordingly, that is essentially specific, i.e. localizing, as I have previously pointed out. In this manner a really scientific and practically useful pathology can be achieved, and we, too, are convinced that this is the only way to the pathology of the future.

Experiments
and Observations
on the Gastric Juice
and the Physiology of Digestion

by WILLIAM BEAUMONT

PREFACE

The present age is prolific of works on physiology; therefore in offering to the public another book relative to an important branch of this science, it will perhaps be necessary to assign my motives.

They are, first, a wish to comply with the repeated and urgent solicitations of many medical men who have become partially acquainted with the facts and observations it is my intention to detail; men, in whose judgment I place confidence, and who have expressed their conviction of the deep importance of the experiments, the result of which I mean herewith to submit to the public: secondly, (and it is that which mainly influences me,) my own firm conviction that medical science will be forwarded by the publication. . . .

The experiments which follow were commenced in 1825, and have been continued, with various interruptions, to the present time (1833). The opportunity for making them was afforded to me in the following way.

Whilst stationed at Michillimackinac, Michigan Territory, in 1822, in the military service of the United States, the following case of surgery came under my care and treatment.

Alexis St. Martin, who is the subject of these experiments, was a Canadian, of French descent, at the above mentioned time about eighteen years of age, of good constitution, robust and healthy. He had been engaged in the service of the American Fur Company, as a voyageur, and was accidentally wounded by the discharge of a musket, on the 6th of June, 1822. . . . The whole mass of materials forced from the musket, together with fragments of clothing and pieces of fractured ribs, were driven into the muscles and cavity of the chest.

I saw him in twenty-five or thirty minutes after the accident occurred, and, on examination, found a portion of the lung, as large as a Turkey's egg, protruding through the external wound, lacerated and burnt; and immediately below this, another protrusion, which, on further examination, proved to be a portion of the stomach, lacerated through all its coats, and pouring out the food

William Beaumont, "Experiments and Observations on the Gastric Juice and the Physiology of Digestion," from an abridged version in *A Source Book in Animal Biology*, ed. Thomas S. Hall (New York: McGraw-Hill, 1951), pp. 201–208. Copyright, 1951, by the President and Fellows of Harvard College. Reprinted by permission of the Harvard University Press, Cambridge, Mass. Originally published as *Experiments and Observations in the Gastric Juice and the Physiology of Digestion* (Plattsburgh, N.Y.: F. G. Allen, 1833).

he had taken for his breakfast, through an orifice large enough to admit the fore finger.

[He then tells the details of his stormy convalescence and gradual recovery with the formation of a gastric fistula through which all his food passed when his side was not tightly bandaged.]

EXPERIMENT I

August 1, 1825. At 12 o'clock M., I introduced through the perforation, into the stomach, the following articles of diet, suspended by a silk string, and fastened at proper distances, so as to pass in without pain—viz.:—a piece of high seasoned *a la mode beef*; a piece of *raw, salted, fat pork*; a piece of *raw, salted, lean beef*; a piece of *boiled, salted beef*; a piece of *stale bread*; and a bunch of *raw, sliced cabbage*; each piece weighing about two drachms; the lad continuing his usual employment about the house.

A 1 o'clock P.M., withdrew and examined them—found the *cabbage* and bread about half digested: the pieces of *meat* unchanged. Returned them into the stomach.

At 2 o'clock P.M., withdrew them—found the *cabbage, bread, pork,* and *boiled beef,* all cleanly digested and gone from the string; the other pieces of meat but very little affected. Returned them into the stomach again.

At 2 o'clock P.M., examined again—found the *a la mode beef* partly digested: the *raw beef* was slightly macerated on the surface, but its general texture was firm and entire. The smell and taste of the fluids of the stomach were slightly rancid; and the boy complained of some pain and uneasiness at the breast. Returned them again.

The lad complaining of considerable distress and uneasiness at the stomach, general debility and lassitude, with some pain in his head, I withdrew the string, and found the remaining portions of aliment nearly in the same condition as when last examined; the fluid more rancid and sharp. The boy still complaining, I did not return them any more.

August 2. The distress at the stomach and pain in the head continuing, accompanied with costiveness, a depressed pulse, dry skin, coated tongue, and numerous white spots, or pustules, resembling coagulated lymph, spread over the inner surface of the stomach, I thought it advisable to give medicine; and, accordingly, dropped into the stomach, through the aperture, half a dozen *calomel pills,* four or five grains each; which, in about three hours, had a thorough cathartic effect, and removed all the foregoing symptoms, and the diseased appearance of the inner coat of the stomach. The effect of the medicine was the same as when administered in the usual way, by the mouth and oesophagus, except the nausea commonly occasioned by swallowing pills.

This experiment cannot be considered a fair test of the powers of the gastric juice. The cabbage, one of the articles which was, in this instance, most speedily dissolved, was cut into small, fibrous pieces, very thin, and necessarily exposed, on all its surfaces, to the action of the gastric juice. The stale bread was porous, and, of course, admitted the juice into all its interstices; and probably fell from the string as soon as softened, and before it was completely dissolved. These circumstances will account for the more rapid disappearance of these substances, than of the pieces of meat, which were in entire solid pieces when put in. To account for the disappearance of the fat pork, it is only necessary to remark, that the fat of meat is always resolved into oil, by the warmth of the stomach, before it is digested. I have generally observed that when he has fed on fat meat or butter, the whole superior portion of the contents of the stomach, if examined a short time after eating, will be found covered with an oily pellicle. This fact may account for the disappearance of the pork from the string. I think, upon the whole, and subsequent experiments have confirmed the opinion, that fat meats are less easily digested than lean, when both have received the same advantages of comminution. Generally speaking, the looser the texture, and the more tender the fiber, of animal food, the easier it is of digestion.

This experiment is important, in a pathological point of view. It confirms the opinion, that undigested portions of food in the stomach produce all the phenomena of fever; and is calculated to warn us of the danger of all excesses, where that organ is concerned. It also admonishes us of the necessity of a perfect comminution of the articles of diet.

Gastric Juice of the Buzzard

by RENÉ ANTOINE RÉAUMUR

It will be easily seen that sponge is the most convenient substance to use in these experiments, for birds of prey do not normally eat it and therefore, judging by previous observations, we may conclude that they cannot digest it. I had no doubt as to the success of the experiment which I was about to undertake, and I accordingly put several small pieces of sponge into a tube, without filling it too full; numerous small holes were then made in the tube and it was swallowed by the bird and brought up as usual. Before the pieces of sponge were placed in the

René Antoine Réaumur, "Gastric Juice of the Buzzard," from an abridged translation by John F. Fulton in *Selected Readings in the History of Pysiology,* 2nd ed., ed. John F. Fulton and Leonard G. Wilson (Springfield, Ill.: Charles C. Thomas, 1966), pp. 169–170. Reprinted by permission. Originally published as "Sur la digestion des oiseaux. Première mémoire. Expériences sur la manière dont se fait la digestion dans les oiseaux qui vivent principalement de grains et d'herbes, et dont l'estomac est un gésier," *Mémoires d l'Académie royale des sciences, Paris* (1752), 266–307. "Seconde mémoire. De la manière dont elle se fait dans l'estomac des oiseaux de proie," *Mémoires de l'Académie royale des sciences, Paris* (1752), 461–495.

tube they weighed only 13 grains, but when I took them out their weight was 63 grains; they therefore absorbed 50 grains of fluid, most of which I was easily able to squeeze out into a vessel prepared for the purpose.

This experiment alone proves that a fairly large quantity of juice can be obtained quite easily. Two or three of these tubes containing sponge, administered in the course of the day would yield double or treble the above amount, *i.e.* 100 or 150 grains of fluid, while for a small outlay two or three birds could be kept for a week or two and thus 200, 300, or even 450 grains of juice obtained daily. . . . My buzzard died before the series of experiments which I had intended to perform upon it were completed, and I blame my negligence in not replacing it by another buzzard or similar bird of prey. However, I shall make amends for this and try some further experiments which seem to me desirable: I shall now indicate which of these I consider to be the most important, in order to encourage other physicians to attempt them if they have the opportunity.

Before my buzzard died I had only twice obtained, by means of sponges, this juice which can dissolve bones and meat. When I squeezed the fluid out of the sponges into a dish it was quite unlike the clear liquid which is got by different distillations, for it was thick and cloudy and a muddy yellowish white in colour. I am not sure whether its natural colour and transparency had been altered, but further observations will elucidate this point. In the first experiments which I made I did not take the precaution of thoroughly washing the sponges, so that if there were any sediment or other matter in them it would change the consistency of the fluid and make it cloudy.

Apart from anything which the fluid might absorb from the sponges, there may be another reason for its impurity. If, before entering the tube, it came in contact with fragments of meat in the stomach it would not fail to act upon them to a certain extent, and some part of this meat would, when digested and reduced to pulp, almost certainly be mixed with the juice. Therefore, although the juice contained in the sponges could dissolve meat it must not be supposed that it is pure. To obtain fluid which is absolutely pure,—or at least much purer than that which we have just mentioned,—it is only necessary to make sure that the bird swallows the tube containing the sponge on an empty stomach, and that it does not have any food while it retains it. This will not be such a hardship as one might imagine, for nature enables these birds to endure very long fasts; they are not always successful in their search for prey and often go for days without catching, and consequently without eating, anything. . . .

When I put some of the juice from the buzzard's stomach on my tongue, it tasted salt rather than bitter, although, on the contrary, the bones which had been reduced to jelly by a similar fluid, and their remains, on which the fluid had acted, had not a salt but a bitter taste.

When blue [litmus?] paper was moistened with the fluid it became red. One of the first experiments that ought to be tried with this fluid,—both because it would be most interesting and because it would prove that it is this juice which reduces meat and bones to pulp,—would be to make it dissolve meat in a vessel just as it dissolves it in the stomach. Actual digestion of aliments taking place under such abnormal conditions would be a most singular and interesting phenomenon.

Effects of Electricity on Muscular Motion

by LUIGI GALVANI

PART I. THE EFFECTS OF ARTIFICIAL ELECTRICITY ON MUSCULAR MOTION

Since I wish to bring to a degree of usefulness those facts which came to be revealed about nerves and muscles through many experiments involving considerable endeavor, whereby their hidden properties may possibly be revealed and we may be able to treat their ailments with more safety, there seems no better way for fulfilling this desire than by publishing these discoveries at length (such as they are). For after reading of our experiments, learned and distinguished scholars will not only be able to develop them through their own studies and investigations, but even to carry out other experiments which we may have attempted but perhaps could not bring to conclusion. . . .

The course of the work has progressed in the following way. I dissected a frog and prepared it as in Tableau I. Having in mind other things, I placed the frog on the same table as an electrical machine, so that the animal was completely separated from and removed at a considerable distance from the machine's conductor. When one of my assistants by chance lightly applied the point of a scalpel to the inner crural nerves, DD, of the frog, suddenly all the muscles of the limbs were seen so to contract that they appeared to have fallen into violent tonic convulsions. Another assistant who was present when we were performing electrical experiments thought he observed that this phenomenon occurred when a spark was discharged from the conductor of the electrical machine, Fig. 1, B. Marvelling at this, he immediately brought the unusual phenomenon to my attention when I was completely engrossed and contemplating other things. Hereupon I became extremely enthusiastic and eager to repeat the experiment so as to clarify the obscure phenomenon and make it known. I myself, therefore, applied the point of the scalpel first to one then to the other crural nerve, while at the same time some one of the assistants produced a spark; the phenomenon

Abridged from Luigi Galvani, "Effects of Electricity on Muscular Motion," in *Commentary on Effects of Electricity on Muscular Motion,* trans. Margaret G. Foley (Norwalk, Conn.: The Burndy Library, 1953), pp. 45–88. Reprinted by permission. Originally published as *De viribus electricitatis in motu musculari* in 1791.

repeated itself in precisely the same manner as before. Violent contractions were induced in the individual muscles of the limbs and the prepared animal reacted just as though it were seized with tetanus at the very moment when the sparks were discharged.

I was fearful, however, that these movements arose from the contact of the point, which might act as a stimulus, rather than from the spark. Consequently I touched the same nerves again in other frogs with the point in a similar manner, and exerted even greater pressure, but absolutely no movements were seen unless someone produced a spark at the same time. Thus I formed the idea that perhaps in order to produce this phenomenon there were required the simultaneous contact of some body and the emission of a spark. I therefore again applied the edge of the scalpel to the nerves and held it motionless. I did this at one time when sparks were discharged and at another when the electrical machine was completely quiet. The phenomenon occurred, however, only as often as a spark was produced.

We repeated the experiments with the same scalpel and found, to our astonishment, that at times, when a spark was produced, the aforementioned movements were evident, and at others, they were absent.

Excited by the novelty of the phenomenon, we began to make tests and experiments of various kinds, but always using the same scalpel, in order to understand, if possible, the reasons for this unexpected difference. Nor was this additional diligence without its reward, for we discovered that the answer to the problem lay in the part of the scalpel we held in our fingers. Since the scalpel had a bone handle, we found that when this handle was held in the hand, no movements were produced at the discharge of a spark. They did occur, however, when the fingers touched the metal blade or the iron nails that secured the blade of the instrument.

Now since dry bones exhibit an idioelectric (or non-conducting) nature, while a metal blade and iron nails exhibit an anelectric (or conducting) nature, as they say, we began to suspect that perhaps when we held the bone handle in our fingers, there was no way for the electric fluid[1] to flow (by whatever means) into the frog, but when we took hold of the blade or nails and brought them in contact with the frog, a path was opened.

To place this conclusion beyond all doubt, therefore, we used at one time a thin glass cylinder, Fig. 2, H, wiped clean of all moisture and fine dust, in place of the scalpel, and at another, one of iron, G. At the time when a spark was discharged, we were not only touching the crural nerves with the glass rod, but were actually rubbing them. Our efforts were unsuccessful, however, since the phenomenon did not reappear although numerous strong sparks were discharged from the conductor of the electrical machine at close range to the animal. On the

---

[1] In the eighteenth and nineteenth centuries it was customary to describe electricity in terms of the flow of a specific "fluid." Benjamin Franklin was one of the most able theoreticians of electricity, and developed the idea that a single electrical fluid exists. An abundance of this fluid in a substance produces a "positive charge," while a depletion of the fluid from a substance produces a "negative charge." Galvani adhered to the Franklin theory in his writings. [*Eds.*]

other hand, when the iron rod was only lightly applied to the same nerves and when only weak sparks were emitted, the phenomenon once again occurred.

This clearly confirmed what we had suspected to be true, namely that the contact of a conducting substance with the nerves is necessary to produce the phenomenon. But in this experiment use had been made of both the substance, by which the nerves were touched and the man who touched them; so we applied the iron rod, G, to the same nerves but did not hold it in our hands. In this way we hoped to ascertain whether the phenomenon should be ascribed to the man and the iron rod together or to the latter alone. When the experiment was made in this way, no movement of the muscles occurred when the spark was emitted. In place of the cylinder, therefore, we used a very long wire, Fig. 2, KK, in order to see whether or not this could somehow compensate for the absence of the man. And behold! the muscles contracted when the sparks were discharged.

From these observations it became clear to us that not only was a conducting substance that touched the nerves required to produce the phenomenon, but one also of determined size and length. Hereafter, for the sake of clearness rather than brevity, allow us to call a conducting substance of this sort a nerve-conductor.

Now, to the end of this conductor, we attached a small hook which was fastened to the frog's spinal cord, Fig. 2. At one time we placed the frog near the electrical machine and at another we arranged its conductor in such a manner that now the frog was near to the electrical machine and now removed at a distance from it. Because at one time the feet and at another the prepared nerves were turned towards the electrical machine, the latter now had the conductor before it and now behind. No matter what the arrangement was, contractions of equal intensity were always produced.

We investigated, moreover, whether the phenomenon took place in prepared animals even when the experiment was performed at a distance from the electrical machine and very long nerve-conductors were employed. We were able to ascertain that when an iron wire of one hundred and more ells in length was attached to the frog, muscular contractions occurred at the emission of a spark, even though the distance from the electrical machine was very great. We carried out the experiment in the following way. We suspended an iron wire, Fig. 3, FF, by silk threads and thereby insulated it, as the natural philosophers say. Then we fastened one end by a silk thread to a nail, F, driven into the wall; the other end we carried away from the electrical machine through various rooms as far as the wire reached. To the latter at point, C, we joined another iron wire, B, from whose end a frog was suspended. For the sake of convenience, we enclosed the frog in a glass jar, A, whose bottom was covered with some conducting material, e.g. water or very small lead shot of the kind used by hunters (the latter brought about the best experimental results). When a spark was discharged from the conductor of the electrical machine, the limbs of the prepared frog moved, even at so great a distance—which was truly extraordinary—and almost jumped. The same phenomenon occurred when the frog was removed from the glass jar and was hung in a similar manner from the conductor, EE. This happened much more quickly if some conducting body, which was in contact with the earth, were fastened to the feet of the animal.

Since these results had been observed with an insulated conductor, we next investigated what would happen with one that was not insulated.

We attached the iron wire, EE, therefore, to the various hinges of the doors of the rooms of my house, six in number. All things were arranged as in the previous experiment. When a spark was discharged, only small contractions were produced in the prepared frog, but nonetheless there were some. . . .

PART II. THE EFFECTS OF ATMOSPHERIC ELECTRICITY ON MUSCULAR MOTION

Having already set forth our discoveries on the effects of artificial electricity on muscular contractions, we wanted nothing better than to investigate whether so-called atmospheric electricity produces the same phenomena or not, or more precisely whether lightning flashes like discharged sparks excite muscular contractions when the same techniques are used.

Therefore in the open air, we set up and insulated a long conductor, appropriately made of iron, Tableau II, Fig. 7, and fastened one end of it to a high part of the house. When a thunderstorm arose we fastened the nerves of prepared frogs or the prepared limbs of warm-blooded animals to the other end. . . . Then we attached to their feet another similar conductor of the greatest possible length so that it might reach down to the water of the well represented in the diagram. As we hoped, the result completely paralleled that in the experiment with artificial electricity. Whenever lightning flashed, all the muscles simultaneously fell into numerous violent contractions. These contractions preceded and as it were gave warning of the thunder to follow, just as the flash and illumination of lightning is wont to do. Indeed, so great was the agreement of the phenomena that contractions occurred without the addition of a muscle-conductor and with an uninsulated nerve-conductor. What is more, we observed these phenomena taking place, contrary to our expectation and belief, even with the conductor attached to a lower part of the house, Tableau II, Fig. 8, particularly if the lightning bolts were great or erupted from clouds overlying the site of the experiment or if a person held the iron wire, F, in his hands at the same time the lightning flashed.

Contractions were evident, moreover, if the animal lay in the open air, or was enclosed in an appropriate jar for the sake of convenience . . ., or was kept within a room. They even took place when the nerve-conductor was set at some distance from the nerves themselves, especially when the lightning was very strong

---

In the reprint of De viribus electricitatis *at Modena in 1792 the four engravings of the previous edition were redrawn and reduced to three. These are shown on the next three pages as Tableaux I, II, and III.* [Ed. note: *The redrawing accounts for the lack of correspondence between the figure*

Tableau I

references in the text and the drawings as shown. Tableaux IV and V, not part of the Commentary translation by Miss Foley, represent alternative versions that may help the reader to follow more easily the explanations given in the text. All engravings reproduced by permission of the Burndy Library, Norwalk , Connecticut.]

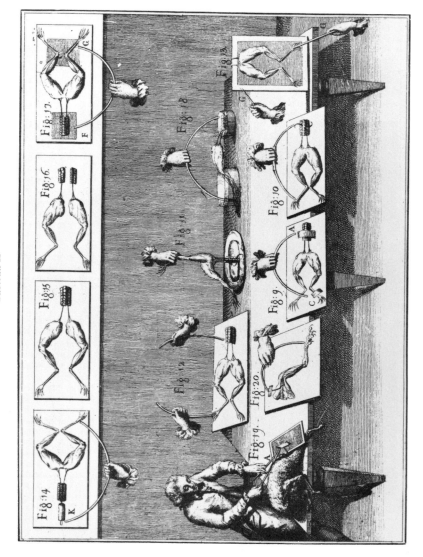

Tableau II

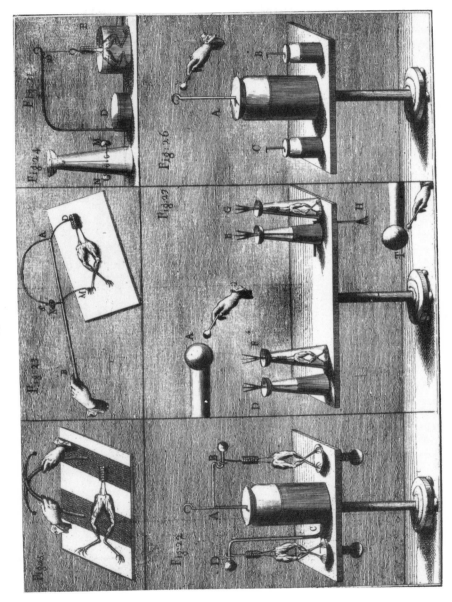

Tableau IV

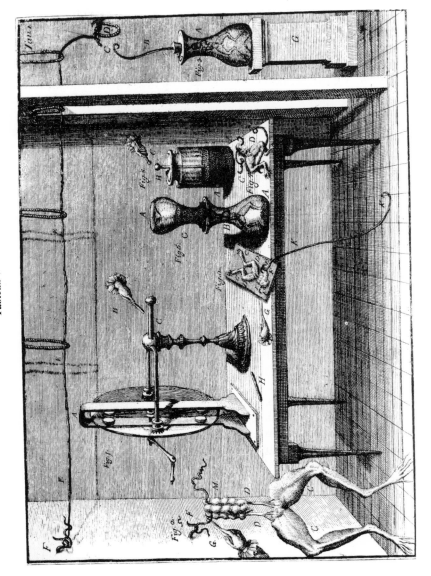

Tableau V

or near at hand. We described a similar phenomenon with artificial electricity when the sparks were particularly strong or were discharged near the animal. It is noteworthy that the entire electrical force in the lightning was not dissipated in only one muscular contraction as with the spark, but with many contractions following one another in turn almost simultaneously. Their number seemed to correspond to the number of peals usually given out by thunder.

Now such contractions were evident not only when lightning flashed, but also appeared quite spontaneously under threatening skies when clouds passed close to the elevated nerve-conductors. When this happened, the electrometers gave out clear indications of electricity and sparks frequently could be discharged from the elevated conductors themselves. With the contractions stimulated by lightning, however, sparks frequently were not discharged and even a very sensitive electrometer scarcely recorded by its movement any trace of electricity.

Experiments of this kind were undertaken not only on dead, but also on living animals, and the phenomenon of contractions appeared in both. No experiment was omitted which we had tried with artificial electricity and the ensuing results were essentially the same. At first sight, indeed, the following difference seemed worthy of notice, namely that prepared frogs which were fitted with a conductor and were enclosed in the little glass instrument, Tableau I, Fig. 6, set at a certain distance from the conductor of the electrical machine were violently moved, as we said, by the discharge of a spark. On the other hand, when lightning flashed from the clouds, these frogs were absolutely unmoved—perhaps because the electricity was too weak, having been carried by a conductor to the little instrument from a cloud bearing an accumulation of electricity, and encompassed too small a part of the instrument's outer surface, with the result that either the electrical force was not strong enough to induce contractions or that none of it reached the little instrument. In the same way and for precisely the same reason, contractions were not evident at the discharge of a spark if the little instrument were set apart from the electrical machine and placed near the end of the conductor, Tableau I, Fig. 3, EE, which was far distant from the machine.

Inasmuch as careful investigation reveals that artificial and atmospheric electricity operate in the same way, perhaps it is necessary that the electrical atmosphere encompass the glass instrument either completely or in large part to produce the aforementioned contractions within that receptacle. From our description of the instrument's position in the experiment, it is evident that this condition was not fulfilled.

We discovered, moreover, after examining the laws of the observed phenomena as well as investigating the muscular contractions, that the former were maintained similarly in experiments involving both atmospheric and artificial electricity.

Since we had observed the effects of the so-called electricity of storms,—both of lightning flashes and thunderbolts—we determined to test how summer evening heat lightning affects animals prepared in the usual way. Consequently we attached the same animals to our open-air conductor when the sky was filled with heat flashes (as we had done previously when there was lightning). No contractions took place at all, perhaps because heat flashes of this kind either do not have their source in electricity, or if they do, they occur a great distance away and operate in a completely different manner from lightning. This is a question, however, that would be of particular interest to the natural philosophers.[2] . . .

PART IV. THE EFFECTS OF ANIMAL ELECTRICITY ON MUSCULAR MOTION

From the things that have been ascertained and investigated thus far, I believe it has been sufficiently well established that there is present in animals an electricity which we, together with Bartholonius and others are wont to designate with the general term, "animal." This electricity is present, if not in all, at least in many parts of animals. It is seen most clearly, however, in the muscles and nerves. Its special characteristic, not recognized before, seems to be that it courses strongly from the muscles to the nerves or rather from the latter to the former, and directly enters an arc, a chain of men, or other conducting bodies which lead from the nerves to the muscles by the shortest and most direct course possible, and passes in all haste from one to the other through them.

From this, two facts are particularly evident, namely that a two-fold electricity is present in these bodily parts, one positive, as one supposes, the other negative, and that each is completely separated from the other by nature: otherwise, if there were a state of equilibrium, no movement, no flow of electricity, and no phenomenon of muscular contraction would take place.

It is clearly difficult to establish in which of the aforementioned parts the one or the other electricity is situated and from which part it flows: whether one is present in the muscle, the other in the nerve, or both together in the former. If one can hazard a guess in a problem so obscure, however, I am inclined to place the source of both kinds of electricity in the muscle.

Now although it is of prime necessity that one apply one end of an arc to the nerves outside of the muscles and the other, as we have indicated, to the muscles themselves, in order to produce muscular contractions, it does not seem to follow, nevertheless, that the nerves are filled with their own electricity, with the concomitant assumption that one kind of electricity has its seat in the nerves and the other in the muscles; just as in the case of the Leyden jar,[3] although we are accustomed to apply one end of an arc to the jar's outer surface and the other to its conductor so that electricity flows from this to the other surface, it cannot be inferred, nevertheless, that the electricity which is present in the conductor, is

---

[2] "Natural philosopher" is the term used in the seventeenth and eighteenth centuries to refer to those who studied nature in both a practical (experimental and observational) and theoretical way. It is not quite the same as our modern term "scientist," but it had many of the same applications. [*Eds.*]

[3] A Leyden jar is a form of electrical condenser, first developed by Pieter Van Musschenbroek in the 1740's. It consisted of a glass jar with an outer or "bottom" conductor of metal foil which covered the jar to within a few inches of the neck. An inner conductor of water, or metal shot, was in contact with a metal rod inserted through the neck of the jar. Static electricity was fed into the jar through contact of the metal rod with a friction machine. After being charged, a Leyden jar could be discharged by bringing the outer conductor in contact with the inner conductor. If a person touched the outer conductor with one hand, and the inner with another, he felt a severe shock. [*Eds.*]

peculiar to that part alone and is dissimilar from that which was collected in the bottom of the jar. Rather it is established that the electricity of the conductor belongs to the inner charged surface of the jar and that both kinds of electricity, although of contrary natures, are contained in the same jar.

For this reason, if one considers the large number of contractions which are produced in a prepared animal and which largely cannot be accounted for by the small residue of electricity present in the tiny section of nerve remaining in the prepared muscles after dissection, and if, moreover, one examines those numerous arguments based on animal functions which plainly prove that the nerve fluid (which we have already demonstrated as being electric), flows out freely and with great speed through the nerves, and finally if a clear and easy explanation of the phenomena is considered as arising from the two kinds of electricity residing in the same muscles, as we shall show later, then one will not be far from the truth in postulating that the muscle is the appropriate seat of the electricity we investigated, with the nerve functioning as a conductor.

If one admits these conclusions, then perhaps the hypothesis is not absurd and wholly speculative which compares a muscle fibre to something like a small Leyden jar or to some other similar electrical body charged with a twofold and opposite electricity, and by comparing a nerve in some measure to the conductor of the jar; in this way one likens the whole muscle, as it were, to a large group of Leyden jars. Anyone who has supposed that a muscle fibre, although simple at first sight is composed of solid as well as fluid parts (substances which produce in it no slight diversity), will readily admit that a two-fold and contrary electricity having its seat in one and the same muscle is not far from the truth: for certainly sensory perception, which is present throughout the fiber, clearly indicates that the nerve substance found therein is wholly different from muscle. Indeed since this nerve substance, which is present throughout the fibre, neither constitutes a nerve nor is perceptible to the eye but is perceived only by feeling, what hinders our supposing that it is at least partially dissimilar to the substance of the visible nerve, or is arranged in a different way, and for this reason has perhaps an electrical nature, but that it is extended as a conducting nerve outside of the muscle fibre? But perhaps this may become clearer from what we will say a little later on about nerves.

That a two-fold electricity exists in one and the same muscle, he will be little able to deny, moreover, who has seen that it is not difficult or improbable for a muscle fibre to have surfaces that oppose one another both externally and internally, either because he has seen the cavity which several people say is present in it, or because of the diversity of substances which we have said compose the fibre—a condition which could not exist without different little hollows and surfaces in the substance of the muscle.

Finally, if one, even briefly, has considered the mineral, tourmaline, which embodies a two-fold and opposite electricity, as the investigations of contemporary experimenters seem to indicate, he has come upon a new argument based on analogy which renders a hypothesis of this kind not at all improbable. But however this may be, we feel sure that the argument of causes and phenomena between the streaming out of electric fluid from a Leyden jar and our contractions is so noticeable that we have scarcely, and not even scarcely, been able to be diverted from this hypothesis and comparison and to restrain ourselves from ascribing a similar cause to the former and the latter.

For electricity has been discharged from the inner surface of a Leyden jar through the employment of three techniques in particular; that is, through the contact of the jar's conductor with some body, but especially with one of a conducting nature, through the application of an arc, and through the discharge of a spark from the conductor of an electrical machine, as we have recently observed.

Using these three techniques, we find muscular contractions are produced through the contact of an armed nerve, which we have made a muscle-conductor, then through the application of the ends of an arc to this nerve as well as to the muscle, and finally through the discharge of a spark.

Inasmuch as the arc is more suitable and efficacious than any other device for evoking the discharge of electricity from a Leyden jar, we now see that the same device is better than all others for exciting muscular contractions. Moreover, just as the arc has little success in evoking a discharge unless the conductor projects beyond the opening of the jar, and particularly beyond the place where the conducting substance is contained within the jar and is removed at a distance from it, so we have already shown that this same arc is of little use in inducing muscular contractions if the nerves have been cut near to the muscles.

Now as to what pertains to the eliciting of a spark, the similarity extends even further than we have set forth thus far. By way of illustration, we noticed through a chance observation on our part that a brush discharge shone continuously in the dark on the pointed conductor of a charged Leyden jar and after some time disappeared of its own accord. After it had disappeared, however, if the jar were set at a certain distance from the conductor of the electrical machine and a spark were produced from the latter's conductor, the same brush discharge again appeared at the very moment the spark was produced, but soon passed away and thus alternately arose when the spark was produced and then disappeared. This brush discharge, which we tested and investigated in various ways presents a significant new argument for the analogy we have already put forward; for just as a brush discharge of this kind is produced at the discharge of a spark, so, as we have pointed out, are contractions excited. Furthermore, just as when a conducting body, particularly one in communication with the earth, touches the external surface of the jar at the precise moment when the same brush discharge has disappeared or is ebbing at the passage of a spark, and is immediately refreshed and revived when a spark is again discharged, in such a way, we contend, failing muscular contractions are restored and weakened ones are increased when this same conducting body is applied to the muscles and sparks are produced. Likewise since this brush discharge becomes evident at the discharge of a spark whether the conductor of the jar is facing the electrical machine or is in the reverse position, in the same way contractions occur, as we have indicated, whether the nerves and their conductors are directed toward the machine or are in a reverse position. If that portion of the conductor which extends beyond the opening of the jar is enclosed in a glass or resin tube, the brush discharge does not appear when a spark is discharged, just as contractions are absent when the nerves are enclosed in the same tube, although the rest of the animal is exposed to the open air.

What is more, just as when a Leyden jar is placed inside some glass receptacle whose outside is covered with metal foil, a weak brush discharge is restored and an ebbing one is revived through the contact alone of this external container when a spark is discharged, so, in a jar containing an animal, as in Tableau I, Fig. 5, which has been set in the same receptacle, weak contractions are revivified and disappearing ones again arise at the discharge of a spark through the contact of this same container.

Now inasmuch as the appearance of this electrical brush discharge is wholly absent when a spark is discharged, if either the conductor of the inner surface does not extend beyond the opening of the Leyden jar or, even though this be the case, if another conductor is attached to it and is extended to the external surface of the jar; in such a way contractions cease, as we have said, at the discharge of a spark if either the nerve, outside of the muscles corresponding to it, does not project from the contiguous parts, or even should it do so, if another conductor, having been attached to it, is directed to the muscles or their conductors.

Now although this hypothesis and comparison has strong elements of truth, nevertheless there are many considerations which seem forcibly to oppose them. For either the nerves are of an idioelectric (or non-conducting) nature, as many affirm, and for this reason function unsuccessfully as conductors, or they are anelectric (or conducting); and how then can they retain the animal electric fluid within them so that it is not diffused and spread to adjacent parts, with a great diminution of muscular contractions? He will easily avoid this objection and difficulty, however, who postulates that the nerves are so constituted that they are hollow internally, or at any rate are composed of some material adapted to carrying electric fluid, and that externally they are oily, or have some other similar substance which prohibits the dissipation and effusion of this electric fluid flowing through the nerves. Indeed such a structure and composition of the nerves will admit their functioning in both ways, namely in conducting the electric nerve fluid and at the same time, in preventing its dissipation, and will be completely consistent with the economy of the animal as well as the experiments, since indeed the economy of the animal seems to require that its life force be confined within the nerves and experiments reveal that the nerves are composed of a particularly oily substance. For not only is a large amount of oil obtained from the nerves through distillation, (and a much greater quantity than from the muscles), but we produced by a newer process a greater amount of inflammable air from them than was ever derived from any other part of the animal. This air showed a capacity for emitting a brighter, clearer, and more lasting flame than the inflammable air drawn from other parts is wont to produce. This is a clear indication of a more abundant oily substance in the nerves.

This idioelectric (or non-conducting) substance in the nerves, however, which seems to prevent the electric nerve fluid from being dispersed with great loss, will not prevent this fluid, coursing through the inner conducting substance of the nerves, from leaving these same nerves, when it has become necessary, to produce contractions and to be transferred to the muscles as quickly as possible through an arc in its own characteristic way.

For just as a discharge is produced in a Leyden jar when an arc is applied to its conductor, although the latter is covered with wax, if the layer of wax is thin, but if it be too thick, it must be covered with metal foil—and even then the wax should not exceed certain limits of thickness, as we have discovered many times—in such a way electric fluid can flow and produce contractions through a nerve constructed by nature in a similar way, particularly when it has been skillfully armed.

Let us adopt, therefore, this extremely convincing hypothesis which we will readily reject, however, should learned scholars contradict it or the discoveries of natural philosophers and new experiments undertaken for this purpose bring forward another that is more suitable.

Now I have selected a few things characteristic of the nature of this animal electricity from those which could be inferred from the experiments I have described. Some of these characteristics animal electricity has in common with artificial and ordinary electricity and others with the electricity of the torpedo and other animals of this class.

The traits in common with ordinary electricity are the following: first of all it has an unimpeded and easy path through the same bodies which common electricity penetrates, that is, through metals, and particularly the most perfect and noble as gold and silver, then through the less noble, like bronze, iron, tin, and lead, following these, through the imperfect metals, an example of which is antimony, and lastly through ores. There is also an unimpeded and easy path through water and through moist bodies, a more difficult one through stones, soils, and woods, and finally interrupted and completely blocked paths through glass, resin, and oily bodies. The result of this is that if metals are laid upon a non-conducting surface, not unlike common and artificial electricity which is accustomed to build up in these and to produce much greater effects, animal electricity is wont to excite contractions that are more powerful and of longer duration, than if these same metals communicated freely with other conducting bodies.

In the second place, animal electricity has a preference in its emanation for a shorter, easier path, that is, for an arc, angles, and points.

In the third place, it has a double and opposite nature, that is, one positive, the other negative.

Fourthly, it adheres to the muscles for a long time and lasts for hours, just as common electricity is accustomed to adhere to bodies by nature.

In the fifth place, its renewal, as it were, is spontaneous and is not restricted to a small interval of time.

Finally, there is an extraordinary increase in the strength of animal electricity when the device of arming is employed and when this covering is made of the very metal with which the natural philosophers are accustomed to encase resin and glass bodies.

Now the characteristics animal electricity has in common with the electricity of the torpedo and other animals of this class are these: there is a kind of circuit of electricity from one part of the animal to the other, which is completed either through an arc or through the water itself functioning as an arc, as the natural philosophers have noticed. From this it is apparent that such a circuit is peculiar not only to torpedoes or other similar animals, but perhaps to most animals if our devices are applied. Furthermore there is absent in both the perception of a delicate enveloping atmosphere, as it were, through the attraction and repulsion of very light bodies or evidences of even slight movements in the most modern electroscopes.

Our animal electricity, furthermore, has the following quality in common with this electricity, namely that it has need of no preliminary device like rubbing, heating, or other similar procedures to excite it, but being prepared, as it were, to manifest itself immediately, it reveals itself by merely a contact. In fact this animal electricity has so great a drive to action, as we have learned through experience, that if the spinal column is touched by a body, even though it is non-conducting, at the place it is armed, contractions frequently are produced, particularly if the animal has been killed and prepared recently. They also occur if the same non-conducting body is pressed against the metal foil in such a way that the contact of the foil with the nerve projecting from the spinal column is either strengthened or altered. I do not know whether this can be affirmed about the electricity of the torpedo.

Now the following seems to be one characteristic and peculiarity of the torpedo in particular, and other related animals, that they can arbitrarily and at their pleasure discharge and eject electricity from their skin in such a way that it completes its circuit outside the body so forcefully and abundantly that a spark is produced, as we learn from the natural philosophers. This produces a strong reaction and concussion, which occasionally assaults the little animals coming in the path of this circuit so that they are either killed or are rendered stunned or dazed. These facts indeed indicate that animals of this kind perhaps possess stronger forces and a greater abundance of electricity than other animals, but do not imply that they are, in truth, of a dissimilar nature. Perhaps techniques will be found someday whereby effects of this kind may be obtained in other animals as well.

Not only the forces and laws of operation which we have discovered and revealed, but also the procedures that are followed and the means that are involved in producing an electric circuit of this kind in other animals, will be able, perhaps, to bear some light on the same circuit in torpedoes and related animals. On the other hand, from a very careful investigation and observation of the organs which serve this function in the latter, our investigations in turn will be enlightened. The means will perhaps be similar but the terminals of the electric circuit will undoubtedly be the same, namely the muscles and nerves. . . .

Now, in closing, let us touch upon several rather important and useful conclusions to be drawn from our experiments.

It seems to be established from these experiments that both artificial and atmospheric electricity exert far greater force upon muscles and nerves than hitherto was known; and that they exercise so great a power on animal electricity (as was seen in our experiments) to be able to incite this same animal electricity to movement, to stimulate its separation from the muscles and its very rapid effluence through the nerves and to excite powerful muscular contractions.

Through such knowledge perhaps a better approach may lie open than seemed possible before for discovering new and more useful methods of employing electricity, or for disclosing the correlation between the vicissitudes of atmospheric electricity and our health and between its sudden changes and certain human diseases.

Experiments of this kind seem to suggest, moreover, that at the discharge of lightning and sparks not only atmospheric electricity, but even perhaps terrestrial electricity flows back to the sky. Can it be that this flowing back results in the mutations and changes which occur in the air of the atmosphere when great storms arise in the sky, not only because of the diverse elements which it transfers with itself from the various regions of the sky, but even because of those substances which it carried from the earth into the air, if electric fluid has this characteristic which many natural philosophers attribute to it, that it expels and dissipates some of the delicate substances of the bodies through which it passes, but removes others and joins them to itself? The natural philosophers, in particular, should investigate these things.

To such a flowing back of terrestrial electricity in the atmosphere, however, one can attribute if not a great, certainly a not inconsiderable part in the very rapid and conspicuous growth of plants after thunder and lightning had occurred which the renowned Gardinius noticed and ascribed particularly to atmospheric electricity in conjunction with vapors.

Finally, since muscular contractions of this kind, which, as we have said, are produced under stormy skies, offer a new, as it were, and clear indication of atmospheric electricity and its effects on the animal organism, these same contractions perhaps can be of great usefulness in revealing not so much the causes of an earthquake as its effects on the organism. For this reason it seems quite worthwhile to investigate these things when there are earthquakes.

But now let us cease and call an end to conjecture. These were the facts in particular which I had discovered and wished to communicate to learned men about the effects of artificial as well as atmospheric, storm, and natural electricity on muscular motion, (which is subject to the will), so that these facts might be of some future use, a hope which we particularly cherish.

What pertains, however, to the effects of these various kinds of electricity on natural motions, on the circulation of the blood, and the secretion of humors, these problems we will present as soon as possible in another treatise, once we enjoy somewhat more leisure.

Conditioned Reflexes

by IVAN PAVLOV

EXPERIMENTAL PSYCHOLOGY AND PSYCHO-PATHOLOGY IN ANIMALS
(Read before the International Congress of Medicine, Madrid, April, 1903.)

Observing the normal activity of these (salivary) glands, it is impossible not to be struck with the high degree in which they are adapted to their work. Give the animal some dry, hard food, and there is a great flow of saliva, but with watery food there is much less. Now it is clear that for the chemical testing of the food and for mixing it and preparing it as a bolus capable of being swallowed, water is necessary. This water is supplied by the salivary glands. From the mucous salivary glands there flows for every kind of food, saliva rich in mucin. This facilitates the passage of the food through the oesophagus. Upon all strongly irritant chemical substances, as acids and salts, there is also a free flow of saliva, varying to a certain degree with the strength of the stimulus. The purpose of this is to dilute or neutralise the irritant, and to cleanse the mouth. This we know from every-day experience. This saliva contains much water and little mucin. For, what could be the use of mucin here?

If you put some quartz pebbles into a dog's mouth he moves them around, or may try to chew them, but finally drops them. There is no flow of saliva, or at most only two or three drops. Indeed, what purpose could saliva serve here? The stones are easily ejected and nothing remains in the mouth. But, if you throw some sand in the dog's mouth (the same stones but pulverised), there is an abundant flow of saliva. It is apparent that without fluid in the mouth, the sand could neither be ejected nor passed on to the stomach. We see here facts which are exact and constant, and which really seem to imply intelligence. The entire mechanism of this intelligence is plain. On the one hand physiology has known for a long time of the centrifugal nerves to the salivary glands which may cause either water or organic material to pass into the saliva. On the other hand, in certain regions, the lining of the oral cavity acts as a receptor for mechanical, chemical and thermal stimuli. These different stimuli may be further subdivided: the chemical, for example, into salts, acids, etc. There is reason for assuming the same in regard to mechanical irritants. From these special regions of the oral cavity the specific centripetal nerves take their origin.

All these reactions of adaptation depend upon a simple reflex act which has its beginning in certain external conditions, affecting only certain kinds of centripetal nerve endings. From here the excitation runs along a certain nerve

Ivan Pavlov, "Conditioned Reflexes," in *Lectures on Conditioned Reflexes* (New York: International Publishers, 1928), pp. 47–50. Reprinted from an abridged version in *A Source Book in Animal Biology*, ed. Thomas S. Hall (New York: McGraw-Hill, 1951), pp. 326–334. Copyright, 1951, by the President and Fellows of Harvard College. Reprinted by permission of the Harvard University Press, Cambridge, Mass.

path to the centres whence it is conducted to the salivary glands, calling out their specific function. . . .

All the foregoing substances, which when placed in the mouth influence specifically the salivary glands, act exactly the same upon these glands, at least in a qualitative way, when they are a certain distance from the dog. Dry food, even from a distance, produces much saliva; moist food, only a little. To the stimulation by food at a distance, there flows into the mouth from the mucous glands a thick, lubricating saliva. Inedible substances also produce a secretion from all the glands, but the secretion from the mucous glands is watery and contains only a small amount of mucin. The pebbles when shown to the dog have no effect on the glands, but the sand provokes an abundant flow of saliva. The above facts were partly discovered, partly systematised by Dr. Wolfson in my laboratory. The dog sees, hears, and sniffs all thise things, directs his attention to them, tries to obtain them if they are eatable or agreeable, but turns away from them and evades their introduction into the mouth if they are undesired or disagreeable. Every one would say that this is a psychical reaction of the animal, a psychical excitation of the salivary glands. . . .

In our "psychical" experiments on the salivary glands (we shall provisionally use the word "psychical"), at first we honestly endeavored to explain our results by fancying the subjective condition of the animal. But nothing came of it except unsuccessful controversies, and individual, personal, incoordinated opinions. We had no alternative but to place the investigation on a purely objective basis. The first and most important task before us, then, is to abandon entirely the natural inclination to transpose our own subjective condition upon the mechanism of the reaction of the experimental animal, and instead, to concentrate our whole attention upon the investigation of the correlation between the external phenomena and the reaction of the organism, which in our case is the salivary secretion. Reality must decide whether the elaboration of these new phenomena is possible in this direction. I dare to think that the following account will convince you, even as I am convinced, that in the given cases there opens before us an un-limited territory for successful research in a second immense part of the physiology of the nervous system as a system which establishes the relation, not between the individual parts of the organism with which we previously dealt, but between the organism and the surrounding world. Unfortunately, up to the present time, the influence of the environment on the nervous system has been explained for the most part subjectively, and this comprises the whole contents of the contemporary physiology of the sense organs.

In our psychical experiments we have before us definite, external objects, exciting the animal and calling forth in it a definite reaction—the secretion of the salivary glands. The effect of these objects, as has been shown, is essentially the same as in the physiological experiments in which they come in contact with the tongue and palate, as in eating. This is nothing more than a further adaptation, i.e., that the object influences the salivary glands if it is brought even *near* the mouth. . . .

It is not difficult to recognise in the first psychical experiments certain important conditions which insure constant results and guarantee the success of the experiment. You stimulate an animal (i.e., his salivary glands) by food from a distance; the success of the experiment depends exactly upon whether the animal has been prepared by a previous period of fasting. In a hungry dog we get a positive result, but, on the contrary, in even the most avaricious and greedy beast we fail to get a response to food at a distance if he has just satiated himself. Thinking physiologically we can say that we have a different excitability of the salivary centre—in the one case greatly increased, in the other decreased. One may rightly suppose that just as the carbonic acid of the blood determines the energy of the respiratory centre, the composition of the blood in the fasting or fed animal likewise regulates the threshold of excitability of the salivary centre, as noted in our experiment. From the subjective point of view this change in excitability could be designated as attention. With an empty stomach the sight of food causes the mouth to "water"; in a satiated animal this reaction is very weak or may be entirely lacking.

Let us go further. If you only show the dog food, or some undesired substance, and repeat this several times, at each repetition you get a weaker result, and finally no reaction whatever. But there is a sure method of restoring the lost reaction: this is by giving the dog some food or by putting any undesired substance into the mouth. This provokes, of course, the usual strong reflex, and the object is again effective from a distance. It is immaterial for our result whether food is given or the undesired substance is put into the mouth. For instance, if meat powder, having been repeatedly brought before the dog, fails to produce a flow of saliva, we may again make it active by either giving it to the dog to eat (after showing it), or by putting an undesired substance into his mouth, e.g., acid. Owing to the direct reflex, the irritability of the salivary centre has been increased, and now the weak stimulus—the object at a distance—becomes strong enough to produce its effect. Does it not happen the same with us when, having no desire for food, an appetite comes as we begin to eat, or also when we have experienced shortly before some unpleasant emotion (anger, etc.)?

Here is another series of constantly recurring facts. The object acts upon the salivary glands at a distance not only as a complex of all its properties, but through each of its individual properties. You can bring near the dog your hand having the odour of the meat powder, and that will be enough to produce a flow of saliva. In the same manner the sight of the food from a further distance, and consequently only its optical effect, can also provoke the reaction of the salivary glands. But the combined action of all these properties always gives at once the larger and more significant effect, i.e., the sum of the stimuli acts more strongly than they do separately.

The object acts from a distance upon the salivary glands not only through its inherent properties but also through accidental qualities accompanying the object. For example, if we colour the acid black, then water to which we add a black colour will affect the salivary glands from a distance. But these accidental properties of the substance become endowed with the quality of stimulating the salivary glands from a distance only if the object with the new property has been introduced into the mouth at least once. The black coloured water acts on the salivary glands only in case the black coloured acid has been previously put into the mouth. To this group of conditioned properties belong stimuli of the olfactory nerves. The experiments of Snarsky in our laboratory showed that there exist simple physiological reflexes from the nasal cavity acting on the salivary glands, and that they are conducted only through the trigeminal nerve; for example, ammonia, oil or mustard, etc., always produce a constant action in the curarised animal. This action fails, however, if the trigeminal nerves are cut. Odours without local irritating effects have no influence on the salivary glands. If you bring before a dog with a salivary fistula oil of anise for the first time, there is no secretion of saliva. If, however, simultaneously with the odour of anise you touch the oral cavity with this oil (producing a strong local reaction), there will afterwards be a secretion of saliva from only the smell of the oil of anise.

If you combine food with an undesired object, or even with the qualities of this object—for instance, if you show the dog meat moistened with acid—notwithstanding the fact that the dog approaches the meat, you note a secretion from the parotid gland (there is no secretion from this gland with pure meat), i.e., a reaction to an undesired object. And further, if the effect of the undesired object at a distance, owing to its repetition, is diminished, combining it with food which attracts the animal always strengthens the reaction. . . .

All the above facts lead, on the one hand, to important and interesting conclusions about the processes in the central nervous system, and, on the other hand, to the possibility of a more detailed and successful analysis. Let us now consider some of our facts physiologically, beginning with the cardinal ones. If a given object—food or a chemical—is brought in contact with the special oral surface, and stimulates it by virtue of those of its properties upon which the work of the salivary glands is especially directed, then it happens that at the same time other properties of the object, unessential for the activity of these glands, or the whole medium in which the object appears, stimulate simultaneously other sensory body surfaces. Now these latter stimuli become evidently connected with the nervous centre of the salivary glands, whither (to this centre) is conducted through a fixed centripetal nervous path also the stimulation of the essential properties of the object. It can be assumed that in such a case the salivary centre acts in the central nervous system as a point of attraction for the impulses proceeding from the other sensory body surfaces. Thus from the other excited body regions, paths are opened up to the salivary centre. But this connection of the centre with accidental pathways is very unstable and may of itself disappear. In order to preserve the strength of this connection it is necessary to repeat time and again the stimulation through the essential properties of the object simultaneously with the unessential. There is established in this way a temporary relation between the activity of a certain organ and the phenomena of the external world. This temporary relation and its law (reinforcement by repetition and weakening if not repeated) play an important role in the welfare and integrity of the organism; by means of it the fineness of the adaptation between the activity of the organism and the environment becomes more perfect. Both parts of this law are of equal value. If the temporary relations to some object are of great significance for the organism, it is also of the highest importance that these relations should be abandoned as soon as they cease to correspond to reality. Otherwise the relations of the animal, instead of being delicately adapted, would be chaotic.

PHYSIOLOGY AND PSYCHOLOGY IN THE STUDY OF THE HIGHER NERVOUS ACTIVITY OF ANIMALS

(Read before the Philosophical Society, Petrograd, November 24, 1916.)

. . . Here you see a diagram of our animal. On it are two black spots, one on the front leg, one on the thigh of the hind leg. These are the places where we attached the apparatus for mechanical stimulation of the skin. We proceeded as follows. After we have started mechanical irritation of these places with the pricking apparatus, then acid is poured into the mouth of the dog. The secretion of saliva produced by the acid is, of course, a simple inborn reflex. This was repeated several times, yesterday, to-day, and day after day. . . . After a number of experiments a state of affairs results in which we get a flow of saliva when we begin only to irritate that spot of the skin; it is just as if we had poured acid into the dog's mouth, though in reality no acid is given.

Now I come to the discussion of our fact, and will do it physiologically and then as far as I can possibly psychologically, as a zoö-psychologist would do it. I can not guarantee that I shall use the correct phrases, because I am out of practice in these expressions, but I shall approximate to those I have heard from others. The facts are these. I apply lightly the mechanical irritation of the skin and then give the acid. Saliva is secreted—the simple reflex. When this has been repeated several times, then only the mechanical irritation of the skin is necessary to call out the flow of saliva. Our explanation was that a new reflex was formed, a new nerve path was made between the skin and the salivary glands. The zoö-psychologist, who wants to penetrate into the dog's soul, says that the dog directed his attention and remembered that when he felt the irritation of the skin at a certain place he would receive the acid and, therefore, when there was only irritation of the skin, he imagined the acid was coming, and he reacted correspondingly—saliva flowed, etc. Let it be so. But let us proceed further. We shall perform another experiment. We had elaborated a reflex and every time it gave perfectly accurate results. Now I start the mechanical irritation and receive as formerly a complete motor and secretory reaction, but this time I do not give the acid. One or two minutes pass and I repeat the experiment. Now the action already is less, the motor reaction is not so marked and there is not so much saliva. Again the acid is not given. We allow two or three minutes to elapse and repeat the mechanical irritation. The resulting reaction is still less. When we have done this four or five times, the reaction is entirely absent; there is no movement and no secretion of saliva. Here you have a clear, absolutely exact fact.

But here is the difference between the physiologist and the zoö-psychologist. I say that there develops our well-known inhibition. This I base on the fact that if I now interrupt the experiment and wait two hours, then the mechanical irritation again has its action on the salivary glands. For me as a physiologist this is perfectly clear. It is known that all processes in the nervous system in the course of time and with the cessation of the active causes become obliterated. The zoö-psychologist is also not at a loss for an explanation, and he says that the dog noticed that now after the mechanical stimulation acid was not given, and therefore after four or five such skin irritations he ceases to react.

So far there is no difference between us. You can agree with one as well as the other. But we shall proceed to more complicated experiments. Now you are aware that when the zoö-psychologist and the physiologist vie with each other to see whose explanations are correct, and more appropriate, then we must be well acquainted with the conditions which the facts are to explain. The prerequisite is, as you know, that the explanation should account for all that really occurs. The facts must all be explained without changing the point of view. This is the first requirement, and the second is even more obligatory. This is that from the given explanation it should be possible to foretell the explained phenomena under consideration. He who can say what will happen is right compared with him who can not give any kind of prediction. The failure of the latter here will mean his bankruptcy.

I shall complicate my experiment as follows. I have a dog in which our reflex has been elaborated at several places, let us say three. After the mechanical stimulation of each of these places there appears the same acid reaction, measured by a definite flow of saliva. This is the simplest way to measure the reaction; the measurement of the motor component would be more difficult. The motor and the salivary reactions go together, they are parallel. They are the components of a single complicated reflex. Now we have several skin reflexes formed. They are all equal, they act with absolute exactness, they give the same number of divisions of the tube used to measure the salivary secretion, for example, 30 divisions for one half-minute stimulation. I stimulate the place on the front leg in the way I have just said, i.e., I do not combine it with the influence of the acid, and so after about five or six times the mechanical irritation does not show any action. To the physiologist this means that I have obtained a complete inhibition of the reflex. When this has happened to the place on the front leg, I can stimulate another spot on the hind leg. And there developed such phenomena. If now I take the mechanical stimulation on the thigh—just as I did on the front leg, where I got zero—so that there is no interval between the end of that stimulation and the beginning of this, then at the new place I obtain a full action, 30 divisions on our tube, and the dog behaves as if this were the first application of the stimulus. Saliva flows freely, the motor reaction occurs, the dog acting as if he were rejecting acid from the mouth with the tongue, although there is no acid present—in short, the whole reaction appears. If in the next experiment I try the effect of the irritation on the front leg until again there is no secretion (by repeating the mechanical stimulation without giving acid), and then irritate the place on the hind leg, not after zero seconds but after five seconds, then I receive not 30 divisions from the new place but only 20. The reflex has become weaker. The next time I use an interval of fifteen seconds, and I get a slight action from the new place,—5 divisions. Finally if I stimulate after twenty seconds there is no action whatever. If I go further and employ a great interval, thirty seconds, then again I get an action from this place. With an interval of about fifty seconds, there is considerable secretion, 25 divisions, and with an interval of sixty seconds we see the full reaction. On the same place, on the shoulder, after we obtained zero result, if the irritation is repeated with an interval of five, ten, fifteen minutes, then we get zero (I do not know if I have made this clear to you). What does this mean?

I invite the zoö-psychologists to give their explanation of these data. More than once I have questioned intelligent people, having a scientific education— doctors, etc., about these same facts, and asked them for an explanation of the phenomena. The majority of the naïve zoö-psychologists gave explanations, but each one his own, and different from the others. In general the result was disastrous. They examined the facts as much as possible, but there was no way of making the various interpretations agree. Why is it that on the shoulder, when the experiment was so conducted that we got zero, the apparatus produced no further action, but here at the other place we obtain now a full action, now nothing, in a fine dependence upon different intervals of time between the stimuli?

I came here to get an answer to this question from the point of view of the zoö-psychologists.

Now I shall tell you what we think. Our explanation is purely physiological, purely objective, purely *spatial*. It is obvious that in our case the skin is a projection of the brain mass. The different points of the skin are a projection of the points of the brain. When at a certain point of the brain, through the corresponding skin area on the shoulder, I evoke a definite nervous process, then it does not remain there, but makes a considerable excursion. It first *irradiates* over the brain mass, and then returns, *concentrating* at its point of origin. Both of these movements naturally require time. Having produced inhibition at the point of the brain corresponding to the shoulder, when I stimulated another place (the thigh) I found the inhibition had not yet spread this far. After twenty seconds it had gotten here; and in twenty seconds, though not before, complete inhibition occurred at this point. The concentration required forty seconds, and after sixty seconds from the end of the zero irritation on the shoulder, we already had a complete restoration of the reflex, on the second spot (the thigh). But on the primary place (the shoulder) the reflex was not yet restored even after five to ten or fifteen minutes.

This is my interpretation, the interpretation of a physiologist. I have had no difficulty in explaining these facts. For me it fits in perfectly with other facts in the physiology of the nervous process.

Now, gentlemen, we shall test the truth of this explanation. I have a means of verifying it. If actually we have a movement, then consequently in all the intervening points we should be able to predict the effect, judging by the fact that this movement occurs in two directions. I take only one intermediate point. What is to be expected at this place? In proportion to its proximity to that area where I produce the inhibition it will be inhibited. Consequently in it the zero effect appears sooner and lasts longer—while the inhibition passes further and then recedes. At this spot the return to the normal irritability occurs later. Thus it came to pass in the actual experiment. Here at the middle point after an interval of zero seconds, there were not 30 but 20 divisions. Then the zero effect appeared already after ten seconds, when the full inhibition had reached here, and this effect remained for a long time, both while the inhibition was spreading further, and also when it was contracting, and passing in the opposite direction. It is clear why on the thigh the normal reactivity returned after one minute, but here only after two minutes.

This is one of the most astonishing facts that I have seen in the laboratory. In the depth of the brain mass there occurs a special process, and its movement can be mathematically foretold.

So here, gentlemen, is the complexity of our experiment, and its relation to the physiologist. I do not know how the zoö-psychologists will answer me, how they will consider these facts, but answer them they must. If, indeed, they refuse to give an explanation, then with full justice I can say that their point of view is in general unscientific, and unsuitable for accurate investigation.

Section III
Heredity
and the
Chromosome Theory

Introduction

Probably no aspect of biology belongs more to the twentieth century than that of genetics. The year 1900 appropriately witnessed the rediscovery of Gregor Mendel's long-forgotten paper on plant hybridization (originally published in 1865); by 1910 Mendelian principles had been shown to apply to a large variety of other organisms. Studies on the fruit fly *Drosophila* between 1910 and 1915 established clearly that Mendel's "factors" (our genes) were located on the chromosomes in the cell nucleus. Somewhat later in the century the pressing problem in genetics became less a structural than a functional one: How do genes function to produce adult characters? Though many lines of work were involved, the most far-reaching and dramatic results were obtained in 1953 when J. D. Watson and F. H. C. Crick elucidated the molecular structure of DNA (deoxyribonucleic acid), the molecule which contained the information of genes. There have thus been two revolutions in the study of heredity in this century: one between 1900 and 1915, and one between 1953 and the present. The selection of papers in this section attempts to capture some of the features of each of these exciting periods.

Gregor Mendel was an Austrian monk at the Catholic monastery of Brünn, in what is now Czechoslovakia. His letter to Carl Nägeli, reprinted here, was written in 1867, in an attempt to elicit a more favorable response from Nägeli for Mendel's breeding experiments with peas *(Pisum)*. The letter presents a condensed summary of Mendel's results and the general laws he drew from them. Although Nägeli was one of the foremost plant breeders and experimental botanists in the nineteenth century, he failed almost completely to see the value of Mendel's work. Many reasons have been suggested for Nägeli's lack of interest. One is that Mendel's results were presented statistically, a form which was unfamiliar to most biologists of the time, and, indeed did not seem very relevant to the problems of heredity. Another is that Nägeli was a professional botanist, who had never heard of Mendel before the latter sent him a reprint of the famous paper of 1865. To Nägeli, Mendel was simply one of any number of amateur gardeners. And, too, since Mendel studied a different plant (pea) from that which interested Nägeli (the hawkweed), his work was not likely to attract the professional botanist's attention. Partly as a result of this total indifference of the scientific community to his work, and partly because of increased administrative duties within the monastery, Mendel wrote little else on plant breeding during the remainder of his life.

Shortly after Mendel's paper came to public notice, a young graduate student at Columbia University, W. S. Sutton, pointed out an interesting phenomenon. In the paper reprinted here, written in 1902, Sutton showed how the segregation of "factors" postulated by Mendel bore a strong resemblance to the physical separation of homologous chromosomes during mitosis of cells in higher plants and animals. Mendel himself had known nothing about the physical structure of cells or the movement of chromosomes. Sutton, a student of cytology, suggested that chromosomes might be the actual Mendelian factors or, at least, the bearers of them.

Three years later, one of Sutton's own professors, E. B. Wilson, showed that chromosomes were associated with the inheritance of sex in insects. Wilson's work (along with the independent studies of Nettie Stevens) demonstrated conclusively for the first time that the chromosomes were associated with specific hereditary characteristics (i.e., sex characters). This was a milestone in developing a comprehensive theory of heredity with a physical basis in cell structure. The later (post-1910) work of T. H. Morgan, in *Studies of Drosophila,* finally established unequivocably the chromosome theory of heredity.

The work of Wilson, Morgan, and others through the 1940's focused primarily on the structure, arrangement, and interaction of genes. Little was known about what genes really were, or how they functioned in a molecular or chemical sense. The work of J. D. Watson and F. H. C. Crick in 1953 provided a basis from which, for the first time, a whole series of molecular questions could be asked about gene function. The two papers reprinted here are adaptations from the investigators' Nobel laureate speeches, presented in Stockholm, Sweden, in December of 1962. Both papers discuss problems which grew out of these initial studies by Watson and Crick on the molecular structure of the DNA molecule. Crick's discussion shows how the nature of the genetic code was determined. Watson's paper deals principally with the transcription of RNA from the DNA template.

It must be emphasized that both papers discuss work which was possible to conceive of and carry out only after the structure of the molecule of heredity —DNA—was known. This was Watson and Crick's chief accomplishment; for this they, together with Maurice Wilkins, were awarded the 1962 Nobel Prize. One of the most significant features of any revolutionary scientific concept is the number of new areas of research it opens up. In this regard the Watson-Crick model of DNA is exemplary. Knowledge of the molecular structure of DNA has led to a much fuller understanding of such problems as how genes replicate, how they direct the construction of proteins, how information is carried within the molecule, how genes interact, and how they control their own rates of activity.

Letter on Hybridization from Mendel to Carl Nägeli

Highly Esteemed Sir:

My most cordial thanks for the printed matter you have so kindly sent me! The papers "die Bastardbildung im Pflanzenreiche," "über die abgeleiteten Pflanzenbastarde," "die Theorie der Bastardbildung," "die Zwischenformen zwischen den Pflanzenarten," "die systematische Behandlung der Hieracien rücksichtlich der Mittelformen und des Umfangs der Species," especially capture my attention. This thorough revision of the theory of hybrids according to contemporary science was most welcome. Thank you again!

With respect to the essay which your honor had the kindness to accept, I think I should add the following information: the experiments which are discussed were conducted from 1856 to 1863. I knew that the results I obtained were not easily compatible with our contemporary scientific knowledge, and that under the circumstances publication of one such isolated experiment was doubly dangerous; dangerous for the experimenter and for the cause he represented. Thus I made every effort to verify, with other plants, the results obtained with Pisum. A number of hybridizations undertaken in 1863 and 1864 convinced me of the difficulty of finding plants suitable for an extended series of experiments, and that under unfavorable circumstances years might elapse without my obtaining the desired information. I attempted to inspire some control experiments, and for that reason discussed the Pisum experiments at the meeting of the local society of naturalists. I encountered, as was to be expected, divided opinion; however, as far as I know, no one undertook to repeat the experiments. When, last year, I was asked to publish my lecture in the proceedings of the society, I agreed to do so, after having re-examined my records for the various years of experimentation, and not having been able to find a source of error. The paper which was submitted to you is the unchanged reprint of the draft of the lecture mentioned; thus the brevity of the exposition, as is essential for a public lecture.

I am not surprised to hear your honor speak of my experiments with mis-

Gregor Mendel, Letter of April 18, 1867, to Carl von Nägeli, in "The Birth of Genetics," supplement to *Genetics* 35 (1950), 3–10. Reprinted by permission.

trustful caution; I would not do otherwise in a similar case. Two points in your esteemed letter appear to be too important to be left unanswered. The first deals with the question whether one may conclude that constancy of type has been obtained if the hybrid *Aa* produces a plant *A*, and this plant in turn produces only *A*.

Permit me to state that, as an empirical worker, I must define constancy of type as the retention of a character during the period of observation. My statements that some of the progeny of hybrids breed true to type thus includes only those generations during which observations were made; it does not extend beyond them. For two generations all experiments were conducted with a fairly large number of plants. Starting with the third generation it became necessary to limit the numbers because of lack of space, so that, in each of the seven experiments, only a sample of those plants of the second generation (which either bred true or varied) could be observed further. The observations were extended over four to six generations. Of the varieties which bred true some plants were observed for four generations. I must further mention the case of a variety which bred true for six generations, although the parental types differed in four characters. In 1859 I obtained a very fertile descendent with large, tasty, seeds from a first generation hybrid. Since, in the following year, its progeny retained the desirable characteristics and were uniform, the variety was cultivated in our vegetable garden, and many plants were raised every year up to 1865. The parental plants were *bcDg* and *BCdG*:

B. albumen yellow	*b*. albumen green
C. seed-coat grayish-brown	*c*. seed-coat white
D. pod inflated	*d*. pod constricted
G. axis long	*g*. axis short

The hybrid just mentioned was *BcDG*.

The color of the albumen could be determined only in the plants saved for seed production, for the other pods were harvested in an immature condition. Never was green albumen observed in these plants, reddish-purple flower color (an indication of brown seed-coat), constriction of the pod, nor short axis.

This is the extent of my experience. I cannot judge whether these findings would permit a decision as to constancy of type; however, I am inclined to regard the separation of parental characteristics in the progeny of hybrids in Pisum as complete, and thus permanent. The progeny of hybrids carries one or the other of the parental characteristics, or the hybrid form of the two; I have never observed gradual transitions between the parental characters or a progressive approach toward one of them. The course of development consists simply in this; that in each generation the two parental characteristics appear, separated and unchanged, and there is nothing to indicate that one of them has either inherited or taken over anything from the other. For an example, permit me to point to the packets, numbers 1035–1088, which I sent you. All the seeds originated in the first generation of a hybrid in which brown and white seed-coats were combined. Out of the brown seed of this hybrid, some plants were obtained with seed-coats of a pure white color, without any admixture of brown. I expect those to retain the same constancy of character as found in the parental plant.

The second point, on which I wish to elaborate briefly, contains the following statement: "You should regard the numerical expressions as being only empirical, because they can not be proved rational."

My experiments with single characters all lead to the same result: that from the seeds of the hybrids, plants are obtained half of which in turn carry the hybrid character *(Aa),* the other half, however, receive the parental characters *A* and *a* in equal amounts. Thus, on the average, among four plants two have the hybrid character *Aa,* one the parental character *A,* and the other the parental character *a.* Therefore $2Aa+A+a$ or $A+2Aa+a$ is the empirical simple, developmental series for two differentiating characters. Likewise it was shown in an empirical manner that, if two or three differentiating characters are combined in the hybrid, the developmental series is a combination of two or three simple series. Up to this point I don't believe I can be accused of having left the realm of experimentation. If then I extend this combination of simple series to any number of differences between the two parental plants, I have indeed entered the rational domain. This seems permissible, however, because I have proved by previous experiments that the development of any two differentiating characteristics proceeds independently of any other differences. Finally, regarding my statements on the differences among the ovules and pollen cells of the hybrids; they also are based on experiments. These and similar experiments on the germ cells appear to be important, for I believe that their results furnish the explanation for the development of hybrids as observed in Pisum. These experiments should be repeated and verified.

I regret very much not being able to send your honor the varieties you desire. As I mentioned above, the experiments were conducted up to and including 1863; at that time they were terminated in order to obtain space and time for the growing of other experimental plants. Therefore seeds from those experiments are no longer available. Only one experiment on differences in the time of flowering was continued; and seeds are available from the 1864 harvest of this experiment. These are the last I collected, since I had to abandon the experiment in the following year because of devastation by the pea beetle, *Bruchus pisi.* In the early years of experimentation this insect was only rarely found on the plants, in 1864 it caused considerable damage, and appeared in such numbers in the following summer that hardly a 4th or 5th of the seeds was spared. In the last few years it has been necessary to discontinue cultivation of peas in the vicinity of Brünn. The seeds remaining can still be useful, among them are some varieties which I expect to remain constant; they are derived from hybrids in which two, three, and four differentiating characters are combined. All the seeds were obtained from members of the first generation, i.e., of such plants as were grown directly from the seeds of the original hybrids.

I should have scruples against complying with your honor's request to send these seeds for experimentation, were it not in such complete agreement with my own wishes. I fear that there has been partial loss of viability. Furthermore the seeds were obtained at a time when *Bruchus pisi* was already rampant, and I cannot acquit this beetle of possibly transferring pollen; also, I must mention again that the plants were destined for a study of differences in flowering time. The other differences were also taken into account at the harvest, but with less care than in the major experiment. The legend which I have added to the packet numbers on a separate sheet is a copy of the notes I made for each individual plant, with pencil, on its envelope at the time of harvest. The dominant characters are designated as A, B, C, D, E, F, G. . . . The recessive characters are designated a, b, c, d, e, f, g; these should remain constant in the next generation. Therefore, from those seeds which stem from plants with recessive characters only, identical plants are expected (as regards the characters studied).

Please compare the numbers of the seed packets with those in my record, to detect any possible error in the designations—each packet contains the seeds of a single plant only.

Some of the varieties represented are suitable for experiments on the germ cells; their results can be obtained during the current summer. The round yellow seeds of packets 715, 730, 736, 741, 742, 745, 756, 757, and on the other hand, the green angular seeds of packets 712, 719, 734, 737, 749, and 750 can be recommended for this purpose. By repeated experiments it was proved that, if plants with green seeds are fertilized by those with yellow seeds, the albumen of the resulting seeds has lost the green color and has taken up the yellow color. The same is true for the shape of the seed. Plants with angular seeds, if fertilized by those with round or rounded seeds, produce round or rounded seeds. Thus, due to the changes induced in the color and shape of the seeds by fertilization with foreign pollen, it is possible to recognize the constitution of the fertilizing pollen.

Let B designate yellow color; b, green color of the albumen.

Let A designate round shape; a, angular shape of the seeds.

If flowers of such plants as produce green and angular seeds by self-fertilization are fertilized with foreign pollen, and if the seeds remain green and angular, then the pollen of the donor plant was, as regards the two characters ab.

If the shape of the seeds is changed, the pollen was taken from Ab.

If the color of the seeds is changed, the pollen was taken from aB.

If both shape and color is changed, the pollen was taken from AB.

The packets enumerated above contain round and yellow, round and green, angular and yellow, and angular and green seeds from the hybrids $ab + AB$. The round and yellow seeds would be best suited for the experiment. Among them . . . the varities AB, ABb, Aab, and $AaBb$ may occur; thus four cases are possible when plants, grown from green and angular seeds, are fertilized by the pollen of those grown from the above mentioned round and yellow seeds, i.e.

I. $ab + AB$

II. $ab + ABb$

III. $ab + AaB$

IV. $ab + AaBb$

If the hypothesis that hybrids form as many types of pollen cells as there are possible constant combination types is correct, plants of the makeup

AB	produce pollen of the type	AB
ABb	,, ,, ,, ,, ,, ,,	AB and Ab
AaB	,, ,, ,, ,, ,, ,,	AB and aB
$AaBb$	,, ,, ,, ,, ,, ,,	$AB, Ab, aB,$ and ab

Fertilization of ovules occurs:

I. Ovules ab with pollen AB

II.   ,, ab ,,   ,, AB and Ab

III.   ,, ab ,,   ,, AB and aB

IV.   ,, ab ,,   ,, $AB, Ab, aB,$ and ab

The following varieties may be obtained from this fertilization:

I. $AaBb$

II. $AaBb$ and Aab

III. $AaBb$ and aBb

IV. $AaBb, Aab, aBb,$ and ab

If the different types of pollen are produced in equal numbers, there should be in

I. All seeds round and yellow

II. one half round and yellow
one half round and green

III. one half round and yellow
one half angular and yellow

IV. one quarter round and yellow
one quarter round and green
one quarter angular and yellow
one quarter angular and green

Furthermore, since the numerical relations between $AB, ABb, AaB, AaBb$ are $1:2:2:4$, among any nine plants grown from round yellow seed there should be found on the average $AaBb$ four times, ABb and AaB twice each, and AB once; thus the IVth case should occur four times as frequently as the Ist and twice as frequently as the IInd or IIIrd.

If on the other hand, plants grown from the round yellow seeds mentioned are fertilized by pollen from green angular plants, the results should be exactly the same, provided that the ovules are of the same types, and formed in the same proportions, as was reported for the pollen.

I have not performed this experiment myself, but I believe, on the basis of similar experiments, that one can depend on the result indicated.

In the same fashion individual experiments may be performed for each of the two seed characters separately, all those round seeds which occurred together with angular ones, and all the yellow ones which occurred with green seeds on the same plant are suitable. If, for instance, a plant with green seeds was fertilized by one with yellow seeds, the seeds obtained should be either 1) all yellow, or 2) half yellow and half green, since the plants originating from yellow seeds are of the varieties *B* and *Bb*. Since, furthermore, *B* and *Bb* occur in the ratio of 1:2, the 2nd fertilization will occur twice as frequently as the 1st.

Regarding the other characters, the experiments may be conducted in the same way; results, however, will not be obtained until next year.

I have all the piloselloid Hieracia which your honor recommends for the experiments; also *H. murorum* and *H. vulgatum* of the Archieracia; *H. glaucum, H. alpinum, H. amplexicaule, H. prenanthoides,* and *H. tridentatum* do not occur in this vicinity. Last summer I found a withered Hieracium, which has the seed color of Prenanthoidea (Fries: Achaenia typice testaces [pallida]), but did not resemble any of the herbarium specimens of this type very closely; finally our botanist declared it to be a hybrid. The rootstock has been transplanted to the garden for further observations, and the seeds have been planted. On the whole, this area is poor in Hieracia, and probably has not been sufficiently searched. Next summer I hope to have the time to roam the sandy lignite country which extends eastward from Brünn for several miles to the Hungarian frontier. Several other rare plants are known from this region. The Moravian plateau also is probably terra incognita as far as the Hieracia are concerned. If I should find anything noteworthy during the summer, I shall hurry to send it to your honor. At the moment permit me to include with the seed packets the plant just mentioned, albeit in a rather defective condition, together with another Hieracium. Last year I found at least 50 specimens of it on an old garden wall. This plant is not found in the local herbaria; its appearance suggests both *H. praealtum* and *H. echioides,* without being one or the other. *H. praealtum* does occur in the environs of the city, *H. echioides* does not.

Several specimens of the hybrid *Geum urbanum*+*G. rivale* (from last year's hybridization) wintered in the greenhouse. Three are now flowering, the others will follow. Their pollen is fairly well developed, and the plants should be fertile, just as Gärtner states. It seems strange that all the plants now flowering are of the exceptional type mentioned by Gärtner. He says: *"Geum urbano-rivale,* mostly with large flowers, like *rivale,* and only a few specimens with small yellow flowers like *urbanum."* In my plants the flowers are yellow or yellow-orange, and about half the size of those of *G. rivale;* the other characters correspond, as far as can be judged at present, to those of *G. intermedium* Ehrh. Could it be that the exceptional type has an earlier flowering season? To judge from the buds, however, the other plants do not have large flowers either. Or could it be that the exception has become the rule? I believe I have good reasons for considering my parental species pure. I obtained *G. urbanum* in the environs of the city, where neither *G. rivale,* nor any other species of the genus occurs; and I got *G. rivale* in a damp mountain meadow, where *G. urbanum* certainly does not occur. This plant has all the characteristics of *G. rivale*; it is being maintained in the garden, and seedlings have been produced from self-fertilization.

The *Cirsium arvense* + *C. oleraceum* hybrids, sown in the fall, have died during the winter; one plant of the *C. arvense* + *C. canum* hybrid survived. I hope the spring seedlings will do better. Two other Cirsium hybrids have wintered well in the greenhouse. Last summer I observed, on a flowering plant of *C. praemorsum* M. *(olerac.* + *rivulare)*, that in those heads which develop first and last on the stems, no pollen is formed, and thus they are completely sterile; on the others (about one half of the total heads) some pollen and fertile seed is formed. Fertilization experiments were conducted with two of the late-developing heads; pollen of *C. palustre* was transferred to one, pollen of *C. canum* to the other. Viable seeds were obtained from both, the resulting plants survived the winter in the greenhouse, and are now developed to a stage at which the success of the hybridization is evident. Some seedlings of *C. praemorsum*, others of a hybrid (probably in the group *C. canum* + *palustre*), and those of a third one, probably *C. rivulare* + *palustre*, have survived the winter in the open quite well. The same may be said of the autumn seedlings of the hybrids *Aquilegia canadensis* + *vulgaris*, *A. canadensis* + *A. atropurpurea*, and *A. canadensis* + *A. Wittmaniana*. However, fall seedlings of some Hieracia which were grown to test constancy of type have suffered considerable damage. In this genus it is preferable to sow in the early spring, but then it is doubtful that the plants will flower in the same year. Nevertheless, FRIES has made this statement concerning the division Accipitrina: "Accipitrina, praecocius sata, vulgo primo anno florent."

I have obtained luxuriant plants of *Linaria vulgaris* + *L. purpurea*; I hope they will flower in the first year. The same may be said of *Calceolaria salicifolia* and *C. rugosa*. Hybrids of *Zea Mays major* (with dark red seeds) + *Z. Mays minor* (with yellow seeds) and of *Zea Mays major* (with dark red seeds) + *Zea Cuzko* (with white seeds) will develop during the summer. Whether *Zea Cuzko* is a true species or not I do not dare to state. I obtained it with this designation from a seed dealer. At any rate it is a very aberrant form. To study color development in flowers of hybrids, cross-fertilizations were made last year between varieties of *Ipomoea purpurea*, *Cheiranthus annuus*, and *Antirrhinum majus*. An experiment with hybrids of *Tropaeoleum majus* + *T. minus* (1st generation) must also be mentioned.

For the current year exploratory experiments with Veronica, Viola, Potentilla, and Carex are planned. Unfortunately, I have only a small number of species.

Because of lack of space the experiments can be started with a small number of plants only; after the fertility of the hybrids has been tested, and when it is possible to protect them sufficiently during the flowering period, each in turn will receive an extensive study. Thus far the three Aquilegia hybrids mentioned above and *Tropaeoleum majus* + *T. minus* are suitable, although the latter has only partial fertility. It is hoped that *Geum urbanum* + *G. rivale* can be included in the group of suitable plants.

As must be expected, the experiments proceed slowly. At first beginning, some patience is required, but later, when several experiments are progressing concurrently, matters are improved. Every day, from spring to fall, one's interest is refreshed daily, and the care which must be given to one's wards is thus amply repaid. In addition, if I should, by my experiments, succeed in hastening the solution of these problems, I should be doubly happy.

Accept, highly esteemed Sir, the expression of most sincere respect from

> Your devoted,
> *G. Mendel*
> (Altbrünn, Monastery of St. Thomas)

Brünn, 18 April, 1867

The Chromosomes in Heredity

by *WALTER S. SUTTON*

In a recent announcement of some results of a critical study of the chromosomes in the various cell-generations of *Brachystola*[1] the author briefly called attention to a possible relation between the phenomena there described and certain conclusions first drawn from observations on plant hybrids by Gregor Mendel in[2] 1865, and recently confirmed by a number of able investigators. Further attention has already been called to the theoretical aspects of the subject in a brief communication by Professor E. B. Wilson.[3] The present paper is devoted to a more detailed discussion of these aspects, the speculative character of which may be justified by the attempt to indicate certain lines of work calculated to test the validity of the conclusions drawn. The general conceptions here advanced were evolved purely from cytological data, before the author had knowledge of the Mendelian principles, and are now presented as the contribution of a cytologist who can make no pretensions to complete familiarity with the results of experimental studies on heredity. As will appear hereafter, they completely

Abridged from Walter S. Sutton, "The Chromosomes in Heredity," *Biological Bulletin* **4** (1902), 231–251. Reprinted by permission.

[1] Sutton, Walter S., "On the Morphology of the Chromosome Group in Brachystola magna," *Biol. Bull.,* IV, 1, 1902.
[2] Mendel, Gregor Johann, "Versuche über Pflanzen-Hybriden," *Verh. naturf. Vers. in Brünn* IV., and in Osterwald's *Klassiker der exakten Wissenschaft*. English translation in *Journ. Roy. Hort. Soc.,* XXVI., 1901. Later reprinted with modifications and corrections in Bateson's "Mendel's Principles of Heredity," Cambridge, 1902, p. 40.
[3] Wilson, E. B., "Mendel's Principles of Heredity and the Maturation of the Germ-Cells," *Science,* XVI., 416.

satisfy the conditions in typical Mendelian cases, and it seems that many of the known deviations from the Mendelian type may be explained by easily conceivable variations from the normal chromosomic processes.

It has long been admitted that we must look to the organization of the germ-cells for the ultimate determination of hereditary phenomena. Mendel fully appreciated this fact and even instituted special experiments to determine the nature of that organization. From them he drew the brilliant conclusion that, while, in the organism, maternal and paternal potentialities are present in the field of each character, *the germ-cells in respect to each character are pure.* Little was then known of the nature of cell-division, and Mendel attempted no comparisons in that direction; but to those who in recent years have revived and extended his results the probability of a relation between cell-organization and cell-division has repeatedly occurred. Bateson[4] clearly states his impression in this regard in the following words: "It is impossible to be presented with the fact that in Mendelian cases the cross-bred produces on an average *equal* numbers of gametes of each kind, that is to say, a symmetrical result, without suspecting that this fact must correspond with some symmetrical figure of distribution of the gametes in the cell divisions by which they are produced."

Nearly a year ago it became apparent to the author that the high degree of organization in the chromosome-group of the germ-cells as shown in *Brachystola* could scarcely be without definite significance in inheritance, for, as shown in the paper[5] already referred to, it had appeared that:

1. The chromosome group of the presynaptic germ-cells is made up of two equivalent chromosome-series, and that strong ground exists for the conclusion that one of these is paternal and the other maternal.

2. The process of synapsis (pseudo-reduction) consists in the union in pairs of the homologous members (*i.e.*, those that correspond in size) of the two series.[6]

3. The first post-synaptic or maturation mitosis is equational and hence results in no chromosomic differentiation.

4. The second post-synaptic division is a reducing division, resulting in the separation of the chromosomes which have conjugated in synapsis, and their relegation to different germ-cells.

5. The chromosomes retain a morphological individuality throughout the various cell-divisions.

It is well known that in the eggs of many forms the maternal and paternal chromosome groups remain distinctly independent of each other for a considerable number of cleavage-mitoses, and with this fact in mind the author was

---

[4] Bateson, W., "Mendel's Principles of Heredity," Cambridge, 1902, p. 30.

[5] Sutton, W. S., *loc. cit.*

[6] The conclusion that synapsis involves a union of paternal and maternal chromosomes in pairs was first reached by Montgomery in 1901. Montgomery, T. H., Jr., "A Study of the Chromosomes of the Germ-Cells of Metazoa," *Trans. Amer. Phil. Soc.*, XX.

at first inclined to conclude that in the reducing divisions all the maternal chromosomes must pass to one pole and all the paternal ones to the other, and that the germ-cells are thus divided into two categories which might be described as maternal and paternal respectively. But this conception, which is identical with that recently brought forward by Cannon,[7] was soon seen to be at variance with many well-known facts of breeding; thus:

1. If the germ-cells of hybrids are of pure descent, no amount of cross-breeding could accomplish more than the condition of a first-cross.

2. If any animal or plant has but two categories of germ-cells, there can be only four different combinations in the offspring of a single pair.

3. If either maternal or paternal chromosomes are entirely excluded from every ripe germ-cell, an individual cannot receive chromosomes (qualities) from more than one ancestor in each generation of each of the parental lines of descent, *e.g.*, could not inherit chromosomes (qualities) from both paternal or both maternal grandparents.

Moved by these considerations a more careful study was made of the whole division-process, including the positions of the chromosomes in the nucleus before division, the origin and formation of the spindle, the relative positions of the chromosomes and the diverging centrosomes, and the point of attachment of the spindle fibers to the chromosomes. The results gave no evidence in favor of parental purity of the gametic chromatin as a whole. On the contrary, many points were discovered which strongly indicate[8] that the position of the bivalent chromosomes in the equatorial plate of the reducing division is purely a matter of chance—that is, that any chromosome pair may lie with maternal or paternal chromatid indifferently toward either pole irrespective of the positions of other pairs—and hence that a large number of different combinations of maternal and paternal chromosomes are possible in the mature germ-products of an individual. To illustrate this, we may consider a form having eight chromosomes in the somatic and presynaptic germ-cells and consequently four in the ripe germ-products. The germ-cell series of the species in general may be designated by the letters A, B, C, D, and any cleavage nucleus may be considered as containing chromosomes A, B, C, D from the father and a, b, c, d, from the mother. Synapsis being the union of homologues would result in the formation of the bivalent chromosomes Aa, Bb, Cc, Dd, which would again be resolved into their components by the reducing division. Each of the ripe germ-cells arising from the

---

[7] Cannon, W. A., "A Cytological Basis for the Mendelian Laws," *Bull. Torrey Botanical Club*, 29, 1902.

[8] Absolute proof is impossible in a pure-bred form on account of the impossibility of distinguishing between maternal and paternal members of any synaptic pair. If, however, such hybrids as those obtained by Moenkhaus (Moenkhaus, W. J., "Early Development in Certain Hybrid Species," Report of Second Meeting of Naturalists at Chicago, *Science*, XIII., 323), with fishes can be reared to sexual maturity absolute proof of this point may be expected. This observer was able in the early cells of certain fish hybrids to distinguish the maternal from the paternal chromosomes by differences in form, and if the same can be done in the maturation-divisions the question of the distribution of chromosomes in reduction becomes a very simple matter of observation.

reduction divisions must receive one member from each of the synaptic pairs, but there are sixteen possible combinations of maternal and paternal chromosomes, that will form a complete series, to wit: a, B, C, D; A, b, C, D; A, B, c, D; A, B, C, d; a, b, C, D; a, B, c, D; a, B, C, d; a, b, c, d; and their conjugates A, b, c, d; a, B, c, d; a, b, C, d; a, b, c, D; A, B, c, d; A, b, C, d; A, b, c, D; A, B, C, D. Hence instead of two kinds of gametes an organism with four chromosomes in its reduced series may give rise to 16 different kinds; and the offspring of two unrelated individuals may present 16×16 or 256 combinations, instead of the four to which it would be limited by a hypothesis of parental purity of gametes. Few organisms, moreover, have so few as 8 chromosomes, and since each additional pair doubles the number of possible combinations in the germ-products[9] and quadruples that of the zygotes it is plain that in the ordinary form having from 24 to 36 chromosomes, the possibilities are immense. The table below shows the number of possible combinations in forms having from 2 to 36 chromosomes in the presynaptic cells.

Chromosomes		Combinations in Gametes	Combinations in Zygotes
Somatic Series	Reduced Series		
2	1	2	4
4	2	4	16
6	3	8	64
8	4	16	256
10	5	32	1,024
12	6	64	4,096
14	7	128	16,384
16	8	256	65,536
18	9	512	262,144
20	10	1,024	1,048,576
22	11	2,048	4,194,304
24	12	4,096	16,777,216
26	13	8,192	67,108,864
28	14	16,384	268,435,456
30	15	32,768	1,073,741,824
32	16	65,536	4,294,967,296
34	17	131,072	17,179,869,184
36	18	262,144	68,719,476,736

Thus if Bardeleben's estimate of sixteen chromosomes for man (the lowest estimate that has been made) be correct, each individual is capable of producing 256 different kinds of germ-products with reference to their chromosome com-

[9] The number of possible combinations in the germ-products of a single individual of any species is represented by the simple formula 2^n in which n represents the number of chromosomes in the reduced series.

binations, and the numbers of combinations possible in the offspring of a single pair is 256×256 or $65,536$; while *Toxopneustes,* with 36 chromosomes, has a possibility of $262,144$ and $68,719,476,736$ different combinations in the gametes of a single individual and the zygotes of a pair respectively. It is this possibility of so great a number of combinations of maternal and paternal chromosomes in the gametes which serves to bring the chromosome-theory into final relation with the known facts of heredity; for Mendel himself followed out the actual combinations of two and three distinctive characters and found them to be inherited independently of one another and to present a great variety of combinations in the second generation.

The constant size-differences observed in the chromosomes of *Brachystola* early led me to the suspicion, which, however, a study of spermatogenesis alone could not confirm, that the individual chromosomes of the reduced series play different *rôles* in development. The confirmation of this surmise appeared later in the results obtained by Boveri[10] in a study of larvæ actually lacking in certain chromosomes of the normal series, which seem to leave no alternative to the conclusion that the chromosomes differ qualitatively and as individuals represent distinct potentialities. Accepting this conclusion we should be able to find an exact correspondence between the behavior in inheritance of any chromosome and that of the characters associated with it in the organism.

In regard to the characters, Mendel found that, if a hybrid produced by crossing two individuals differing in a particular character be self-fertilized, the offspring, in most cases, conform to a perfectly definite rule as regards the differential character. Representing the character as seen in one of the original parents by the letter A and that of the other by a, then all the offspring arising by self-fertilization of the hybrid are represented from the standpoint of the given character by the formula AA:2Aa:aa.—that is, one fourth receive only the character of one of the original pure-bred parents, one fourth only that of the other; while one half the number receive the characters of both original parents and hence present the condition of the hybrid from which they sprang.

We have not heretofore possessed graphic formulæ to express the combinations of chromosomes in similar breeding experiments, but it is clear from the data already given that such formulæ may now be constructed. The reduced chromosome series in *Brachystola* is made up of eleven members, no two of which are exactly of the same size. These I distinguished in my previous paper by the letters A, B, C, . . . K. In the unreduced series there are twenty-two elements [11] which can be seen to make up two series like that of the mature germ-cells, and hence may be designated as A, B, C . . . K—A, B, C . . . K. Synapsis results in the union of homologues and the production of a single series of double-elements

[10] Boveri, Th., "Ueber Mehrpolige Mitosen als Mittel zur Analyse des Zellkerns," *Verh. d. Phys.-Med. Ges. zu Würzburg,* N. F., Bd. XXXV., 1902. It appears from a personal letter that Boveri had noted the correspondence between chromosomic behavior as deducible from his experiments and the results on plant hybrids—as indicated also in footnote 1, *l. c.,* p. 81.

[11] Disregarding the accessory chromosome which takes no part in synapsis.

thus: AA, BB, CC . . . KK, and the reducing division affects the separation of these pairs so that one member of each passes to each of the resulting germ-products.

There is reason to believe that the division-products of a given chromosome in *Brachystola* maintain in their respective series the same size relation as did the parent element; and this, taken together with the evidence that the various chromosomes of the series represent distinctive potentialities, make it probable that a given size-relation is characteristic of the physical basis of a definite set of characters. But each chromosome of any reduced series in the species has a homologue in any other series, and from the above consideration it should follow that these homologues cover the same field in development. If this be the case chromosome *A* from the father and its homologue, chromosome *a*, from the mother in the presynaptic cells of the offspring may be regarded as the physical bases of the antagonistic unit-characters A and a of father and mother respectively. In synapsis, copulation of the homologues gives rise to the bivalent chromosome *Aa*, which as is indicated above would, in the reducing division, be separated into the components *A* and *a*. These would in all cases pass to different germ-products and hence in a monœcious form we should have four sorts of gametes,

$$A\,♂ \quad a\,♂$$
$$A\,♀ \quad a\,♀$$

which would yield four combinations,

$$A\,♂ \; + \; A\,♀ = AA$$
$$A\,♂ \; + \; a\,♀ = Aa$$
$$a\,♂ \; + \; A\,♀ = aA$$
$$a\,♂ \; + \; a\,♀ = aa$$

Since the second and third of these are alike the result would be expressed by the formula *AA* : *2Aa* : *aa* which is the same as that given for any character in a Mendelian case. *Thus the phenomena of germ-cell division and of heredity are seen to have the same essential features, viz., purity of units (chromosomes, characters) and the independent transmission of the same;* while as a corollary, it follows in each case that each of the two antagonistic units (chromosomes, characters) is contained by exactly half the gametes produced.

The observations which deal with characters have been made chiefly upon hybrids, while the cytological data are the result of study of a pure-bred form; but the correlation of the two is justified by the observation of Cannon[12] that the maturation mitoses of fertile hybrids are normal. This being the case it is necessary to conclude, as Cannon has already pointed out, that the course of variations in hybrids either is a result of normal maturation processes or is entirely independent of the nature of those divisions. If we conclude from the evidence already given that the double basis of hybrid characters is to be found

---

[12] Cannon, W. A., *loc. cit.*

in the pairs of homologous chromosomes of the presynaptic germ-cells, then we must also conclude that in pure-bred forms likewise, the paired arrangement of the chromosomes indicates a dual basis for each character. In a hypothetical species breeding absolutely true, therefore, all the chromosomes or subdivisions of chromosomes representing any given character would have to be exactly alike, since the combination of any two of them would produce a uniform result. As a matter of fact, however, specific characters are not found to be constant quantities but vary within certain limits; and many of the variations are known to be inheritable. Hence it seems highly probable that homologous chromatin-entities are not usually of strictly uniform constitution, but present minor variations corresponding to the various expressions of the character they represent. In other words, it is probable that specific differences and individual variations are alike traceable to a common source, which is a difference in the constitution of homologous chromatin-entities. Slight differences in homologues would mean corresponding, slight variations in the character concerned—a correspondence which is actually seen in cases of inbreeding, where variation is well known to be minimized and where obviously in the case of many of the chromosome pairs both members must be derived from the same chromosome of a recent common ancestor and hence be practically identical. . . .

We have seen reason, in the foregoing considerations, to believe that there is a definite relation between chromosomes and allelomorphs[13] or unit characters but we have not before inquired whether an entire chromosome or only a part of one is to be regarded as the basis of a single allelomorph. The answer must unquestionably be in favor of the latter possibility, for otherwise the number of distinct characters possessed by an individual could not exceed the number of chromosomes in the germ-products; which is undoubtedly contrary to fact. We must, therefore, assume that some chromosomes at least are related to a number of different allelomorphs. If then, the chromosomes permanently retain their individuality, it follows that all the allelomorphs represented by any one chromosome must be inherited together. On the other hand, it is not necessary to assume that all must be apparent in the organism, for here the question of dominance enters and it is not yet known that dominance is a function of an entire chromosome. It is conceivable that the chromosome may be divisible into smaller entities (somewhat as Weismann assumes), which represent the allelomorphs and may be dominant or recessive independently. In this way the same chromosome might at one time represent both dominant and recessive allelomorphs.

Such a conception infinitely increases the number of possible combinations of characters *as actually seen* in the individuals and unfortunately at the same time increases the difficulty of determining what characters are inherited together, since usually recessive chromatin entities (allelomorphs?) constantly associated in the same chromosome with usually dominant ones would evade detection for generations and then becoming dominant might appear as reversions in a very confusing manner. . . .

---

[13] Bateson's term.

Dominance is not a conception which grows out of purely cytological consideration. Cytology merely shows us the presence in a cell of two chromosomes, either of which is capable of producing some expression of a given character, and it is left to experiment in each case to show what the effect of this combined action will be. The experiment[14] has shown that any one of the three theoretical possibilities may be realized, viz: (1) One or the other may dominate and obscure its homologue. (2) The result may be a compromise in which the effect of each chromosome is to be recognized. (3) The combined action of the two may result in an entirely new cast of character. In cases belonging to the first category, the visible quality (allelomorph, chromatin-entity) was described by Mendel as dominant and the other as recessive, and the experiments of Bateson and Saunders and others, as well as those of Mendel, have shown that in many cases a dominant character tends to remain dominant during successive generations if the environment is not materially changed. Nevertheless, some experiments cited by Bateson[15] go to show that dominance may be variable or defective. Furthermore, it is not only conceivable, but highly probable that in most, if not all cases, there are many different expressions of each character (*i.e.,* many different allelomorphs as suggested by Bateson[3] in regard to human stature), which on various combinations would necessarily exhibit relative dominance. The experiments with peas show an almost constant dominance of certain allelomorphs, such as round over wrinkled in seeds, and of yellow over green in cotyledons; but it is worthy of note that here, as in most Mendelian experiments, only two antagonistic characters have been used. Investigations on varieties, in general similar, but exhibiting different expressions of some particular character, will certainly yield instructive results. Bateson's observations on crosses between single-, rose- and pea-combed fowls, represent a simple form of such a case and may be expected on completion to add much to our knowledge of the nature of dominance. . . .

---

[14] Bateson and Saunders, Experimental Studies in the Physiology of Heredity. Reports to the Evolution Committee, I. London, 1902, p. 81, paragraphs 11 and 12.

[15] *Cf.* Bateson and Saunders, *loc. cit.*

The Chromosomes in Relation to the Determination of Sex in Insects

by EDMUND B. WILSON

Material procured during the past summer demonstrates with great clearness that the sexes of Hemiptera show constant and characteristic differences in the chromosome groups, which are of such a nature as to leave no doubt that a definite connection of some kind between the chromosomes and the determination of sex exists in these animals. These differences are of two types. In one of these, the cells of the female possess one more chromosome than those of the male; in the other, both sexes possess the same number of chromosomes, but one of the chromosomes in the male is much smaller than the corresponding one in the female (which is in agreement with the observations of Stevens on the beetle *Tenebrio*). These types may conveniently be designated as *A* and *B*, respectively. The essential facts have been determined in three genera of each type, namely, (type *A*) *Protenor belfragei, Anasa tristis* and *Alydus pilosulus,* and (type *B*) *Lygoeus turcicus, Euschistus fissilis* and *Coenus delius.* The chromosome groups have been examined in the dividing oogonia and ovarian follicle cells of the female and in the dividing spermatogonia and investing cells of the testis in case of the male.

Type *A* includes those forms in which (as has been known since Henking's paper of 1890 on *Pyrrochoris*) the spermatozoa are of two classes, one of which contains one more chromosome (the so-called 'accessory' or heterotropic chromosome) than the other. In this type the somatic number of chromosomes in the female is an even one, while the somatic number in the male is one less (hence an odd number) the actual numbers being in *Protenor* and *Alydus* ♀ 14, ♂ 13, and in *Anasa* ♀ 22, ♂ 21. A study of the chromosome groups in the two sexes brings out the following additional facts. In the cells of the female all the chromosomes may be arranged two by two to form pairs, each consisting of two chromosomes of equal size, as is most obvious in the beautiful chromosome groups of *Protenor,* where the size differences of the chromosomes are very marked. In the male all the chromosomes may be thus symmetrically paired with the exception of one which is without a mate. This chromosome is the 'accessory' or heterotropic one; and it is a consequence of its unpaired character that it passes into only one half of the spermatozoa.

Edmund B. Wilson, "The Chromosomes in Relation to the Determination of Sex in Insects," *Science* **22** (October 20, 1905), 500–502. Reprinted by permission of the American Association for the Advancement of Science.

In type *B* all of the spermatozoa contain the same number of chromosomes (half the somatic number in both sexes), but they are, nevertheless, of two classes, one of which contains a large and one a small 'idiochromosome.' Both sexes have the same somatic number of chromosomes (fourteen in the three examples mentioned above), but differ as follows: In the cells of the female (oogonia and follicle-cells) all of the chromosomes may, as in type *A*, be arranged two by two in equal pairs, and a small idiochromosome is not present. In the cells of the male all but two may be thus equally paired. These two are the unequal idiochromosomes, and during the maturation process they are so distributed that the small one passes into one half of the spermatozoa, the large one into the other half.

These facts admit, I believe, of but one interpretation. Since all of the chromosomes in the female (oogonia) may be symmetrically paired, there can be no doubt that synapsis in this sex gives rise to the reduced number of symmetrical bivalents, and that consequently all of the eggs receive the same number of chromosomes. This number (eleven in *Anasa*, seven in *Protenor* or *Alydus*) is the same as that present in those spermatozoa that contain the 'accessory' chromosome. It is evident that both forms of spermatozoa are functional, and that in type *A* females are produced from eggs fertilized by spermatozoa that contain the 'accessory' chromosome, while males are produced from eggs fertilized by spermatozoa that lack this chromosome (the reverse of the conjecture made by McClung). Thus if n be the somatic number in the female $n/2$ is the number in all of the matured eggs, $n/2$ the number in one half of the spermatozoa (namely, those that contain the 'accessory'), and $n/2-1$ the number in the other half. Accordingly: In fertilization

$$\text{Egg } \frac{n}{2} + \text{spermatozoon } \frac{n}{2} \quad = n \text{ (female).}$$

$$\text{Egg } \frac{n}{2} + \text{spermatozoon } \frac{n}{2}-1 = n-1 \text{ (male).}$$

The validity of this interpretation is completely established by the case of *Protenor*, where, as was first shown by Montgomery, the 'accessory' is at every period unmistakably recognizable by its great size. The spermatogonial divisions invariably show but one such large chromosome, while an equal pair of exactly similar chromosomes appear in the oogonial divisions. One of these in the female must have been derived in fertilization from the egg-nucleus, the other (obviously the 'accessory') from the sperm-nucleus. It is evident, therefore, that all of the matured eggs must before fertilization contain a chromosome that is the maternal mate of the 'accessory' of the male, and that females are produced from eggs fertilized by spermatozoa that contain a similar group (*i.e.*, those containing the 'accessory'). The presence of but one large chromosome (the 'accessory') in the somatic nuclei of the male can only mean that males arise from eggs fertilized by spermatozoa that lack such a chromosome, and that the single 'accessory' of the male is derived in fertilization from the egg nucleus.

In type *B* all of the eggs must contain a chromosome corresponding to the large idiochromosome of the male. Upon fertilization by a spermatozoon containing the large idiochromosome a female is produced, while fertilization by a spermatozoon containing the small one produces a male.

The two types distinguished above may readily be reduced to one; for if the small idiochromosome of type *B* be supposed to disappear, the phenomena become identical with those in type *A*. There can be little doubt that such has been the actual origin of the latter type, and that the 'accessory' chromosome was originally a large idiochromosome, its smaller mate having vanished. The unpaired character of the 'accessory' chromosome thus finds a complete explanation, and its behavior loses its apparently anomalous character.

The foregoing facts irresistibly lead to the conclusion that a causal connection of some kind exists between the chromosomes and the determination of sex; and at first thought they naturally suggest the conclusion that the idiochromosomes and heterotropic chromosomes are actually sex determinants, as was conjectured by McClung in case of the 'accessory' chromosome. Analysis will show, however, that great, if not insuperable, difficulties are encountered by any form of the assumption that these chromosomes are specifically male or female sex determinants. It is more probable, for reasons that will be set forth hereafter, that the difference between eggs and spermatozoa is primarily due to differences of degree or intensity, rather than of kind, in the activity of the chromosome groups in the two sexes; and we may here find a clue to a general theory of sex determination that will accord with the facts observed in hemiptera. A significant fact that bears on this question is that in both types the two sexes differ in respect to the behavior of the idiochromosomes or 'accessory' chromosomes during the synaptic and growth periods, these chromosomes assuming in the male the form of condensed chromosome nucleoli, while in the female they remain, like the other chromosomes, in a diffused condition. This indicates that during these periods these chromosomes play a more active part in the metabolism of the cell in the female than in the male. The primary factor in the differentiation of the germ cells may, therefore, be a matter of metabolism, perhaps one of growth.

On the Genetic Code

by FRANCIS H. C. CRICK

It now seems certain that the amino acid sequence of any protein is determined by the sequence of bases in some region of a particular nucleic acid molecule. Twenty different kinds of amino acid are commonly found in protein, and four main kinds of base occur in nucleic acid. The genetic code describes the way in

Francis H. C. Crick, "On the Genetic Code," *Science* **139** (February 8, 1963), 461–464. This paper is a modified version of the author's Nobel Lecture delivered on December 11, 1962. Copyright © Nobel Foundation, 1964. Reprinted by permission of Elsevier Publishing Company, Amsterdam.

which a sequence of 20 or more things is determined by a sequence of four things of a different type.

It is hardly necessary to stress the biological importance of the problem. It seems likely that most if not all of the genetic information in any organism is carried by nucleic acid—usually by DNA, although certain small viruses use RNA as their genetic material. It is probable that much of this information is used to determine the amino acid sequence of the proteins of that organism. (Whether the genetic information has any other major function we do not yet know). This idea is expressed by the classic slogan of Beadle, "one gene—one enzyme," or, in the more sophisticated but cumbersome terminology of today, "one cistron—one polypeptide chain."

It is one of the more striking generalizations of biochemistry—one which surprisingly is hardly ever mentioned in the biochemical text books—that the 20 amino acids and the four bases, are, with minor reservations, the same throughout nature. As far as I am aware, the presently accepted set of 20 amino acids was first drawn up by Watson and myself in the summer of 1953 in response to a letter of Gamow's.

Here I shall not deal with the intimate technical details of the problem, if only for the reason that I have recently written such a review *(1)* which will appear shortly. Nor shall I deal with the biochemical details of messenger RNA and protein synthesis. Rather, I shall ask certain general questions about the genetic code and ask them how far we can now answer them.

Let us assume that the genetic code is a simple one and ask how many bases code for one amino acid. This coding can hardly be done by a pair of bases, as from four different things we can only form 4×4 $(= 16)$ different pairs, whereas we need at least 20 and probably one or two more to act as spaces or for other purposes. However, triplets of bases would give us 64 possibilities. It is convenient to have a word for a set of bases which codes one amino acid, and I shall use the word *codon* for this.

This brings us to our first question. Do codons overlap? In other words, as we read along the genetic message do we find a base which is a member of two or more codons? It now seems fairly certain that codons do *not* overlap. If they did, the change of a single base, due to mutation, should alter two or more (adjacent) amino acids, whereas the typical change is to a single amino acid, both in the case of the "spontaneous" mutations, such as occur in the abnormal human hemoglobins, and in chemically induced mutations, such as those produced by the action of nitrous acid and other chemicals on tobacco mosaic virus *(2)*. In all probability, therefore, codons do not overlap.

This leads us to the next problem. How is the base sequence divided into codons? There is nothing in the backbone of the nucleic acid, which is perfectly regular, to show us how to group the bases into codons. If, for example, all the codons are triplets, then in addition to the correct reading of the message there are two *in*correct readings which we shall obtain if we do not start the grouping into sets of three at the right place. My colleagues and I *(3)* have recently obtained experimental evidence that each section of the genetic message is indeed read from a fixed point, probably from one end. This fits in very well with the experimental evidence, most clearly shown in the work of Dintzis *(4)*, that the amino acids are assembled into the polypeptide chain in a linear order, starting at the amino end of the chain.

SIZE OF THE CODON

This leads us to the next general question: the size of the codon. How many bases are there in any one codon? The experiments to which I have just referred *(3)* strongly suggest that all (or almost all) codons consist of a triplet of bases, though a small multiple of 3, such as 6 or 9, is not completely ruled out by our data. We were led to this conclusion by the study of mutations in the A and B cistrons of the r_{11} locus of bacteriophage T4. These mutations are believed to be due to the addition or subtraction of one or more bases from the genetic message. They are typically produced by acridines, and cannot be reversed by mutagens which merely change one base into another. Moreover, these mutations almost always render the gene completely inactive, rather than partly so.

By testing such mutants in pairs we can assign them all, without exception, to one of two classes which we call plus and minus. For simplicity one can think of the plus class as having one extra base at some point or other in the genetic message and of the minus class as having one base too few. The crucial experiment is to put together, by genetic recombination, three mutants of the same type into one gene. That is, either (+ with + with +) or — with — with —). Whereas a single + or a pair of them (+ with +) makes the gene completely inactive, a set of three, suitably chosen, has some activity. Detailed examination of these results shows that they are exactly what we should expect if the message were read in triplets, starting from one end.

We are sometimes asked what the result would be if we put four +'s in one gene. To answer this my colleagues have recently put together not merely four but six +'s. Such a combination is active, as expected on the basis of our theory, although sets of four or five of them are not. We have also gone a long way toward explaining the production of "minutes," as they are called—that is, combinations in which the gene is working at very low efficiency. Our detailed results fit the hypothesis that in some cases when the mechanism comes to a triplet which does not stand for an amino acid (called a "nonsense" triplet) it very occasionally makes a slip and reads, say, only two bases instead of the usual three. These results also enable us to tie down the direction of reading of the genetic message, which in this case is from left to right, as the r_{11} region is conventionally drawn. A final proof of our ideas can only be obtained through detailed studies on the alterations produced in the amino acid sequence of a protein by mutations of the type discussed here.

One further conclusion of a general nature is suggested by our results. It appears that the number of nonsense triplets is rather low, since we only occasionally come across them. However, this conclusion is less secure than our other deductions about the general nature of the genetic code.

COLINEARITY

It has not yet been shown directly that the genetic message is colinear with its product—that is, that one end of the gene codes for the amino end of the poly-peptide chain and the other for the carboxyl end, and that as one proceeds along the gene one comes in turn to the codons in between in the linear order in which the amino acids are found in the polypeptide chain. This seems highly likely, especially as it has been shown that in several systems mutations affecting the same amino acid are extremely near together on the genetic map. The experi-mental proof of the colinearity of a gene and the polypeptide chain it produces may be confidently expected within the next year or so.

UNIVERSALITY

There is one further general question about the genetic code which we can ask at this point. Is the code universal—that is, the same in all organisms? Preliminary evidence suggests that it may well be. For example, something very like rabbit hemoglobin can be synthesized in a cell-free system of which part comes from rabbit reticulocytes and part from *Escherichia coli (5)*. That this would be the case if the code was very different in these two organisms is not very probable. However, as we shall see, it is now possible to test the universality of the code by more direct experiments.

ATTACK ON THE GENETIC CODE

It is believed, not that DNA itself controls protein synthesis directly in a cell in which DNA is the genetic material, but that the base sequence of the DNA—probably of only one of its chains—is copied onto RNA, and that this special RNA then acts as the genetic messenger and directs the actual process of joining up the amino acids into polypeptide chains. The breakthrough in the coding problem has come from the discovery, made by Nirenberg and Matthaei *(6)*, that one can use synthetic RNA for this purpose. In particular, they found that polyuridylic acid—an RNA in which every base is uracil—would promote the synthesis of polyphenylalanine when added to a cell-free system already known to synthesize polypeptide chains. Thus, one codon for phenylalanine appears to be the sequence UUU (where U stands for uracil; in the same way we use A, G, and C for adenine, guanine, and cytosine, respectively). This discovery has opened the way to a rapid, although somewhat confused, attack on the genetic code.

It would not be appropriate to review this work in detail here. I have discussed critically the earlier work in the review mentioned *(1)*, but such is the pace of work in this field that more recent experiments have already made the discussion out of date, to some extent. However, some general conclusions can safely be drawn.

The technique mainly used so far, both by Nirenberg and his colleagues *(6)* and by Ochoa and his group *(7)*, has been to synthesize enzymatically "random" polymers of two or three of the four bases. For example, use of a polynucleotide [which I shall call poly (U,C)], having about equal amounts of uracil and cytosine in (presumably) random order, will increase the incorporation of the amino acids phenylalanine, serine, leucine, and proline, and possibly threonine. By using polymers of different composition and assuming a triplet code one can deduce limited information about the composition of certain triplets.

From such work it appears that, with minor reservations, each polynucleotide incorporates a characteristic set of amino acids. Moreover, the four bases appear quite distinct in their effects. A comparison between the triplets tentatively deduced by these methods with the *changes* in amino acid sequence produced by mutation shows a fair measure of agreement. Moreover, the incorporation requires the same components that are needed for protein synthesis and is inhibited by the same inhibitors. Thus, the system is most unlikely to be a complete artifact and is very probably closely related to genuine protein synthesis.

As to the actual triplets so far proposed, it was first thought that possibly every triplet had to include uracil, but this was neither plausible on theoretical grounds nor supported by the experimental evidence. The first direct evidence that this was not so was obtained by my colleagues Bretscher and Grunberg-Manago *(8)*, who showed that a poly (C, A) would stimulate the incorporation of several amino acids. Recently other workers *(9, 10)* have reported further evidence of this sort for other polynucleotides not containing uracil. It now seems very likely that many of the 64 triplets, possibly most of them, may code one amino acid or another, and that in general several distinct triplets may code one amino acid. In particular, a very elegant experiment *(11)* suggests that both (UUC) and (UUG) code leucine (the parentheses imply that the order within the triplets is not yet known). This general idea is supported by several indirect lines of evidence which cannot be presented in detail here. Unfortunately it makes the unambiguous determination of triplets by these methods much more difficult than would be the case if there were only one triplet for each amino acid. Moreover, it is not possible, by using polynucleotides of "random" sequence, to determine the *order* of bases in a triplet. A start has been made to construct polynucleotides whose exact sequence is known at one end, but the results obtained so far are suggestive rather than conclusive *(12)*. It seems likely, however, from this and other (unpublished) evidence, that the amino end of the polypeptide chain corresponds to the "right-hand" end of the polynucleotide chain—that is, the one with the 2′, 3′ hydroxyls on the sugar.

It seems virtually certain that a single chain of RNA can act as messenger RNA, since poly U is a single chain without secondary structure. If poly A is added to poly U to form a double or triple helix, the combination is inactive. Moreover, there is preliminary evidence *(9)* which suggests that secondary structure within a polynucleotide inhibits the power to stimulate protein synthesis.

It has yet to be shown by direct biochemical methods, as opposed to the indirect genetic evidence mentioned earlier, that the code is indeed a triplet code.

Attempts have been made, from a study of the changes produced by mutation, to obtain the relative order of the bases within various triplets, but my own view is that such attempts are premature until there are more extensive and more reliable data on the composition of the triplets.

Evidence presented by several groups *(8, 9, 11)* suggest that poly U stimulates the incorporation of both phenylalanine and a lesser amount of leucine. The meaning of this observation is unclear, but it raises the unfortunate possibility of ambiguous triplets—that is, triplets which may code more than one amino acid. However, one would certainly expect such triplets to be in a minority.

ORIGIN OF THE GROUPING

It seems likely, then, that most of the 64 possible triplets will be grouped into 20 groups. The balance of evidence, both from the cell-free system and from the study of mutation, suggests that this grouping does not occur at random, and that triplets coding the same amino acid may well be rather similar. This raises the main theoretical problem now outstanding. Can this grouping be deduced from theoretical postulates? Unfortunately, it is not difficult to see how the grouping might have arisen at an extremely early stage in evolution by random mutations. so that the particular code we have may perhaps be the result of a series of historical accidents. This point is of more than abstract interest. If the code does indeed have some logical foundation, then it is legitimate to consider all the evidence, both good and bad, in any attempt to deduce it. This is not true if the codons have no simple logical connection. In that case, it makes little sense to guess a codon; the important thing is to provide enough evidence to prove each codon independently. It is not yet clear what evidence can safely be accepted as establishing a codon. What is clear is that most of the experimental evidence so far presented falls short of proof in almost all cases.

UNSUPPORTED PROPOSALS

In spite of the uncertainty of many of the experimental data, there are certain codes which have been suggested in the past which we can now reject with some degree of confidence.

1. Comma-less triplet codes. All such codes are unlikely, not only because of the genetic evidence but also because of the detailed results from the cell-free system.

2. Two-letter or three-letter codes—for example, a code in which A is equivalent

to C, and G to U. As already stated, the results from the cell-free system rule out all such codes.

3. The combination triplet code. In this code all permutations of a given combination code the same amino acid. The experimental results can only be made to fit such a code by very special pleading.

4. Complementary codes. There are several classes of these. Consider a certain triplet in relation to the triplet which is complementary to it on the other chain of the double helix. The second triplet may be considered as being read either in the same direction as the first or in the opposite direction. Thus, if the first triplet is UCC, we consider it in relation to either AGG or (reading in the opposite direction) GGA.

It has been suggested that if a triplet stands for an amino acid its complement must necessarily stand for the same amino acid, or, alternatively in another class of codes, that its complement will stand for no amino acid—that is, will be nonsense.

It has recently been shown by Ochoa's group that poly A stimulates the incorporation of lysine *(10)*. Thus, presumably AAA codes lysine. However, since UUU codes phenylalanine, these facts rule out all the foregoing proposed codes. It is also found that poly (U, G) incorporates quite different amino acids from poly (A, C). Similarly, poly (U, C) differs from poly (A, G) *(9, 10)*. Thus, there is little chance that any of the theories of this class will prove correct. Moreover they are all, in my opinion, unlikely for general theoretical reasons.

A start has already been made on investigations of the role of the same polynucleotides in cell-free systems from different species, to see if the code is the same in all organisms. Eventually it should be relatively easy to discover in this way whether the code is universal and, if it is not, how it differs from organism to organism. The preliminary results presented so far disclose no clear difference, with respect to the code, between *E. coli* and mammals, and this is encouraging *(10, 13)*.

GENERAL PROPERTIES

At the present time, therefore, the genetic code appears to have the following general properties.

1. Most, if not all, codons consist of three (adjacent) bases.

2. Adjacent codons do not overlap.

3. The message is read in the correct groups of three by starting at some fixed point.

4. The code sequence in the gene is colinear with the amino acid sequence, the polypeptide chain being synthesized sequentially from the amino end.

5. In general, more than one triplet codes each amino acid.

6. It is possible that some triplets may code more than one amino acid—that is, they may be ambiguous.

7. Triplets which code the same amino acid are probably rather similar.

8. It is not known whether there is any general rule in accordance with which such codons are grouped together, or whether the grouping is mainly the result of historical accident.

9. The number of triplets which do not code an amino acid is probably small.

10. Certain codes proposed earlier—such as comma-less codes, two- or three-letter codes, the combination code, and various transposable codes—are all unlikely to be correct.

11. The code is probably much the same in different organisms. It may be the same in all organisms, but this is not yet known.

Finally, one should add that in spite of the great complexity of protein synthesis and in spite of the considerable technical difficulties in synthesizing polynucleotides with defined sequences, it is not unreasonable to hope that all these points will be clarified in the near future, and that the genetic code will be completely established on a sound experimental basis within the next few years.

REFERENCES

1. F. H. C. Crick, in *Progress in Nucleic Acid Research,* J. N. Davidson and Waldo E. Cohn, Eds. (Academic Press, New York, in press).

2. H. G. Wittmann, *Z. Vererbungslehre,* in press; A. Tsugita, *J. Mol. Biol.* **5**, 284, 293 (1962).

3. F. H. C. Crick, L. Barnett, S. Brenner, R. J. Watts-Tobin, *Nature* **192**, 1227 (1961).

4. M. A. Naughton and H. M. Dintzis, *Proc. Natl. Acad. Sci. U.S.* **48**, 1822 (1962).

5. G. von Ehrenstein and F. Lipmann, *ibid.* **47**, 941 (1961).

6. J. H. Matthaei and M. W. Nirenberg, *ibid.* **47**, 1580 (1961); M. W. Nirenberg and J. H. Matthaei, *ibid.* **47**, 1588 (1961); M. W. Nirenberg, J. H. Matthaei, O. W. Jones, *ibid.* **48**, 104 (1962); J. H. Matthaei, O. W. Jones, R. G. Martin, M. W. Nirenberg, *ibid.* **48**, 666 (1962).

7. P. Lengyel, J. F. Speyer, S. Ochoa, *ibid.* **47**, 1936 (1961); J. F. Speyer, P. Lengyel, C. Basilio, S. Ochoa, *ibid.* **48**, 63 (1962); P. Lengyel, J. F. Speyer, C. Basilio, S. Ochoa, *ibid.* **48**, 282 (1962); J. F. Speyer, P. Lengyel, C. Basilio, S. Ochoa, *ibid.* **48**, 441 (1961); C. Basilio, A. J. Wahba, P. Lengyel, J. F. Speyer, S. Ochoa, *ibid.* **48**, 631 (1962).

8. M. S. Bretscher and M. Grunberg-Manago, *Nature* **195**, 283 (1962).

9. O. W. Jones and M. W. Nirenberg, *Proc. Natl. Acad. Sci. U.S.,* in press.

10. R. S. Gardner, A. J. Wahba, C. Basilio, R. S. Miller, P. Lengyel, J. F. Speyer, *ibid.,* in press.

11. B. Weisblum, S. Benzer, R. W. Holley, *ibid.* **48**, 1449 (1962).

12. A. J. Wahba, C. Basilio, J. F. Speyer, P. Lengyel, R. S. Miller, S. Ochoa, *ibid.* **48**, 1683 (1962).

13. H. R. V. Arnstein, R. A. Cox, J. A. Hunt, *Nature* **194**, 1042 (1962); E. S. Maxwell, *Proc. Natl. Acad. Sci. U.S.* **48**, 1639 (1962); I. B. Weinstein and A. N. Schechter, *ibid.* **48**, 1686 (1962).

Involvement of RNA in the Synthesis of Proteins

by JAMES D. WATSON

I arrived in Cambridge in the fall of 1951. Though my previous interests were largely genetic, Luria had arranged for me to work with John Kendrew. I was becoming frustrated with phage experiments and wanted to learn more about the actual structures of the molecules which the geneticists talked about so passionately. At the same time John needed a student and hoped that I would help him with his x-ray studies on myoglobin. I thus became a research student of Clare College with John as my supervisor.

But almost as soon as I set foot in the Cavendish Laboratory I knew I would never be of much help to him. For I had already started talking with Francis Crick. Perhaps even without Francis, I would have quickly tired of myoglobin. But with Francis to talk to, my fate was sealed. For we quickly discovered that we thought the same way about biology. The center of biology was the gene and its control of cellular metabolism. The main challenge in biology was to understand gene replication and the way in which genes control protein synthesis. It was obvious that these problems could be logically attacked only when the structure of the gene became known. This meant solving the structure of DNA. This objective then seemed out of reach to the interested geneticists. But in our cold, dark Cavendish room we thought the job could be done, quite possibly within a few months. Our optimism was partly based on Linus Pauling's feat *(1)* in deducing the α-helix, largely by following the rules of theoretical chemistry so persuasively explained in his classical *The Nature of the Chemical Bond*. We also knew that Maurice Wilkins had crystalline x-ray diffraction photographs of DNA, and so DNA must have a well-defined structure. There was thus an answer for somebody to get.

James D. Watson, "Involvement of RNA in the Synthesis of Proteins," *Science* **140** (April 5, 1963), 17–26. This paper is a modified version of the author's Nobel Lecture delivered on December 11, 1963. Copyright © Nobel Foundation, 1964. Reprinted by permission of Elsevier Publishing Company, Amsterdam.

During the next 18 months, until the double-helical structure became elucidated, we frequently discussed the necessity that the correct structure have the capacity for self-replication. And in pessimistic moods we often worried that the correct structure might be dull—that is, that it would suggest absolutely nothing and excite us no more than something inert like collagen.

The finding of the double helix *(2)* thus brought us not only joy but great relief. It was unbelievably interesting and immediately allowed us to make a serious proposal *(3)* for the mechanism of gene duplication. Furthermore, this replication scheme involved thoroughly understood conventional chemical forces. Previously, some theoretical physicists, among them Pascual Jordan *(4),* had proposed that many biological phenomena, particularly gene replication, might be based on long-range forces arising from quantum-mechanical resonance interactions. Pauling *(5)* thoroughly disliked this conjecture and firmly insisted that known short-range forces between complementary surfaces would prove to be the basis of biological replication.

The establishment of the DNA structure reinforced our belief that Pauling's arguments were sound and that neither long-range forces nor, for that matter, any form of mysticism was involved in protein synthesis. But for the protein-replication problem, mere inspection of the DNA structure then gave no immediate bonus. This, however, did not worry us, since there was much speculation that RNA, not DNA, was involved in protein synthesis.

The notion that RNA is involved in protein synthesis goes back over 20 years to the pioneering experiments of Brachet and Casperson *(6),* who showed that cells actively synthesizing protein are rich in RNA. Later, when radioactive amino acids became available, this conjecture was strengthened by the observation *(7)* that the cellular site of protein synthesis is the microsomal component, composed in large part of spherical particles rich in RNA. Still later experiments *(8)* revealed that these ribonucleoprotein particles (now conveniently called ribosomes), not the lipoprotein membranes to which they are often attached, are the sites where polypeptide bonds are made. Most ribosomes are found in the cytoplasm, and, correspondingly, most cellular protein synthesis occurs without the direct intervention of the DNA located in the nucleus. The possibility was thus raised that the genetic specificity present in DNA is first transferred to RNA intermediates, which then function as templates controlling assembly of specific amino acids into proteins.

We became able to state this hypothesis in more precise form when the structure of DNA became known in 1953. We then realized that DNA's genetic specificity resides in the complementary base sequences along its two inter-twined chains. One or both of these complementary chains must serve as templates for specific RNA molecules whose genetic information again must reside in specific base sequences. These RNA molecules would then assume three-dimensional configurations containing surfaces complementary to the side groups of the 20 specific amino acids.

X-RAY STUDIES ON RNA AND RNA-CONTAINING VIRUSES

The direct way to test this hypothesis was to solve the RNA structure. Already in 1952 I had taken some preliminary x-ray diffraction pictures of RNA. These, however, were very diffuse, and it was not until I returned to the United States in the fall of 1953 that serious x-ray studies on RNA began. Alexander Rich and I, then both at California Institute of Technology, obtained RNA samples from various cellular sources. We *(9)* were first very much encouraged to find that all the RNA samples no matter what their cellular origin, gave similar x-ray diffraction patterns. A general RNA structure thus existed. This gave us hope that the structure, when solved, would be interesting. Our first pictures already showed large systematic absences of reflections on the meridian, suggesting a helical structure. But despite much effort to obtain native undegraded samples of high molecular weight, no satisfactory x-ray diffraction pattern was obtained. The reflections were always diffuse; no evidence of crystallinity was seen. Though there were marked similarities to the DNA pattern, we had no solid grounds for believing that these arose from a similar, helical molecule. The problem of whether RNA was a one-chain or a several-chain structure remained unanswered.

We then considered the possibility that RNA might have a regular structure only when combined with protein. At that time (1955) there was no good evidence for RNA's existing free from protein. All RNA was thought to exist either as a viral component or to be combined with protein in ribonucleoprotein particles. It thus seemed logical to turn attention to a study of ribonucleoprotein particles (ribosomes), since upon their surfaces protein was synthesized. Our hope, again, was that the establishment of their structure would reveal the long-sought cavities specific for the amino acids.

Then we were struck by the morphological similarity between ribosomes and small RNA-containing viruses like turnip yellow mosaic virus and polio-myelitis virus. By then (1955–56) I was back in Cambridge with Crick to finish formulating some general principles of viral structure *(10)*. Our main idea was that the finite nucleic-acid content of viruses severely restricted the number of amino acids they could code for. As a consequence, the protein coat could not be constructed from a very large number of different protein molecules. Instead, it must be constructed from a number of identical small subunits arranged in a regular manner. These ideas already held for TMV, a rod-shaped virus, and we were very pleased when D. L. D. Caspar *(11)*, then working with us at the Cavendish Laboratory, took some elegant diffraction pictures of bushy stunt virus crystals and extended experimental support to the spherical viruses.

STRUCTURAL STUDIES OF RIBOSOMES

At that time almost no structural studies had been done with ribosomes. They were chiefly characterized by their sedimentation constants; those from higher organisms *(12)* were in the 70S to 80S range, while those from bacteria *(13)* appeared smaller and to be of two sizes (30*S* and 50*S*). Because the bacterial particles seemed smaller, they seemed preferable for structural studies. Thus, when Alfred Tissières and I came to Harvard's Biological Laboratories in 1956, we initiated research on the ribosomes of the commonly studied bacteria *Escherichia coli*. We hoped that their structure would show similarities to the structures of the small spherical RNA viruses. Then we might have a good chance to crystallize them and eventually to use x-ray diffraction techniques to establish their three-dimensional structure.

But from the beginning of our Harvard experiments it was obvious that ribosome structure was more complicated than RNA virus structure. Depending upon the concentration of divalent cations (in all our experiments, Mg^{++}), four classes of *E. coli* ribosomes were found, characterized by sedimentation constants of 30*S*, 50*S*, 70*S*, and 100*S*. Our first experiments with $10^{-4}M$ Mg^{++} revealed 30*S* and 50*S* ribosomes. At the same time Bolton and his co-workers *(14)*, at the Carnegie Institute of Washington, employing higher levels of Mg^{++}, saw ribosomes with a higher rate of sedimentation and suggested that they were observing aggregates of the smaller particles. Soon after, more experiments *(15–17)* revealed that, as the concentration of Mg^{++} is raised, one 30*S* particle and one 50*S* particle combine to form a 70*S* ribosome. At still higher concentrations of Mg^{++} two 70*S* ribosomes dimerize to form a 100*S* ribosome (Figs. 1 and 2).

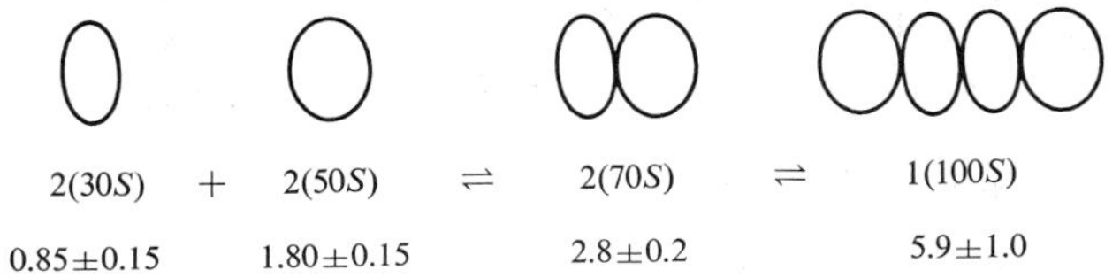

2(30*S*)	+	2(50*S*)	⇌	2(70*S*)	⇌	1(100*S*)
0.85±0.15		1.80±0.15		2.8±0.2		5.9±1.0

Fig. 1. *Diagrammatic representation of* E. coli *ribosome subunits and their aggregation products. The values in the bottom line indicate the molecular weight with a factor of* 10^{-6}. *The data are from Tissières* et al. *(15). All particles are composed of 64 percent RNA and 36 percent protein.*

Ribosomes from every cellular source have a similar subunit construction. In all cases the level of divalent cations determines which ribosomes are predominant. Bacterial ribosomes require higher levels of Mg^{++} in order to aggregate into the larger sizes. Conversely, they break down much faster to the 30*S* and 50*S* forms when the Mg^{++} level is lowered. It is often convenient *(18)* when using mammalian ribosomes to add a chelating agent to rapidly break down the 80*S* ribosomes (homologous to the 70*S* ribosomes of bacteria) to their 40*S* and 60*S* subunits. Bacterial ribosomes are thus not significantly smaller than mammalian ribosomes. It is merely easier to observe the smaller subunits in bacterial systems.

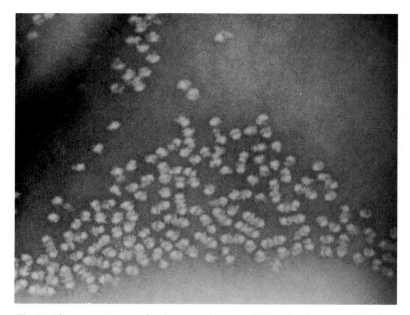

Fig. 2. *Electron micrograph of negatively stained* E. coli *ribosomes (Huxley and Zubay, 17). Two particle types are predominant: (i) 70S, containing two subunits of unequal size, and (ii) 100S, consisting of two 70S ribosomes joined together at their smaller (30S) subunits.*

Ribosomes   30*S*   50*S*

m.w.$\times 10^{-6}$ 0.85±0.15   1.80±0.15

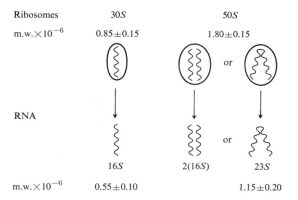

RNA

              16*S*   2(16*S*)   23*S*

m.w.$\times 10^{-6}$ 0.55±0.10   1.15±0.20

Fig. 3. *Molecular weights of RNA isolated from* E. coli *ribosomes. This picture is diagrammatic and does not represent the true conformation of ribosomal RNA.*

Already in 1958 there were several reports *(19)* that ribosomal RNA sedimented as two distinct components (18*S* and 28*S*). We thought that the smaller molecules most likely arose from the smaller subunit, while the faster-sedimenting RNA came from the larger of the ribosomal subunits. Experiments of Kurland *(20)* quickly confirmed this hunch. The *Escherichia coli* 30*S* ribosome was found to contain one RNA chain (16*S*) with a molecular weight of 5.5×10^5. Correspondingly, a larger RNA molecule *(23S)* of molecular weight 1.1×10^6 was found in most 50*S* ribosomes (Fig. 3).

RIBOSOME PROTEINS

Analysis of the protein component revealed a much more complicated picture. In contrast to the small RNA viruses, where the protein coat is constructed from the regular arrangement of a large number of identical protein molecules, each ribosome most likely contains a large number of different polypeptide chains. At first our results suggested a simple answer when Waller and J. I. Harris analyzed *E. Coli* ribosomes for their amino terminal groups. Only alanine and methionine, with smaller amounts of serine, were present in significant amounts. This hinted that only several species of protein molecules were used for ribosome construction. Further experiments by Waller *(21)*, however, suggested the contrary. When ribosomal protein fractions were analyzed by starch-gel electrophoresis, more than 20 distinct bands were seen. Almost all these proteins migrated toward the anode at *p*H 7, confirming the net basic charge of ribosomal protein *(22)*. A variety of control experiments suggested that these bands represented distinct polypeptide chains, not merely aggregated states of several fundamental subunits. Moreover, the band pattern from 30*S* ribosomes was radically different from that of 50*S* proteins.

As yet we have no solid proof that each 70*S* ribosome contains all the various protein components found in the total population. But so far, all attempts by Waller to separate chromatographically intact ribosomes into fractions with different starch-gel patterns have failed. The total protein component of a 70*S* ribosome amounts to about 9×10^5 daltons. Since the end group analysis suggests an average molecular weight of about 30,000, approximately 20 polypeptide chains must be used in the construction of the 50*S* ribosome, and ten for the 30*S* ribosome. It is possible that all the polypeptide chains in a 30*S* particle are different. Waller already has evidence for ten distinct components in 30*S* ribosomes, and the present failure to observe more in the 50*S* protein fraction may merely mean that the same electrophoretic mobility is shared by several polypeptide chains.

We believe that most, if not all, these basic proteins have primarily a structural role. That is, they are not enzymes but function largely to hold the ribosomal RNA and necessary intermediates in the correct position for peptide bond formation. In addition a number of enzymes are bound tightly to ribosomes. As yet their function is unclear. One such enzyme is a bacterial ribonuclease found by Elson *(23)* to be specifically attached to 30*S* ribosomes in a latent form. No ribonuclease activity is present prior to ribosome breakdown. Spahr *(24)* in our laboratories has purified this enzyme and shown its specificity, and from specific activity measurements he concludes that it is present on less than one

$30S$ particle in 20. It is clear that this enzyme, if present in a free active form, would be rapidly lethal to its host cell. Thus its presence in latent form is to be expected. But why it is stuck to ribosomes is still a complete mystery.

CHEMICAL INTERMEDIATES IN PROTEIN SYNTHESIS

Our early experiments with ribosomes were almost unrelated to the efforts of biochemists. At that time our research objectives seemed very different. The enzymologically oriented biochemists hoped to find the intermediates and enzymes necessary for peptide bond formation. On the contrary, those of us with a generic orientation wanted to see the template and discover how it picked out the correct amino acid. Very soon, however, these separate paths came together, partly because of a breakthrough in work on the nature of the amino acid intermediates and partly because of an incisive thought of Crick's.

The biochemical advances arose largely from work *(25)* in Paul Zamecnik's laboratory at Massachusetts General Hospital. There was developed a reproducible in vitro system containing ribosomes, supernatant factors, and adenosine triphosphate (ATP) which incorporated amino acids into proteins. Using this system, Hoagland helped make two important discoveries. First, he showed *(26)* that amino acids are initially activated by ATP to form high-energy complexes of amino acid and adenosine monophosphate. Second, together with Zamecnik he demonstrated *(27)* that the activated amino acids are then transferred to low-molecularweight RNA molecules (now known as soluble or transfer RNA), again in an activated form. These amino-acyl-sRNA compounds then function as the intermediates for peptide bond formation (Fig. 4*)*.

a) $AA + ATP \rightarrow AMP{\sim}AA + PP$

b) $AMP{\sim}AA + sRNA \rightarrow AA{\sim}sRNA + AMP$

c) $(AA{\sim}sRNA)_n + GTP \xrightarrow{\text{ribosomes}} AA_1 - AA_2 \cdots AA_n + GDP \ (GMP?) +$

$$(sRNA)_n$$

Fig. 4. *Enzymatic steps in protein peptide bond formation. Steps a and b are catalyzed by single enzymes. The number of enzymes required in c is unknown.*

It had previously been obvious that amino acid activation would have to occur. However, Hoagland and Zamecnik's second discovery (in 1956) of the involvement of a hitherto undiscovered RNA form (sRNA) was unanticipated by almost everybody. Several years previously (in 1954), Leslie Orgel and I had spent a quite frustrating fall attempting to construct hypothetical RNA structures which contained cavities complementary in shape to the amino acid side groups. Not only did plausible configurations for the RNA backbone fail to result in good cavities, but even when we disregarded the backbone, we also failed to find convincing holes which might effectively distinguish between such similar amino acids as valine and isoleucine. Crick, at the same time (early 1955) sensed the same dilemma and suggested a radical solution to the paradox. He proposed *(28)* that the amino acids do not combine with the template. Instead each should first combine with a specific adaptor molecule, capable of selectively interacting with the hydrogen bonding surfaces provided by RNA's purine and pyrimidine bases. This scheme requires at least 20 different adaptors, each specific for a given amino acid. These are very neatly provided by the specific sRNA molecules. Soon after the discovery of sRNA, many experiments, particularly by Hoagland and Paul Berg *(29)*, established that the sRNA molecules are in fact specific for a given amino acid. It thus became possible to imagine, in accordance with Crick's reasoning, that the ribosomal template for protein synthesis combined not with the amino acid side groups but, instead, with a specific group of bases on the soluble RNA portion of the amino-acyl-sRNA precursors.

PARTICIPATION OF ACTIVE RIBOSOMES IN PROTEIN SYNTHESIS

Very little protein synthesis occurred in the cell-free system developed by the Massachusetts General Hospital group. Only by using radio-active amino acids could they convincingly demonstrate amino acid incorporation into proteins. This fact initially seemed trivial, and there was much hope that when better experimental conditions were found, significant net synthesis would occur. But despite optimistic claims from several laboratories, no real improvement in the efficiency of cell-free synthesis resulted. Some experiments (1959) of Tissières and Schlessinger *(30)* with *Escherichia coli* extracts illustrate this point well. At 30°C, cell-free synthesis occurs linearly for 5 to 10 minutes and then gradually stops. During this interval the newly synthesized protein amounts to 1 to 3 micrograms of protein per milligram of ribosomes. Of this, about one-third is released from the ribosomes, the remainder being bound to the ribosomes.

Cell-free synthesis in *E. coli* extracts requires the high ($\sim 10^{-2} M$) Mg^{++} levels which favor the formation of $70S$ ribosomes from their $30S$ and $50S$ sub-units. After incorporation, the ribosomes possessing nascent polypeptide chains become less susceptible to breakdown to $30S$ and $50S$ ribosomes. When cell-free extracts (after synthesis) are briefly dialyzed against $10^{-4} M$ Mg^{++}, about 80 to 90 percent of the $30S$ and $50S$ ribosomes become free. There remain, however, 10 to 20 percent of the original $70S$ ribosomes, and it is upon these "stuck" ribosomes that most ribosomal-bound nascent protein is located. This suggests, first, that protein synthesis occurs on $70S$ ribosomes, not upon free $30S$ or $50S$ ribosomes. Second, in the commonly studied *E. coli* extract, only a small ribosome fraction is functional. Tissières and Schlessinger named these particles "active ribosomes" and suggested that they contained a functional component lacking in other ribosomes.

Each active ribosome synthesizes on the average between 15,000 and 50,000 daltons of protein. This is in the size range of naturally occurring polypeptide chains. Thus, while we remained unsatisfied by the small net synthesis, sufficient synthesis occurred to open the possibility that some complete protein molecules had been made. This encouraged us to look for synthesis of β-galactosidase. None, however, was then found *(31)*, despite much effort.

Another important point emerged from these early (1959) incorporation studies with *E. coli* extracts. The addition of small amounts of purified deoxyribonuclease decreased protein synthesis to values 20 to 40 percent of those found in untreated extracts *(30)*. This was completely unanticipated, for it suggested that DNA functions in the commonly studied bacterial extracts. But since a basal level of synthesis remains after DNA is destroyed by deoxyribonuclease, the DNA itself must not be directly involved in the formation of peptide bonds. This finding suggested, instead, synthesis of new template RNA upon DNA in untreated extracts. This raised the possibility, previously not seriously considered by biochemists, that the RNA templates themselves might be unstable, and hence a limiting factor in cell-free protein synthesis.

METABOLIC STABILITY OF RIBOSOMAL RNA

In all our early ribosome experiments we had assumed that the ribosomal RNA was the template. Abundant evidence existed that proteins were synthesized on ribosomes, and since the template must be RNA, it was natural to assume that it was ribosomal RNA. Under this hypothesis ribosomal RNA was a collection of molecules of different base sequences, synthesized on the functioning regions of chromosomal DNA. After synthesis, they combined with the basic ribosomal proteins to form ribosomes. We thus visualized that the seemingly morphologically identical ribosomes were, in fact, a collection of a very large number of genetically distinct particles masked by the similarity of their protein components.

At that time there existed much evidence suggesting that ribosomal RNA molecules were stable in growing bacteria. As early as 1949, experiments showed that RNA precursors, once incorporated into RNA, remained in RNA. The distinction between ribosomal and soluble RNA was not then known, but later experiments by the ribosome group of the Carnegie Institute of Washington and at Harvard indicated similar stabilities for both fractions. In these experiments, however, the fate of single molecules was not followed; and the possibility remained that a special trick allowed ribosomal RNA chains to be broken down to fragments that were preferentially re-used to make new ribosomal RNA molecules. Davern and Meselson *(32)*, however, ruled out this possibility by first growing bacteria in heavy (C^{13}, N^{15}) medium, and then transferring the cells to light (C^{12}, N^{14}) medium for several additional generations of growth. They then separated the light from the heavy ribosomal RNA in cesium formate density gradients and showed that the heavy molecules remained completely intact for at least two generations. This result predicts, if ribosomes are assumed to be genetically specific, that the protein templates will persist indefinitely in growing bacteria.

But already, by the time of the Davern and Meselson experiment (1959), evidence had begun to accumulate, chiefly at the Institut Pasteur, that some, if not all, bacterial templates were unstable, with lives of only several percent of a generation time. None of these experiments, by themslves, were convincing. Each could be interpreted in other ways which retained the concept of stable templates. But taken together, they argued a strong case.

These experiments were of several types. In one, the effect of suddenly adding or destroying specific DNA molecules was studied. Sudden introduction was achieved by having a male donor introduce a molecule from a specific chromosomal region absent in the recipient female. Simultaneously, the ability of the male gene to function (to produce an enzymatically active protein) in the female cell was measured. Riley, Pardee, Jacob, and Monod *(33)* obtained the striking finding that β-galactosidase, genetically determined by a specific male gene, begins to be synthesized at its maximum rate within several minutes after gene transfer. Thus, the steady-state number of β-galactosidase templates was achieved almost immediately. Conversely, when the *E. coli* chromosome was inactivated by decay of P^{32} atoms incorporated into DNA, they observed that active enzyme formation stopped within several minutes. It thus appeared that the ribosomal templates could not function without concomitant DNA function.

At the same time, François Gros discovered *(34)* that bacteria grown in 5-fluorouracil produced abnormal proteins, most likely altered in amino acid sequences. 5-Fluorouracil is readily incorporated into bacterial RNA, and its presence in RNA templates may drastically raise the "mistake" level. More unexpected was the observation that after addition of 5-fluorouracil the production of all normal proteins ceases within several minutes. This again argues against the persistence of *any* stable templates.

UNSTABLE RNA MOLECULES IN PHAGE-INFECTED CELLS

At first it was thought that no RNA synthesis occurred in T2-infected cells. But in 1952 Hershey *(35)* observed that new RNA molecules are synthesized at a rapid rate. But no net accumulation occurs since there is a correspondingly fast breakdown. Surprisingly, almost everybody ignored this discovery. This oversight was partly due to the tendency, then still prevalent, to suspect that the metabolism of virus-infected cells might be qualitatively different from that of uninfected cells.

Volkin and Astrachan *(36)* were the first (1956) to treat Hershey's unstable fraction seriously. They measured its base composition and found it different from that of uninfected *E. coli* cells. It bore a great resemblance to the infecting viral DNA, a finding which suggested that it was synthesized on T2 DNA templates. Moreover, and most importantly, this RNA fraction must be the template for phage-specific proteins. Unless we assume that RNA is not involved in phage protein synthesis, it necessarily follows that the Volkin-Astrachan DNA-like RNA provides the information for determining amino acid sequences in phage-specific proteins.

Not till the late summer of 1959 was the physical form of this DNA-like RNA investigated. Then Nomura, Hall, and Spiegelman *(37)* examined its relationship to the already characterized soluble and ribosomal RNA's. Immediately they observed that none of the T2 RNA was incorporated into stable ribosomes. Instead, in low concentrations of Mg^{++} ($10^{-4}M$) it existed free, while in $10^{-2}M$ Mg^{++}, they thought, it became part of $30S$ ribosomal-like particles. At the same time, Risebrough in our laboratories began studying T2 RNA, also using sucrose gradient centrifugation. He also found that T2 RNA was not typical ribosomal RNA. In addition, he was the first to notice (in the early spring of 1960) that in $10^{-2}M$ Mg^{++} most T2 RNA sedimented not with $30S$ particles but with the larger $70S$ and $100S$ ribosomes.

Risebrough's result leads naturally to the hypothesis that phage protein synthesis takes place on genetically non-specific ribosomes to which are attached metabolically unstable template RNA molecules. Independently of our work, Brenner and Jacob, motivated by the aforementioned metabolic and genetic experiments at the Institut Pasteur, were equally convinced that conditions were ripe for the direct demonstration of the existence of metabolically unstable RNA templates, to which Jacob and Monod *(38)* gave the name "messenger RNA." In June of 1960 Brenner and Jacob traveled to Pasadena for a crucial experiment in Meselson's laboratory. They argued that all the T2 messenger RNA should be attached to old ribosomes synthesized before infection. This they elegantly demonstrated *(39)* by infecting heavy (C^{13} and N^{15}) labeled bacteria in light (C^{12} and N^{14}) medium with T2. Subsequent CsCl equilibrium centrifugation revealed that most of the T2 messenger RNA was indeed attached to "old" ribosomes, as was all the ribosomal-bound nascent protein, labeled by pulse exposure to radioactive amino acids.

MESSENGER RNA MOLECULES IN UNINFECTED BACTERIA

We were equally convinced that similar messenger RNA would be found in uninfected bacteria. Its demonstration presented greater problems because of the simultaneous synthesis of ribosomal and soluble RNA. François Gros had then (May 1960) just arrived for a visit to our laboratory. Together with Kurland and Gilbert, we decided to look for labeled messenger molecules in cells briefly exposed to a radioactive RNA precursor. Experiments with T2-infected cells suggested that the T2 messenger comprised about 2 to 4 percent of the total RNA and that most of its molecules had lives of less than several minutes. If a similar situation held for uninfected cells during any short interval most RNA synthesized would be messenger RNA. There would be no significant accumulation, since the RNA would be broken down almost as fast as it was made.

Again, the messenger hypothesis was confirmed *(40)*. The RNA labeled during pulse exposures was largely attached to $70S$ and $100S$ ribosomes in $10^{-2}M$ Mg^{++}. In low concentrations of Mg^{++} ($10^{-4}M$) it came off the ribosomes and sedimented free, with an average sedimentation constant of $14S$. Base ratio analysis revealed DNA-like RNA molecules, in agreement with the expectation that such RNA is produced on very many DNA templates along the bacterial chromosome.

Soon afterwards, Hall and Spiegelman (see *41*) formed artificial T2 DNA–T2 messenger RNA hybrids molecules, and in several laboratories *(42)* hybrid molecules were subsequently formed between *E. coli* DNA and *E. coli* pulse RNA. The DNA-template origin for messenger RNA was thus established beyond doubt.

ROLE OF MESSENGER RNA IN CELL-FREE PROTEIN SYNTHESIS

It was then possible to suggest why deoxyribonuclease partially inhibits amino acid incorporation in *E. coli* extracts. The messenger hypothesis prompts the idea that DNA in the extract is a template for messenger RNA. This newly made messenger then attaches to ribosomes, where it serves as additional protein templates. Since deoxyribonuclease only destroys the capacity to make messenger RNA, it has no effect upon the messenger RNA present at the time of extract formation. Hence, no matter how high the deoxyribonuclease concentration employed, a residual fraction of synthesis will always occur. Experiments by Tissières and Hopkins *(43)* in our laboratories and by Berg, Chamberlain, and Wood *(44)* at Stanford confirmed these ideas. First it was shown that the addition of DNA to extracts previously denuded of DNA significantly increased amino acid incorporation. Second, RNA synthesis occurs simultaneously with in vitro protein synthesis. This RNA has a DNA-like composition, attaches to ribosome in $10^{-2} M$ Mg^{++}, and physically resembles messenger RNA synthesized in vivo.

Furthermore, Tissières showed that addition of fractions rich in messenger RNA increased in vitro protein synthesis two- to five-fold. More striking results came from Nirenberg and Mathaei *(45)*. They reasoned that in vitro destruction of messenger RNA might be the principal reason why cell-free systems stop synthesizing protein. If so, previously incubated extracts deficient in natural messenger RNA should respond more to the addition of new messenger RNA than other extracts. This way they were able to demonstrate a 20-fold increase in protein synthesis after the addition of a phenol-purified *E. coli* RNA. Like Tissières active fraction, their stimulating fraction sedimented heterogeneously, arguing against an effect due to either ribosomal or soluble RNA. More convincing support came when they next added TMV RNA to previously incubated extracts of *E. coli*. Again there was a 10- to 20-fold increase. Here there could be no confusion with possible ribosomal RNA templates. Even more dramatic *(46)* was the effect of adding polyuridylic acid (like TMV RNA, single-stranded). This specifically directed incorporating phenylalanine into polyphenylalanine. With this experiment (June 1961) the messenger concept became established. Direct proof then existed that single-stranded messenger RNA was the protein template.

In in-vitro systems ordinarily only 10 to 20 percent of *E. coli* ribosomes contain attached messenger RNA. This was first shown in experiments of Risebrough *(47)*, who centrifuged extracts of T2-infected cells through a sucrose gradient. Ribosomes containing labeled messenger RNA were found to centrifuge faster than ordinary ribosomes. Similarly, Gilbert *(48)* showed that these faster-sedimenting ribosomes are "active"—that is, they are able to incorporate amino acids into proteins. A fresh cell-free extract was centrifuged through a sucrose gradient. Samples along the gradient were collected and then tested for their ability to make protein. A complete parallel was found between "activity" and the presence of messenger RNA.

Furthermore, if an extract is centrifuged *after* it has incorporated amino acids, the nascent protein chains also sediment attached to a small fraction of fast-sedimenting ribosomes *(47)*. These ribosomes still contain messenger RNA. For when the messenger RNA molecules are destroyed by ribonuclease (ribosomes remain intact in the presence of microgram amounts of ribonuclease), the ribosomal-bound nascent protein sediments as $70S$ ribosomes. The nascent protein is thus not attached to messenger RNA but must be directly bound to ribosomes.

BINDING OF sRNA TO RIBOSOMES

Experiments by Schweet *(49)* and Dintzes *(50)* show that proteins grow by the stepwise addition of individual amino acids, beginning at the amino terminal end. Since the immediate precursors are amino-acyl-sRNA molecules, Schweet and Dintzes's result predicts that the polypeptide chain is terminated at its carboxyl growing end by an sRNA molecule (Fig. 5). To test this scheme, we began some studies to see whether sRNA was bound specifically to ribosomes. Cannon and Krug *(51)* first examined binding in the absence of protein synthesis. They showed that, in $10^{-2}M$ Mg^{++}, each $50S$ subunit of the $70S$ ribosome reversibly

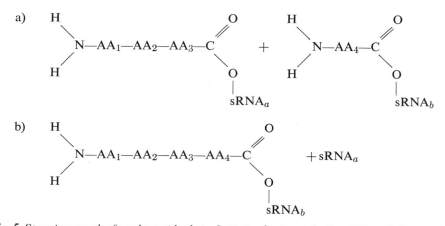

Fig. 5. Stepwise growth of a polypeptide chain. Initiation begins at the free NH_2 end, the growing point being terminated by an sRNA molecule.

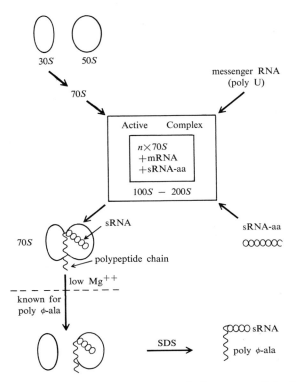

Fig. 6. *Diagrammatic summary of ribosome participation in protein synthesis. The active complex is shown schematically in Fig. 7. SDS, sodium dodecyl sulfate (Duponal).*

bound one sRNA molecule. The same amount of reversible binding occurs with amino-acyl-sRNA or with free sRNA, and in the presence or absence of protein synthesis.

Protein synthesis, however, effects the binding observed in $10^{-4}M$ Mg^{++}. In the absence of protein synthesis no sRNA remains bound to the ribosomes when the Mg^{++} level is lowered from $10^{-2}M$ to $10^{-4}M$. On the contrary, after amino acid incorporation, sRNA molecules become tightly fixed to the "stuck" 70S ribosomes, whose nascent polypeptide chains hinder dissociation to 30S and 50S ribosomes. One sRNA molecule appears to be attached to each stuck ribosome. Prolonged dialysis against $10^{-4}M$ Mg^{++} eventually breaks apart the stuck ribosomes. Then all the bound sRNA, as well as almost all the nascent protein, is seen to be attached to the 50S component—an observation which supports the hypothesis that these bound sRNA molecules are directly attached to nascent chains (Fig. 6). Direct proof comes from recent experiments in which Gilbert *(52)* used the detergent Duponol to further dissociate the 50S ribosomes into their protein and RNA components. Then the nascent protein and bound sRNA remained together during both sucrose gradient centrifugation and separation on G200 Sephadex columns. After exposure, however, to either weak alkali or hydroxylamine (treatments known to break amino-acyl bonds), the sRNA and nascent proteins move separately.

The significance of the reversible binding by nonactive (no messenger) ribosomes is not known. Conceivably, inside growing cells, all ribosomes have attached messenger RNA and synthesize protein. Under these conditions only those sRNA molecules corresponding to the specific messenger sequence can slip into the ribosomal cavities. But when most ribosomes lack messenger templates, as in our in vitro extracts, then any sRNA molecule, charged or uncharged, may fill the empty site.

All the evidence suggests that covalent bonds are not involved in holding nascent chains to ribosomes. Instead, it seems probable that the point of firm attachment involves the terminal sRNA residue, bound by Mg^{++}-dependent secondary forces to a cavity in the $50S$ ribosome. Extensive dialysis against $5 \times 10^{-5} M$ Mg^{++} (which leaves intact $30S$ and $50S$ ribosomes) strips the nascent chains off the $50S$ ribosomes *(52, 53)*. The released polypeptides have a sedimentation constant of about $4S$, and if the latent ribonuclease is not activated, they most likely still have terminally bound sRNA. When the Mg^{++} level is again brought to $10^{-2} M$, many released chains again stick to ribosomes.

MOVEMENT OF THE MESSENGER TEMPLATE OVER THE RIBOSOMAL SURFACE

At any given time, each functioning ribosome thus contains only one nascent chain. As elongation proceeds, the NH_3-terminal end moves away from the point of peptide bond formation and, conceivably, may assume much of its final three-dimensional configuration before the terminal amino acids are added to the carboxyl end. The messenger RNA must be so attached that only the correct amino-acyl-sRNA molecules are inserted into position for possible peptide bond formation. This requirement demands formation of specific hydrogen bonds (base pairs?) between the messenger template and several (probably three) nucleotides along the sRNA molecule. Then, in the presence of the necessary enzymes, the amino-acyl linkage to the then-terminal sRNA breaks and a peptide bond forms with correctly placed incoming amino-acyl-RNA (Fig. 5). This must create an energetically unfavorable environment for the now free sRNA molecule, causing it to be ejected from the sRNA binding site. The new terminal sRNA then moves into this site, completing a cycle of synthesis. It is not known whether the messenger template remains attached to the newly inserted amino-acyl-sRNA. If it does, the messenger necessarily moves the correct distance over the ribosomal surface to place its next group of specific nucleotides in position to correctly select the next amino acid. But no matter what the mechanism is, the messenger tape necessarily moves over the ribosome. It cannot remain in static orientation if there is only one specific ribosomal site for peptide bond formation.

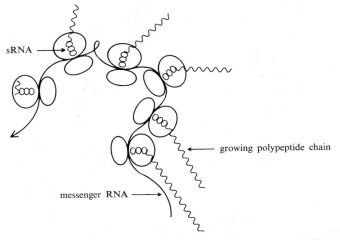

sRNA

growing polypeptide chain

messenger RNA

Fig. 7. *Messenger RNA attachment to several ribosomes. This illustration is schematic, since the site of messenger attachment to ribosomes is not known.*

ATTACHMENT OF SINGLE MESSENGER RNA MOLECULES

Addition of the synthetic messenger polyuridylic acid to extracts containing predominantly 70S ribosomes creates new active ribosomes which sediment in the 150 to 200S region *(54)*. Fixation of a single polyuridylic acid molecule (molecular weight, 100,000) to a 70S ribosome (molecular weight, 3×10^6) should not significantly increase ribosomal sedimentation. Nor is it likely that a very large number of polyuridylic acid molecules have combined with individual ribosomes; in these experiments the molar ratio of fixed polyuridylic acid to 70S ribosomes was less than 1/5. Instead, the only plausible explanation is formation of ribosomal aggregates attached to single polyuridylic acid molecules. The 300 nucleotides in a polyuridylic acid molecule of molecular weight $\sim 10^5$ will have a contour length of about 1000 angstroms if the average internucleotide distance is 3.4 angstroms. Simultaneous attachment is thus possible to groups of four to eight ribosomes (diameter, ~ 200 Å), depending upon the way the messenger passes over (or through) the ribosomal surface. This estimate agrees well with the average aggregate size suggested by the sedimentation rate of the "active" complexes. Sedimentation of extracts *after* incorporation reveals that most polyphenylalanine is attached to the rapidly sedimenting "active" ribosomes.

Single messenger molecules thus most likely move simultaneously over the surfaces of several ribosomes, functioning on each as protein templates (Fig. 7). A progression of increasingly long polypeptide chains should be attached to successive ribosomes, depending upon the fraction of the messenger tape to which they were exposed. When all the messenger has moved across the site of synthesis, some mechanism, perhaps itself triggered by a specific template nucleotide sequence, must release the finished protein. The now vacant ribosome then becomes competent to receive the free end of another (or perhaps even the same) messenger molecule and start a new cycle of protein synthesis.

The realization that a single messenger molecule attaches to many ribosomes resolves a bothersome paradox which accompanied the messenger hypothesis. About 2 to 4 percent of *E. coli* RNA is messenger RNA *(42, 55)*. Its average sedimentation constant of 14S *(56)* suggests an average molecular weight of about 500,000. This value may be too low, since it is very difficult to completely prevent all enzymatic degradation. There thus must be at least six to eight 70S ribosomes for every messenger molecule. It was very difficult to believe that only 10 to 20 percent of the ribosomes functioned at a given moment, for under a variety of conditions the rate of protein synthesis is proportional to ribosome concentration *(57)*. Instead it seems much more likely that, in vivo, almost all ribosomes are active. During the preparation of cell extracts, however, many ribosomes may lose their messenger RNA and become inactive. If this is the case, we may expect that use of more gentle techniques to break open *E. coli* cells will reveal larger fractions of fast-sedimenting active material. Already there are reports *(58)* that over 50 percent of mammalian reticulocyte ribosomes exist as aggregates of five to six 80S particles. Furthermore, it is these aggregated ribosomes which make protein, both in vivo and in vitro.

TEMPLATE LIFETIME

Under the scheme just described, a messenger molecule might function indefinitely. On the contrary, however, the unstable bacterial templates function on the average only 10 to 20 times. This fact comes from experiments done in Levinthal's laboratory *(59)*, where synthesis of new messenger RNA was blocked by addition of the antibiotic actinomycin D. Pre-existing messenger (*Bacillus subtilus* growing with a 60-minute generation time) then broke down with a half-life of 2 minutes. Correspondingly, protein synthesis ceased at the expected rate. A mechanism (or mechanisms) must thus exist to specifically degrade messenger molecules. Several enzymes (polynucleotide phosphorylase and a K^+-dependent diesterase) which rapidly degrade free messenger RNA are ative in bacterial cell extracts *(60)*. They function, however, much less efficiently when the messenger is attached to ribosomes *(61)*. Conceivably, a random choice exists, whether the free forward-moving end of a messenger tape attaches to a vacant ribosome or is enzymatically degraded. If this is the case, this important decision is settled by a chance event unrelated to the biological need for specific messengers.

CONCLUSION

We can now have considerable confidence that the broad features of protein synthesis are understood. The involvement of RNA is very much more complicated than was imagined in 1953. There is not one functional RNA. Instead, protein synthesis demands the ordered interaction of three classes of RNA—ribosomal, soluble, and messenger. Many important questions, however, remain unanswered. For instance, there is no theoretical framework for the ribosomal subunits, nor for that matter, do we understand the functional significance of ribosomal RNA. Most satisfying is the realization that all the steps in protein replication will be shown to involve well-understood chemical forces. As yet we do not know all the details. For example, are the DNA base pairs involved in messenger RNA selection of the corresponding amino-acyl-sRNA? With luck, this will soon be known. We can thus have every expectation that future progress in understanding selective protein synthesis (and its consequences for embryology) will have a similarly well-defined and, when understood, easy-to-comprehend chemical basis *(62)*.

REFERENCES AND NOTES

1. L. Pauling and R. B. Corey, *Proc. Natl. Acad. Sci. U.S.* **37**, 235 (1951).

2. J. D. Watson and F. H. C. Crick, *Nature* **171**, 737 (1953).

3. ——, *ibid.,* p. 964.

4. P. Jordan, *Phys. Z.* **39**, 711 (1938); the reader is also referred to the discussion of possible implications of long-range forces in biology by H. J. Muller in his 1946 Pilgrim Trust lecture, *Proc. Roy. Soc. London* **B** (1947).

5. A sample of Pauling's views is found in his note with M. Delbrück, *Science* **92**, 77 (1940).

6. J. Brachet, *Arch. Biol. Liege* **53**, 207 (1942); T. Caspersson, *Naturwissenschaften* **28**, 33 (1941).

7. H. Borsook, C. L. Deasy, A. J. Hagen-Smit, G. Keighley, P. H. Lowy, *J. Biol. Chem.* **187**, 839 (1950); T. Hultin, *Exptl. Cell Res.* **1950-1**, 376 (1950).

8. J. W. Littlefield, E. B. Keller, J. Gross, P. C. Zamecnik, *J. Biol. Chem.* **217**, 111 (1955); V. G. Allfrey, M. M. Daly, A. E. Mirsky, *J. Gen. Physiol.* **37**, 157 (1953).

9. A. Rich and J. D. Watson, *Nature* **173**, 995 (1954); *Proc. Natl. Acad. Sci. U.S.* **40**, 759 (1954).

10. F. H. C. Crick and J. D. Watson, *Nature* **177**, 473 (1956); ——, in *Ciba Foundation Symposium on the Nature of Viruses,* G. E. W. Wolstenholme and C. M. O'Connor, Eds. (Little, Brown, Boston, 1957).

11. D. L. D. Caspar, *Nature* **177**, 475 (1956).

12. M. L. Petermann and M. G. Hamilton, *J. Biol. Chem.* **224**, 725 (1957); P. Tso, J. Bonner, J. Vinograd, *J. Biophys. Biochem. Cytol.* **2**, 451 (1956).

13. H. K. Schachman, A. B. Pardee, R. Y. Stanier, *Arch Biochem. Biophys.* **38**, 245 (1952).

14. E. T. Bolton, B. H. Hoyer, D. B. Ritter, *Microsomal Particles and Protein Synthesis* (Pergamon, New York, 1958), p. 18.

15. A. Tissières and J. D. Watson, *Nature* **182**, 778 (1958); A. Tissières, J. D. Watson, D. Schlessinger, B. R. Hollingsworth, *J. Mol. Biol.* **1**, 221 (1959).

16. C. E. Hall and H. S. Slayeter, *J. Mol. Biol.* **1**, 329 (1959).

17. H. E. Huxley and G. Zubay, *ibid.* **2**, 10 (1960).

18. H. Lamfrom and E. R. Glowacki, *J. Mol. Biol.* **5**, 97 (1962); P. Tso and J. Vinograd, *Biochim. Biophys. Acta* **49**, 113 (1961).

19. B. Hall and P. Doty, *J. Mol. Biol.* **1**, 111 (1959); U. Z. Littauer and H. Eisenberg, *Biochim. Biophys. Acta* **32**, 320 (1959); S. M. Timasheff, A. Brown, J. S. Colter, M. Davies, *ibid.* **27**, 662 (1958).

20. C. G. Kurland, *J. Mol. Biol.* **2**, 83 (1960).

21. J. P. Waller and J. I. Harris, *Proc. Natl. Acad. Sci U.S.* **47**, 18 (1961).

22. P. F. Spahr, *J. Mol. Biol.* **4**, 395 (1962).

23. D. Elson, *Biochim. Biophys. Acta* **27**, 216 (1958); *ibid.* **36**, 372 (1959).

24. P. F. Spahr and B. R. Hollingworth, *J. Biol. Chem.* **236**, 823 (1961).

25. J. W. Littlefield, E. B. Keller, J. Gross, P. C. Zamecnik, *ibid.* **217**, 111 (1955); J. W. Littlefield and E. B. Keller, *ibid.* **224**, 13 (1957); P. C. Zamecnik and E. B. Keller, *ibid.* 209, 337 (1954); E. B. Keller and P. C. Zamecnik, *ibid.* **221**, 45 (1956).

26. M. B. Hoagland, P. C. Zamecnik, M. L. Stephenson, *Biochim. Biophys. Acta* **24**, 215 (1957).

27. M. B. Hoagland, M. L. Stephenson, J. F. Scott, L. I. Hecht, P. C. Zamecnik, *J. Biol. Chem.* **231**, 241 (1958).

28. F. H. C. Crick, *Symp. Soc. Exptl. Biol.* **12**, 138 (1958).

29. P. Berg and E. J. Ofengand, *Proc. Natl. Acad. Sci. U.S.* **44**, 78 (1958).

30. A. Tissières, D. Schlessinger, F. Gros, *ibid.* **46**, 1450 (1960).

31. F. Gros and D. Schlessinger, unpublished experiments (1961–62).

32. C. I. Davern and M. Meselson, *J. Mol. Biol.* **2**, 153 (1960).

33. M. Riley, A. Pardee, F. Jacob, J. Monod, *ibid.* **2**, 216 (1960).

34. S. Naono and F. Gros, *Compt. Rend.* **250**, 3889 (1960).

35. A. D. Hershey, J. Dixon, M. Chase, *J. Gen. Physiol.* **36**, 777 (1953).

36. E. Volkin and L. Astrachan, *Virology* **2**, 149 (1956).

37. M. Nomura, B. D. Hall, S. Spiegelman, *J. Mol. Biol.* **2**, 306 (1960).

38. F. Jacob and J. Monod, *ibid.* **3**, 318 (1961).

39. S. Brenner, F. Jacob, M. Meselson, *Nature* **190**, 576 (1961).

40. F. Gros, H. Hiatt, W. Gilbert, C. G. Kurland, R. W. Risebrough, J. D. Watson, *ibid.*, p. 581.

41. B. D. Hall and S. Spiegelman, *Proc. Natl. Acad. Sci. U.S.* **47**, 137 (1961).

42. M. Hayashi and S. Spiegelman, *ibid.*, p. 1564. F. Gros, W. Gilbert, H. Hiatt, G. Attardi, P. F. Spahr, J. D. Watson, *Cold Spring Harbor Symp. Quant. Biol.* **26** (1961).

43. A. Tissières and J. W. Hopkins, *Proc. Natl. Acad. Sci. U.S.* **47**, 2015 (1961).

44. M. Chamberlin and P. Berg, *ibid.* **48**, 81 (1962); W. B. Wood and P. Berg, *ibid.* **48**, 94 (1962).

45. M. W. Nirenberg and J. H. Matthaei, *Biochem. Biophys. Res. Commun.* **4**, 404 (1961).

46. ——, *Proc. Natl. Acad. Sci. U.S.* **47**, 1588 (1961).

47. R. W. Risebrough, A. Tissières, J. D. Watson, *ibid.* **48**, 430 (1962).

48. W. Gilbert, *J. Mol. Biol.,* in press.

49. J. Bishop, J. Leahy, R. Schweet, *Proc. Natl. Acad. Sci. U.S.* **46**, 1030 (1960).

50. H. Dintzes, *ibid,* **47**, 247 (1961).

51. M. Cannon, R. Krug, W. Gilbert, in preparation.

52. W. Gilbert, *J. Mol. Biol.,* in press.

53. D. Schlessinger and F. Gros, in preparation.

54. S. H. Barondes and M. W. Nirenberg, *Science* **138**, 813 (1962); G. J. Spyrides and F. Lipman, *Proc. Natl. Acad. Sci. U.S.* **48**, 1977 (1962); W. Gilbert, *J. Mol. Biol.,* in press.

55. S. S. Cohen, H. D. Barner, J. Lichtenstein, *J. Biol. Chem.* **236**, 1448 (1961).

56. R. Monier, S. Naono, D. Hayes, F. Hayes, F. Gros, *J. Mol. Biol.* **5**, 311 (1962); K. Asano, unpublished experiments (1962).

57. O. Maaløe, *Cold Spring Harbor Symp. Quant. Biol.* **26**, 45 (1961); F. C. Neidhardt and D. Fraenkel, *ibid.,* p. 63.

58. A. Gierer, *J. Mol. Biol.,* in press; J. R. Warner, P. M. Knopf, A. Rich, *Proc. Natl. Acad. Sci. U.S.,* in press.

59. C. Levinthal, A. Keynan, A. Higa, *ibid.* **48**, 1631 (1962).

60. S. S. Cohen, *J. Biol. Chem.,* in press. D. Schlessinger and P. F. Spahr, in preparation.

61. R. Gesteland and J. D. Watson, in preparation.

Section IV
Development:
The Nature of
Cell Differentiation

Introduction

The question of how a fertilized egg develops into an adult organism has attracted attention from the time of Aristotle down to the present day. Couched in terms of cell theory during the latter part of the nineteenth century, the problem became: How does a single cell (fertilized egg, or zygote), by undergoing a number of cell divisions, give rise to a variety of descendents which are morphologically and physiologically different? All the papers in this section contain approaches to that question.

The first papers, by Wilhelm Roux (1888) and Hans Driesch (1892), are among the first truly experimental approaches to this problem. The last paper, by Jacob and Monod (1961), represents the most recent and most theoretical approach. The work of each of the other authors contains varying mixtures of theory and experiment. In studying these papers the reader should try to determine what theoretical interpretations the authors are placing on their experimental work; that is, to what degree do they maintain that differentiation is a self-controlled process, and to what degree do they see it as brought about by influences from the external environment?

One basic question continues to pervade most of the studies on differentiation since Roux's paper of 1888. That is: To what extent is the differentiation of a cell (i.e., its degree of specialization) irreversible? Or, put another way, is the nucleus of a differentiated cell totipotent? Can it, under proper conditions, revert to the embryonic state? If not, why not? If it can, under what conditions? In one form or another, this question appears in each of the papers in this section. It is the unifying and still unsolved problem of modern embryology.

The concept of operator genes, developed by Francois Jacob and Jacques Monod in 1961, is one of the most revolutionary ideas in modern biology. Eminently simple, the model provides a mechanism for understanding how gene expression in different cells could be turned on and off under different conditions. Developed out of highly detailed and elegant studies of bacterial enzyme induction, the model applies to such diverse biological phenomena as aging, regeneration, the conversion of specialized cells into malignant cells (i.e., cancer), and embryonic differentiation. Although the Jacob-Monod concept is only theoretical, the new insights which it has provided are significant enough to have won for its authors the Nobel Prize in Medicine and Physiology for 1965.

Contributions to the Developmental Mechanics of the Embryo.
On the Artificial Production of Half-Embryos by Destruction of One of the First Two Blastomeres, and the Later Development (Postgeneration) of the Missing Half of the Body

by WILHELM ROUX

. . . The following investigation represents an effort to solve the problem of self-differentiation[1]—to determine whether, and if so how far, the fertilized egg is able to develop independently as a whole and in its individual parts. Or whether, on the contrary, normal development can take place only through direct formative influences of the environment on the fertilized egg or through the differentiating interactions of the parts of the egg separated from one another by cleavage.

For the egg as a whole I answered this question by rotating eggs in a perpendicular plane in such a way that, while the centrifugal force did not inhibit their development, the eggs continuously altered their orientation with respect to gravitational force, to the magnetic meridian and to the source of light and warmth. The result was that normal development was neither suspended, altered, nor even retarded by this process. We can conclude from this that the typical structures of the developing egg and embryo do not need any formative influence by such external agencies for their formation, and that in this sense the morphological development of the fertilized egg may be considered as self-differentiation. Nevertheless, several possibilities of external formative influence still remain that have not been tested by this experiment. These are of a very general character,

Abridged from Wilhelm Roux, "Contributions to the Developmental Mechanics of the Embryo. On the Artificial Production of Half-Embryos by Destruction of One of the First Two Blastomeres, and the Later Development (Postgeneration) of the Missing Half of the Body," trans. Hans Laufer, in *Foundations of Experimental Biology,* ed. Benjamin H. Willier and Jane M. Oppenheimer (Englewood Cliffs, N.J.: Prentice-Hall, 1964), pp. 4–37. Originally published in *Virchows Archiv für pathologische Anatomie und Physiologie und für klinische Medizin* **114** (1888), 113–153. Reprinted by permission of Springer-Verlag, Heidelberg, Germany.

[1] Cf. W. Roux, Beiträge zur Entwickelungsmechanik des Embryo. No. 1. Zeitschr. f. Biologie. 1885. Bd. XXI.

for example His[2] made the hypothesis that many cells have a tendency to move toward the direction from which oxygen enters, thus enlarging the surface of the embryo. It is also conceivable that the blastomeres lying on the surface of the blastula and the gastrula gradually become flatter on their external surfaces only because influences from outside cause their transformation into functional epithelia, thereby producing a mechanical tendency towards the densest concentration possible and toward the minimizing of the external surface, in contrast to the previous tendency towards the greatest possible sphericity for each individual cell. These speculations must still be checked against reality. The fact also must not be overlooked that the influence of external agencies may be a necessary condition for development, even though these influences may have no directly formative effect. For example, no development at all will take place without a certain amount of heat and also, later, of oxygen. But it cannot be deduced from this that such agencies determine which part of the egg produces the eyes, the blastopore, or the neural groove, or that they are the cause for the specific formation of the parts, despite the fact that abnormal formations result from an abnormal rise in temperature according to Panum, Dareste and Gerlach.

It has thus been shown that the development of the form of the fertilized egg, apart from that of several more general structures, occurs without external formative forces. We therefore have to look for the formative forces in the egg itself, which imposes a very pleasant limitation on further investigation.

As the result of this insight, it seems to me necessary to determine first of all whether all or many parts of the egg must collaborate if its structures are to form normally, or whether, on the contrary, the parts of the egg separated from one another by cleavage are able to develop independently of one another, and to show also, if possible, what share in the normal development each of the two principles has—that of differentiating interaction of the parts with one another, and that of self-differentiation of the parts. . . .

. . . Yet only direct experimentation with the egg can clarify for us with perfect certainty the actual participation of self-differentiation of the parts of the egg in normal development. Years ago[3] I worked along these lines and verified, in general, that operations that produce an extrusion of material from the cleaving and cleaved egg do not prevent development or cause general malformation. The resulting embryos develop rather normally and have only a localized defect or a localized malformation.

In order to acquire more specialized knowledge, I used the portion of the spawning period in the spring of 1887 that remained, after the conclusion of

---

[2] W. His, Untersuchungen über die Bildung des Knochenfischembryo (Salmen). Arch. f. Anat. u. Physiol., anat. Abth. 1878, S. 220.

[3] "Vorläufige Mittheilung über causal-autogenetische Experimente," Vortrag gehalten am 15. Febr. 1884. in der Schlesischen Gesellschaft für vaterländische Cultur. (Lecture delivered on February 15th, 1884 to the Silesian Society for Native Culture.) My neglect in sending in a review resulted in there being no notice of that lecture in the corresponding annual report of the Silesian Society. The report was first published in Beitrag 1 zur Entwickelungsmechanik, Zeitschrift für Biologie 1885.

time-consuming experiments, for pertinent investigations on which I will report in the present article. . . .

The plan of the experiments was as follows:

In the first experiment the eggs of the green frog, *Rana esculenta,* were placed individually in glass dishes, and the oblique position of the black hemisphere and the direction of cleavage were sketched during the formation of the first cleavage. Then one of the first two blastomeres was pricked once or more with a fine needle. The present position of the egg was then compared with the drawing. A new sketch was made if there was a difference, and the location of the puncture points was indicated, along with the position of the egg material exuded through them, the exovates. Unfortunately most of these eggs in the first experiments either did not develop at all or developed normally, in spite of the fact that the punctured blastomere often discharged large amounts of material and became filled up again by a flow of substances from the neighboring cell. As a result, in addition to their loss, an extreme disorder of the egg substances must have been present. Therefore, after the destruction of a single blastomere I could observe the externally visible processes in a few eggs only. In many of the eggs, the unoperated control eggs as well as the experimental ones, occasional malformations were already occurring, as is customary toward the end of the spawning period. I have already described this effect briefly in a previous publication. Since ability of the eggs to develop normally might cease completely at any time, I operated after the formation of the first cleavage on great numbers of unisolated eggs lying together in clusters. After several hours, or the next day, I selected and placed in separate dishes those eggs in which the operated blastomere had not cleaved. Occasionally the second cleavage occurred during the operation on the first egg, and I then pierced two of the blastomeres lying next to one another, or perhaps only one of four.

Even after repeated puncture of a cell with a fine needle, and in spite of considerable exovation, the cell often developed normally. So, beginning on the third day, I heated the needle by holding it against a brass sphere for a heat supply, heating the sphere as necessary. In this case only a single puncture was made, but the needle was ordinarily left in the egg until an obvious light brown discoloration of the egg substance appeared in its vicinity. Some of this discolored material stuck to the needle when it was pulled out and formed a broad slightly protruding cone—a sign that it had become firmer and thus was partly coagulated. As a result of this, exovates no longer issued even out of the puncture points. I now had better results; they were as follows. In about 20 % of the operated eggs only the undamaged cell survived the operation, while the majority were completely destroyed and a very few, where the needle had possibly already become too cold, developed normally. I thus developed and preserved over a hundred eggs with one of their halves destroyed, and, of these, 80 were sectioned completely. Eggs that were intended for the latter purpose were taken out and killed from time to time. More were taken from the early stages, those of the morula and the blastula, than from the later stages already provided with the rudiments of special organs.

In each experiment we likewise, although more rarely, observed in the unoperated control egg a failure of one of the two or four first blastomeres to develop as well as other malformations. These eggs were also preserved at various stages and sectioned for comparison with the operated eggs. The same was done with eggs which did not develop in spite of their having been placed in seminal fluid. . . .

. . . Coming now to the report of our experimental results, we will first present the processes which take place in the untreated egg-half after this crude interference.

In many cases no developmental phenomena were perceptible in this cell. More often the symptoms of death already described were apparent, gray discoloration and the formation of spots.[4] In other cases these blastomeres went through several further cleavages only to die likewise, as I have elsewhere described, with an accompanying maximal flattening of the cells against one another, occasionally leading to the disappearance of the externally visible cleavage planes. On the basis of the third type of behavior, about to be described, we can properly assume that in these first two cases the supposedly and undamaged cells had actually been directly affected by the operation and died from its effects and not as a result of the failure of interaction with the other cells.

In the third type of development, which was achieved in approximately 20% of the treated eggs in the last experiments, the untreated cell continued to survive. Various results might have been expected from this: for example, abnormal processes might intervene which would lead to bizarre structures. Or the single half of the egg, which, after all, according to many authors, is a complete cell with a nucleus completely equivalent in quality to the first segmentation nucleus, might develop into a correspondingly small individual. These authors see in the mechanism of indirect nuclear segmentation, on my authority as it were, only a contrivance for qualitative halving. I have repeatedly and clearly opposed this opinion. But instead of the possible surprises as postulated above an even more amazing thing happened; the one cell developed in many cases into a half-embryo generally normal in structure, with small variations occurring only in the region of the immediate neighborhood of the treated half of the egg. These variations will be mentioned in the section on the behavior of this latter half.

By repeated cleavages of the undamaged half of the egg a structure was at first produced which deserves the name of a *semimorula verticalis*,[5] since it is built substantially like the vertical half of a morula. I mean by this that it was a hemispherical structure which consisted, in its upper region, of tightly packed small pigmented cells, and in its lower region of larger unpigmented cells. One

---

[4] Beitr. zur Entwickelungsmechanik No. 1 Zeitschr. f. Biologie. 1885.

[5] Very similar to normal development. [*Eds.*]

component, however, of the normal morula was not properly developed in the eleven *semimorulae verticales* that were sectioned. This was the segmentation cavity. It should have been represented by an approximately hemispherical cavity adjacent to the undeveloped half and delimited by closely packed cells. Instead of this, the internal cells are merely loosely arranged with interstices between them. Sometimes there is a larger but not sharply delimited cavity that is separated from the undeveloped half by a layer of cells. Occasionally there is no indication at all of the formation of the cavity, not even the loose arrangement of the cells [see Figs. 1–4].

The next stage, the blastula, is not distinctly separated from the morula stage, since the blastula develops from the morula mainly by a further diminution in size of the cells and an enlargement of the internal cavity. This latter results from a gradual thinning of the roof of the cavity, which can be extremely varied in different individuals.

I found several *semiblastulae verticales* corresponding to this stage and sectioned them. The interesting thing here is that at this stage the internal cavity proves to be well defined, bordered by densely packed cells in the majority of cases, so that in comparison with the condition in the semimorulae the cells must have subsequently rearranged themselves and approximated themselves closely together. The blastocoele thus formed sometimes lies completely enclosed in the developed half, i.e., it is separated from the undeveloped half by a single or multiple layer of cells (Fig. 1). Sometimes it borders directly on the boundary surface, which is approximately flat. In one case, however, it extends into this half (Fig. 2) and has thus acquired approximately the shape of a complete blastocoele; this however was caused merely by an abnormally large secretion of fluid by the developing half. In another case there is no indication at all of the formation of a cavity; the cells lie tightly together at all points and therefore border directly on the undeveloped half. . . .

The median plane can already be clearly distinguished in the normal gastrula as a plane passing through the center of the whole spherical structure and dividing symmetrically both the horseshoe-shaped blastopore and, internally, the cavity of the archenteron that is continuous with it. The cavity of the archenteron is covered on the outside by a thin double layered sheet that is dark on the outside. The horseshoe-shaped rim of this sheet forms, together with the adjacent white yolk mass, the blastopore. The dark sheet develops into the dorsal half of the embryo and I have therefore designated it as the dorsal plate. The middle of the horseshoe-shaped rim represents the head region and the open part of the arc the tail region of the embryo. Later the two halves of the horseshoe-shaped edge of the dorsal plate approach one another, proceeding in the cephalocaudal direction, and then merge. Normally the horseshoe-shaped rim is divided symmetrically by the median plane of the embryo.

As has been mentioned, because of the turning in of the free edge of the living half it is extremely difficult in half-embryos to identify the pertinent structural features by superficial examination and to judge whether the semigastrula is a lateral or an anterior or a posterior one.

Figure 3 represents a rather advanced stage, where one would be inclined to identify the section as a median one through a *semigastrula anterior*. Since however the direction of the cut is not perpendicular to the surface separating the developed from the undeveloped half, but runs almost parallel to it, and since the dorsal plate is present in almost its entire length, the section figured proves to be one through a *semi-gastrula lateralis*. This diagnosis is easily and certainly confirmed if we mentally integrate the appearance of all the sections. The lumen of the archenteron is still only a slit in spite of its great length. The outer layer, the ectoderm, is clearly distinguishable from the inner layer, the endoderm. The blastula fluid and therefore the blastocoele also is still maintained, which is not normally the case at this time. The incorrectness of the view of previous authors, according to which the side of the egg adjacent to the blastocoele becomes the dorsal side of the embryo, is clearly evident in the more lateral sections where the blastocoele is located on the ventral side of the egg opposite to the dorsal plate. This is true in the developed as well as the undeveloped halves. . . .

I must mention in this connection that even in normal embryos the shape of the folds at various ages is not always so constant and stereotyped as in the beautiful models by Ecker-Ziegler so frequently reproduced by later authors. On the contrary, rather high degrees of variation occur that have already been partially described by O. Hertwig[6] and myself.[7] Many of these variations seem to represent reversions to processes that are known in fishes, and that are caused primarily by anachronisms in differentiation and growth of the various parts. Such anachronisms are also evident in the relative delay or acceleration of the development of the individual germ layers. For example, many otherwise normal embryos possessing rather undifferentiated neural folds already show development within the mesoderm, the endoderm and in the chorda dorsalis that normally does not occur until nearly the time that the neural tube closes. In these cases there is an obvious retardation in the ectoderm as compared with the development of the two other germ layers. Such variations can easily lead to differences of opinion between observers should one of them attempt general deductions on the basis of insufficient material. The rates of development of the two lateral halves of the body also show variations of a lesser degree and provide the advantageous opportunity of permitting two stages of development to be observed in the same specimen.[8]

Such variations, caused by inhibiting factors and the retardation of various processes, occur frequently toward the end of the spawning period, or as the result of an insufficient supply of air. Frequently, however, they are compensated for during the further course of development.

I sectioned six of the *hemiembryones laterales* that were obtained as a result of the above operation. Inspection of the cross-sections shows only half of the

---

[6] O. Hertwig, Die Entwickelung des mittleren Keimblattes der Wirbelthiere. Jena 1883. Taf. V. Fig. 5.

[7] Beitrag 1 zur Entwickelungsmechanik des Embryo. Zeitschr. f. Biol. 1885. Bd. XXI.

[8] Note that Roux here brings up the important point that variations in embryonic development occur even under normal conditions; hence interpretations of abnormalities under experimental conditions must be made with reference to the normal range of variation. [*Eds.*]

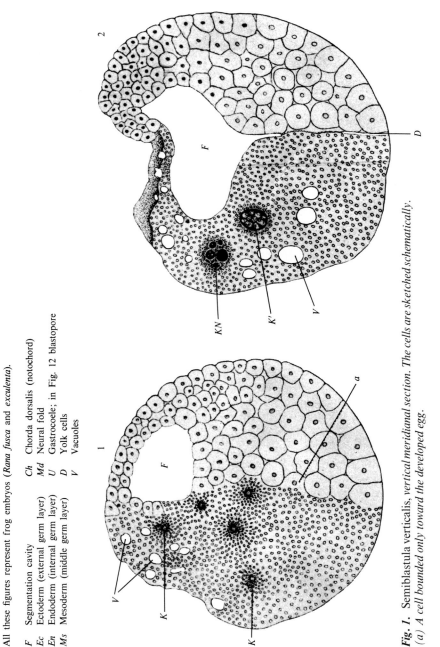

All these figures represent frog embryos (*Rana fusca* and *exculenta*).

F	Segmentation cavity	*Ch*	Chorda dorsalis (notochord)
Ec	Ectoderm (external germ layer)	*Md*	Neural fold
En	Endoderm (internal germ layer)	*U*	Gastrocoele; in Fig. 12 blastopore
Ms	Mesoderm (middle germ layer)	*D*	Yolk cells
		V	Vacuoles

Fig. 1. Semiblastula verticalis, *vertical meridianal section. The cells are sketched schematically.* (a) A cell bounded only toward the developed egg.

Fig. 2. Semiblastula verticalis, *section of the same. Extension of the cleavage cavity into the undeveloped half of the egg. KN nuclear test. K' a very large nucleus with reticular structure.*

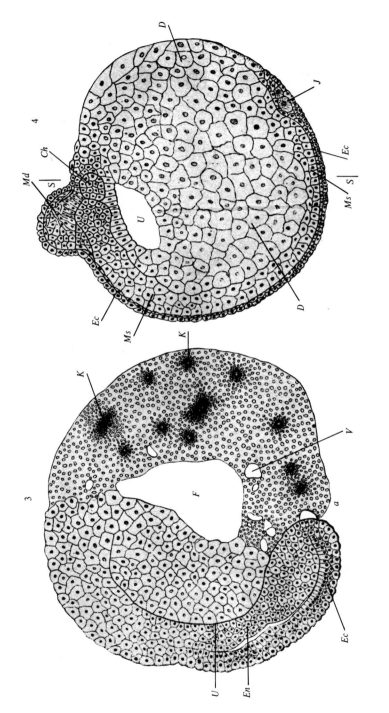

Fig. 3. Semigastrula lateralis, *oblique longitudinal section.*

Fig. 4. Hemiembryo sinister, *cross section. S–S the median place. The right half of the egg is already completely cellular as a result of the post-generation of the germ layers which has begun. Notochord has already caught up in its development to the normal size of the cross section. J two yolk cells, which have remained young.*

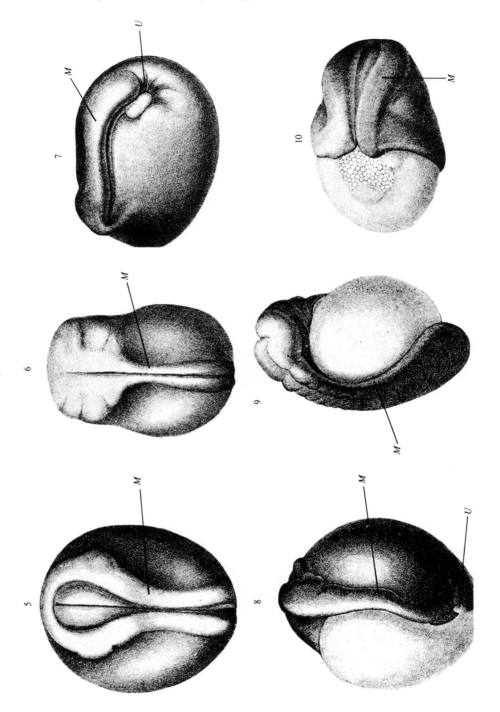

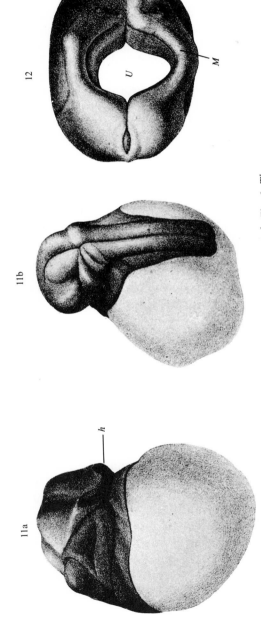

Fig. 5. *Dorsal surface of a normal frog embryo with neural folds still separated.* **Fig. 6.** *The same, with neural folds already united.* **Fig. 7.** *Hemiembryo dexter, with post-generation of the external germ layer already almost completed.* **Fig. 8.** *The same, older, but with less post-generation.* **Fig. 9.** *Hemiembryo sinister, still older, almost without post-generation.* **Fig. 10.** *Hemiembryo anterior, already in the process of post-generation.* **Fig. 11.** *Hemiembryo anterior, older. (a) Ventral side. (h) The adhesive gland. (b) Dorsal side. Post-generation of the neural folds is already far advanced.* **Fig. 12.** *Three-quarter embryo with asyntaxia medullaris (Roux). The left half of the head is not developed, the ectoderm is nevertheless already post-generated in its area. (U) A part of the blastopore that has remained open.*

neural plate to be present. This is especially noticeable in the more advanced stages where the neural fold is already formed and typical in structure (Fig. 4). The typical arrangement of the cells of the more advanced neural tube is already nicely attained in many preparations but not so obvious in other places. The older embryos show the neural tissue in the cephalic region to be thickened and appropriately shaped. The originally lateral side of the ectoderm (the horny layer) had previously joined with the lateral edge of the neural plate, and in the course of the formation of the neural fold had been raised along with it to approach the midline. In the oldest embryo this horny layer had already separated from the neural part, although there is no opportunity here for it to merge with a similar layer of the other half. For the time being it projects unattached toward the other undeveloped half. This free edge, as well as the dorsal edge of the *semi-medulla lateralis,* is curved ventrally, which also occurs in normal embryos.

The cavity of the archenteron has taken form only in the developed half and likewise extends only as far as the chorda. Its lumen is often too narrow and still slit-shaped. In other cases it has enlarged somewhat but is still constricted in the cephalic region by too great a concentration of yolk. The endoderm is normally constituted.

The formation of the mesoderm and the chorda dorsalis is normally a new feature of this phase. Our half-embroys also have formed these parts. I have no specimen in the very short phase in which we could gain clear insight into the origin of the mesoderm. In all the preparations it is already completely separated and in some cases it shows the normal cross-sectional appearance and the normal arrangement of the cells. In the older embryos the separation into lateral plate and somitic mesoderm is taking place or is already completed. In the oldest embryo the latter is already split up into somites. The lateral half of the mesoderm is thus normally developed (compare Fig. 4, Ms). . . .

INFERENCES FROM THESE FINDINGS

In general we can infer from these results that each of the two first blastomeres is able to develop independently of the other and therefore does develop independently under normal circumstances. . . .

All this provides a new confirmation of the insight we had already achieved earlier that developmental processes may not be considered a result of the interaction of all parts, or indeed even of all the nuclear parts of the egg. We have, instead of such differentiating interactions, the self-differentiation of the first blastomeres and of the complex of their derivatives into a definite part of the embryo. This is valid both for the case when the first cleavage to appear separates, as normally, the right and left half and for the case when it anachronistically separates the cephalic and caudal halves. Each of these blastomeres contains therefore not only the formative substance for a corresponding part of the embryo but also the differentiating and formative forces. The assumption[9] that I had

---

[9] Ueber die Bedeutung der Kerntheilungsfiguren. Leipzig 1883. S. 15 und Beiträge zur Entwickelungs-mechanik des Embryo. No. 3. Bresl. ärztl. Zeitschr. 1885. No. 6 u.ff. Separ.-Abdr. S. 45.

previously made with respect to the significance of cleavage becomes a certainty for the first cleavages. We can say: cleavage divides qualitively that part of the embryonic, especially the nuclear material that is responsible for the direct development of the individual by the arrangement of the various separated materials which takes place at that time, and it determines simultaneously the position of the later differentiated organs of the embryo. (This applies also to subsequent typical rearrangements of material.) . . .

Although according to this assertion the first cleavage separates the material of the right and left halves of the body from one another and even though I have introduced the expression "qualitatively halved" embryonic material, still we must not ignore the fact that this material is not morphologically similar although it is qualitatively alike in its chemical and percentage composition. Its arrangement is, after all, such that a right half of the body is produced on one side and a left half on the other. There are several questions in this connection which must be answered separately and which I mention here merely to prevent incorrect views being imputed to me as a result of excessive brevity in my presentation. These concern the arrangements which are the cause of this fundamental dissimilarity, at the time of the first cleavage, on which bilateral symmetry is based. Is it merely in the hemispheric shape of the yolk material and the controlling effect of that shape on the possibly various nuclear components, or is it in their independent arrangement?

It is an obvious further step to extend to the subsequent cleavages the above conclusion regarding qualitative separation of material. I hope to be able to verify by further experiments to what point this extension can be justified. It must similarly be determined whether the derivatives of later blastomeres are capable of self-differentiation or whether the progressive differentiation that forms the embryo is dependent on the coexistence of a whole group, perhaps all the descendants of one of the first four blastomeres. We would then have obtained with each of the first four blastomeres the smallest possible part of the ovum which is capable of self-differentiation. I do not, however, presume this to be the case, in spite of the mechanism of gastrulation which I will describe immediately and which appears to argue for that point.

Let us now proceed to special inferences for developmental mechanics which result from the facts mentioned. First of all it is to be deduced from the normal course of development of the undamaged blastomere that the qualitative division of the cell body and of the nuclear material, which we have just explained and which takes place at the time of cleavage, can proceed properly without any influence from the neighboring cells—and therefore probably does proceed in the normal case without this influence. Secondly, it can be deduced that the nucleus reaches its proper position in the blastomere, so important for the correct arrangement of the separated materials, without being affected by the vital activity of the neighboring cells. The same is true of later cleavages within the region in the neighborhood of the treated cells; therefore this independence can probably correctly be considered general. I further deduce from the dispensability of one vertical half of the egg that the formation of the blastula proceeds without extensive strains in the material, such as far-reaching mechanical interactions of the parts. Because of this I am inclined to attribute the typical formation of the blastula to an active rearrangement of the cells. A contributing factor perhaps is the tendency of many cells to approach the surface as a source of oxygen, which is His' view. . . .

The development of the frog gastrula and of the embryo initially produced from it is, from the second cleavage on, a mosaic of at least four vertical pieces developing independently.

How far this mosaic formation of at least four pieces is now reworked in the course of further development by unilaterally directed rearrangements of material and by differentiating correlations, and how far the independence of its parts is restricted, must still be determined. . . .

REFERENCES

Boveri, Th., Über die Polarität des Seeigeleies. Verhandl. d. Phys.-Med. Ges. zu Würzburg. N. F. Bd. 34. 1901.

Braus, H., Ist die Bildung des Skelettes von den Muskelanlagen abhängig? Morphol. Jarhb. Bd. 35, S. 38 bis 110. 1906.

Lewis, W. H., Transplantation of the lips of the blastopore in *Rana palustris*. Americ. Journ. of Anat. Vol. 7. S. 137–143. 1907.

Mangold, O. Transplantationsversuche zur Ermittelung der Eigenart der Keimblätter. Verhandl. d. dtsch. zool. Ges. Bd. 27, S. 51–52. 1922.

——, Transplantationsversuche zur Frage der Spezifität und Bildung der Keimblätter bei *Triton*. Arch. f. mikrosk. Anat. u. Entwicklungsmech. Bd. 100. S. 198–301, 1923.

Ruud, G. and Spemann, H., Die Entwicklung isolierter dorsaler und lateraler Gastrulahälften von *Triton taeniatus* und *alpestris*, ihre Regulation und Postgeneration. Arch. f. Entwicklungsmech. d. Organismen. Bd. 52, S. 95–165. 1923.

Spemann, H., Über die Determination der ersten Organanlagen des Amphibienembryo I–IV. Ibid. Bd. 43, S. 448–555. 1918.

——, Mikrochirurgische Operationstechnik. *Abderhaldens* Handb. d. biol. Arbeitsmethoden, 2. Aufl., S. 1–30. 1920.

——, Über die Erzeugung tierischer Chimären durch heteroplastische embryonale Transplantation zwischen *Triton cristatus* und *Triton taeniatus*. Arch. f. Entwicklungsmech. d. Organismen Bd. 48, S. 533–570. 1921.

v. Ubisch, L., Das Differenzierungsgefälle des Amphibienkörpers und seine Auswirkungen. Ibid. Bd. 52, S. 641–670. 1923.

Vogt, W., Die Einrollung und Streckung der Urmundlippen bei *Triton* nach Versuchen mit einer neuen Methode embryonaler Transplantation. Verhandl. d. dtsch, zool. Ges. Bd. 27, S. 49–51. 1922.

The Potency of the First Two Cleavage Cells in Echinoderm Development. Experimental Production of Partial and Double Formations

by HANS A. E. DRIESCH

"Granting that the primordium of a part originates during a certain period, one must, for greater accuracy, describe this by stating that the material for the primordium is already present in the blastoderm while the latter is still flat but the primordium is not as yet morphologically segregated and hence not recognizable as such. By tracing it back we shall be able for every primordium to determine its exact location even in the period of incomplete or deficient morphological organization; indeed, to be consistent, we should extend this determination back to the newly fertilized, even the unfertilized, egg. The principle according to which the blastoderm contains organ primordia preformed in a flat pattern and, vice versa, every point in the blastoderm can be rediscovered in a later organ, I call the principle of organ-forming germ-areas."

In these words, he [His, 1874] formulated the principle so designated by him. Continuing this train of thought, Roux[1] discussed in a perceptive manner the difference between evolution, or the *metamorphosis* of manifoldness, and epigenesis, or the *new formation* of manifoldness; in his well-known experiments on "half-embryos" (of which only the first part concerns us here) he decided the question under consideration, for the frog egg, in favor of evolution.

A not very generally known work by Chabry is the only further investigation of this kind known to me. His specific explanations and figures make it clear that his results are fundamentally contrary to those of Roux. I wish to mention here that I came to know of Chabry's work only after the completion of my own experiments.

As to these, I was interested in repeating Roux's experiments on material which would be resistant, easily obtainable, and readily observable; all three of these conditions are most satisfactorily fulfilled by the Echinoids, which had

Hans A. E. Driesch, "The Potency of the First Two Cleavage Cells in Echinoderm Development. Experimental Production of Partial and Double Formations," from an abridged translation by L. Metzger, M. and V. Hamburger, and Thomas S. Hall, in *A Source Book in Animal Biology,* ed. Thomas S. Hall (New York: McGraw-Hill, 1951), pp. 418–426. Copyright, 1951, by The President and Fellows of Harvard College. Reprinted by permission of Harvard University Press, Cambridge, Mass. References, Figs. 1–14, and figure explanations added by Benjamin H. Willier and Jane M. Oppenheimer, eds., *Foundations of Experimental Biology* (Englewood Cliffs, N.J.: Prentice-Hall, 1964), pp. 40–50. Originally published in *Zeitschrift für wissenschaftliche Zoologie* **53** (1892), 160–178, 183–184.

[1] *Beitrage zur Entwicklungsmechanik des Embryo.* I. *Zeitschr. f. Biol.* Bd. XXI. III. *Breslauer ärztl. Zeitschr.* 1885. V. *Virchow's Arch.* Bd. CXIV.

already served as a basis for so many investigations. My own experiments were carried out upon Echinus microtuberculatus.

The investigations were made in March and April of 1891. They have led me to many other problems closely connected with the present one, problems whose eventual solution will deepen materially our understanding of the part already solved. Nevertheless, I present my results at this time because they have decided with certainty, for my material, the cardinal point, that is, the potency of the first blastomeres.

MATERIALS AND METHODS

The first week of my stay in Trieste was lost, inasmuch as I obtained almost exclusively useless material. Whereas the following work follows the above mentioned experiments of Roux in content, the method was taken from the excellent cellular researches of the Hertwig brothers. These investigators, by shaking unfertilized eggs, split off pieces and raised them successfully. It is well known that Boveri used the same method for the production of his "organisms produced sexually without maternal characters," although other factors prevented him from carrying out the procedure exactly.

I therefore went to Trieste with the intention of obtaining one of the first half-blastomeres of Echinus by shaking at the two-cell stage, in order to see, provided it lived, what would become of it.

At an average temperature of about 15° C., cleavage of Echinus eggs occurred $1\frac{1}{2}$ to 2 hours after artificial fertilization. Good material, and only such was used, displayed in only a very few instances immediate division into four cells, an inevitable result, according to Fol and Hertwig, of bispermy.

Shaking was done in small glass containers 4 cm long and about 0.6 cm in diameter. Fifty to one hundred eggs were placed in a small quantity of water. In order to obtain results, one must shake as vigorously as possible for five minutes or more; even then one obtains at best only about ten isolated blastomeres and about as many eggs whose membranes are still intact but whose cells are more or less separated within these membranes.

If shaking is done at the moment of completion of first cleavage, events are, so to speak reversed; the furrow disappears and one obtains a sausage-shaped body whose two nuclei again show connections. In these recombined eggs the furrow reappears in a short time and normal development follows. On the other hand if one shakes too late, the second cleavage occurs prematurely during the shaking. It is therefore necessary to watch carefully for the right moment.

About one half of the blastomeres are, in addition to being isolated, dead; nevertheless I obtained about fifty capable of development. This appears not unfavorable considering the strength of the mechanical treatment, and considering the fact that the isolated blastomeres are in direct contact with the water on at least one side,—a completely abnormal situation. Isolation is obviously possible only where the membrane bursts.

During cleavage the preparations were observed microscopically as often as possible, and during later development usually once every morning and evening.

One more thing about the treatment of the isolated cells. The contents of the glass used for shaking must be poured into fresh sea water as soon as possible since the water has naturally warmed and evaporated.

It was to be expected that the small quantity of water would not be exactly beneficial, nor the bacteria which were especially numerous toward the end of my experiment and were encouraged by disintegrating pieces which had died.

At any rate my method guarantees that one is observing the same pieces on successive days. Unfortunately, Boveri, in his very important experiments, did not succeed in this respect.

But here I anticipate my results. I turn now to a systematic presentation of findings starting with [cleavage].

CLEAVAGE

First a few words about the normal course of events as revealed in Selenka's excellent investigations.

Following two meridional cleavages there is an equatorial one and the germ now consists of eight cells of equal size. Four of these now give off, toward one pole, four smaller cells, and at the same time the others divide approximately meridionally.

The germ now consists of 16 cells and shows a marked polarity with the four small cells, easily recognized, occupying one pole. Further divisions lead to stages with 28, 32, 60, and 108 cells (Selenka). The four small cells which originated at the 16-cell stage clearly indicate the animal pole for a long time. I was unable to establish certainly any differences between the cells of the blastula. At a later stage of development, but before the epithelial flattening due to close union of cells has led to the blastula proper, the Echinus germ, especially in the half containing the smaller-celled pole, consists of cellular rings.

How, then, do the blastomeres of the first division stages after isolation by shaking accomplish cleavage, assuming they survive?

I shall first describe the behavior observed in a majority of cases. Not once did I observe a completely spherical rounding up of the isolated cell. It is true that the normally flat surface tends toward sphericalness but its radius of curvature always remains greater than that of the original free surface of the hemisphere. The cell now divides into two and then, perpendicularly to this, into four parts. Normal controls fertilized at the same time now have eight similar cells the same size as our four. Simultaneously fertilized normal controls have at this time eight similar cells.

In the Echinoids no "gliding" of cells normally occurs either in the four-cell stage nor the $\frac{1}{2}$ eight-cell stage (i.e., my four-cell stage). This is significant because it facilitates considerably the interpretation of the following fact.

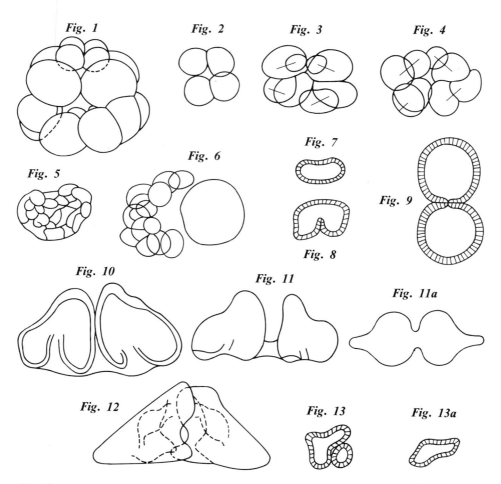

Fig. 1. *Sixteen-cell stage, copied from Selenka. Magnification about 400×.* **Fig. 2.** *Half-embryo made up of 4 cells (half of an 8-cell stage). Compare with Fig. 1. Apochrom. 16 mm. Oc. 8.* **Figs. 3 and 4.** *Half-embryo made up of 8 cells (half of a 16-cell stage). Compare with Fig. 1. Apochrom. 16 mm. Oc. 12.* **Fig. 5.** *Half-embryo; cleavage is completed and the half sphere is closing. Apochrom. 16 mm. Oc. 12.* **Fig. 6.** *Half-embryo; one-half of the egg is dead. Late cleavage stage. Same magnification as Figs. 3 and 4. (The figure attempts merely to give a general impression, only the outlines of the uppermost cells are drawn.)* **Fig. 7.** *Blastula that developed from an extremely distorted 2-cell stage. Although it looks as though it is dividing, it did not form two partial embryos but a single one that was misshapen.* **Fig. 8.** *Blastula in the process of dividing, developed from a very misshapen egg. It formed two partial embryos.* **Fig. 9.** *Blastula in the process of dividing. It formed two conjoined twins.* **Fig. 10.** *The same set of embryos shown as twin gastrulae. Lateral view.* **Fig. 11.** *The same set of embryos shown at the prismatic gastrula stage. Lateral view.* **Fig. 11a.** *Seen from above.* **Fig. 12.** *The same set of embryos as twin plutei. The oral fields face toward each other, and the plutei are somewhat compressed and are therefore seen partially from the side. Apochrom. 16 mm. Oc. 8. (From a Canada balsam preparation, somewhat shrunken. The three divisions of the gut may be seen.)* **Fig. 13.** *Blastula from a greatly misshapen 2-cell stage that at the next division separate into $\frac{3}{4}$ and $\frac{1}{4}$ blastomeres.* **Fig. 13a.** *The fragment from the $\frac{1}{4}$ blastomere has been constricted off. Figures 7 to 13a, except Fig. 12, were drawn without a camera lucida, but as accurately as possible. Several of them (Figs. 7, 8, 13, and 13a) were drawn at a low magnification, others at higher magnification.*

About $5\frac{1}{2}$ hours after fertilization occurs, untreated germs have divided into 16 parts, as described above, and isolated blastomeres into 8 parts.

At this point begins the really interesting part of my experiment in that the last-mentioned division brings into existence a typical single half of the 16-cell stage as described; that is, it behaves in the way expected of it according to absolute self-differentiation; it is actually a half of what Selenka's figure shows.

I will no go on to a description of the normal division of my blastomeres, later speaking about the abnormal cases (about 25%).

I carefully followed the formation of a half-germ of 16 cells, i.e., a typical $\frac{1}{2}$ 32-cell stage. Each of the normal concentric cell rings is present, but each consists of half its normal number of cells. The entire structure now presents the appearance of an open hemisphere with a polarly differentiated opening.

In the majority of cases here referred to as normal, the half-germ presented, on the evening of the day of fertilization, the appearance of a typical, many-celled, open hemisphere, although the opening often seemed somewhat narrowed. As especially characteristic, I will mention here a case upon which I chanced in doing the Roux-Chabry experiment. Instead of one of the blastomeres being isolated, it was killed by the shaking. The living one, which had developed in the above manner into a typical half-formation, was in the afternoon attached to the dead one in the shape of a hemisphere; but by evening its edges were already clearly curled inward.

The cleavage of isolated blastomeres of the two-cell stage of Echinus micro-tuberculatus is accordingly a half-formation as described by Roux for operated frog's eggs.

As already mentioned, this is by far the most frequent behavior. One will not be surprised to find modifications of it in view of damage caused by the strong mechanical insult due to shaking. A few words about these exceptions:

In some cases, germs consisting of about 32 cells ($\frac{1}{2}$ 64-cell stage) presented by late afternoon a spherical appearance; development was here more compact, so to speak, though following the typical scheme. This occurs because of a closer union of the cells and is a phenomenon possibly similar to Chabry's "gliding." Normally, the blastomeres of Echinus make contact in only small areas, until shortly before blastula formation.

In other cases—nine were observed in all—there was from the outset (i.e. from the 8 or half 16-cell stage) little to be seen of the usual scheme except as to cell number; specifically, the half germ was spherical from the very beginning, and "gliding" was even more pronounced. I wish to mention especially a case in which the eight cells (half 16) were of almost equal size. Had the role of first cleavage here been different and had I here, to put it briefly, perhaps separated the animal from the vegetal pole instead of the left from the right? By analogy with the experiments of Rauber, Hallez, etc., this seems not unlikely.

The first time I was fortunate enough to make the observations described above, I awaited in excitement the picture which was to present itself in my dishes the next day. I must confess that the idea of a free-swimming hemisphere or a half gastrula with its archenteron open lengthwise seemed rather extraordinary. I thought the formations would probably die. Instead, the next morning I found in their respective dishes typical, actively swimming blastulae of half size.

I have already described how toward the evening of the day of fertilization the, as yet not epithelial, hemisphere had a rather narrowed opening and I have emphasized that tracing of individual cells and hence of the side of the opening corresponding to the animal pole proved impossible. True, I occasionally saw two smaller cells somewhere along the edge but attached no meaning to them. The question as to the actual mode of closing of the blastula must for the time being, therefore, remain unsolved. I may perhaps be briefly permitted to indicate the significance of this.

Now another general question the solution of which I intend soon to undertake: how far does the totipotency of the blastomeres go? That is, up to what stage are blastomeres still able to produce a complete, small organism? In the future I shall call these "part-formations" in contrast to Roux's "half-formations." The polar course of the cleavage, as well as the above hypothesis concerning the closure of the blastula, suggested that perhaps elements of all concentric rings must be present; that would mean, however, that the four-cell stage would be the last from which isolated cells could produce part-formations, since the equatorial cleavage (namely, the third) divides the material into north and south polar rings, so to speak. This is, as stated, for the time being still merely a question; the totipotency of the cells of the four-cell stage seems to me probable in view of the three-quarter + one-quarter blastulae which will be briefly mentioned later. If, on the other hand, the above-mentioned assumption concerning differences in the effect of the first cleavage should prove true, the latter hypothesis, that material from all three rings is necessary for part-formation, would no longer hold.

But let us leave these conjectures and return to the facts. Thirty times I have succeeded in seeing small free-swimming blastulae arise from cleavage as described above of isolated blastomeres; the rest, about 20 cases, died during cleavage or were sacrificed so I could inspect them under higher magnification. Almost all of them at this stage were still transparent and entirely normal structurally though half-sized. I was not, by a method of estimation, able to discover any difference in size between these cells and those of the normal blastula; therefore, the number of cells is probably half the normal number, which is also to be expected from their cleavage behavior.

At the end of the second day, the fate of the experimental cases seemed to be sealed; they showed the effects of strong mechanical insult and of the small amount of water. For germs still transparent at this time, one could count on raising them further; unfortunately, this was the case with 15 specimens only, that is half the total.

The Gastrula and Pluteus

In healthy specimens invagination at the vegetal pole usually begins at the end of the second day; on the morning of the third day little gastrulae swam about actively in the dishes. As stated, I succeeded in observing 15 such specimens.

Three of the formations finally became actual plutei, differing from the normal only in size.

Therefore, these experiments show that, under certain circumstances, each of the first two blastomeres of Echinus microtuberculatus is able to produce a normally developed larva, whole in form and hence a part-, not half-, formation.

This fact is in fundamental contradiction to the theory of organ-forming germ areas, as the following simple consideration specifically demonstrates.

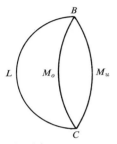

Fig. 14

Imagine a normal blastula split along the median plane of the future pluteus; let us now examine one of the hemispheres preserved this way, for instance the left (see Fig. 14[2]). The material at $M_o M_u$ would normally supply material for the median region, that at L material for the left side. But suppose that we imagine the hemisphere closing, as explained above, to form a sphere but still maintaining polarity along BC. Then M_o will come to lie upon M_u, and hence possibly upon the right side of the future part-formation. Or, if in closure the original median areas supplied materials for the median region of the part-formation, then this could be thought of only as the upper or lower median region. If it is thought of as the upper, then the lower would come from a part which would otherwise have formed the left side. However one regards it, one cannot escape the fundamental difference in the role which identical material is called upon to play depending upon whether one whole- or two part-formations arise from it,—something which can be brought about artificially. "I'l n'est pas des lors permis de croire que chaque sphere de segmentation doit occuper une place et jouer un role, qui sont assignés a l'avance" (Hallez); not, at any rate, in Echinus.

That this is a particularly pleasing result one could scarcely contend; it seems almost a step backward along a path considered already established.

When compared with Roux's, my results reveal a difference in behavior in the sea urchin and frog. Yet perhaps this difference is not so fundamental after all. If the frog blastomeres were really isolated and the other half (which was probably not dead in Roux's case) really removed, would they not perhaps

---

[2] This text figure replaces an incorrect one in the translation. [Editors of *Foundations of Experimental Embryology*.]

behave like my Echinus cells? The cohesion of the blastomeres, conforming to the law of minimal surface formation, is much greater in the frog than in my object.

I have tried in vain to isolate amphibian blastomeres; let those who are more skillful than I try their luck.

It will not have escaped the reader that the results described might throw light on at least one aspect of the theory of [double formation].

Double Formation

On this subject, I am in a position to supplement what has already been said. If, from one isolated cell of the two-cell stage, a perfect embryo of half-size is formed (namely a part-formation, in contrast to mere division which yields half-formation as in the case of Roux's frog embryos), it follows unequivocally that both cells of this stage if they are isolated and kept intact will form separate embryos, or twins.

It is highly probable that the separation of blastomeres by shaking was the direct cause of double formation and that without shaking whole-formation would have resulted.

This is certain since part-formations show that an isolated blastomere, provided it lives at all, always develops into a structure which differs from the normal only in size. With other twins, the situation is different, since they are too numerous to be considered accidental formations of this kind, such having never been seen in thousands of larvae observed by the Hertwig brothers and me.

Roux's theory of double formation, must, together with the principle of organ-forming germ-areas previously discussed, be discarded, at least in its general form. I have already remarked that, for our theoretical conceptions, this might be considered a backward rather than a forward step if establishment of facts did not always constitute progress.

Whether or not mechanical isolation or separation of the first two cleavage cells is the only way to obtain twin formation will be left open at this time.

It is an old controversy whether double-formation takes place by fusion or fission; birds and fish would, as mentioned, elsewhere, provide rather unfavorable material for a solution of this problem which in its usual formulation is rather a descriptive than a fundamental one. The observations communicated by other workers as well as my own experiments establish splitting as a cause, to which I may add on the basis of my results, splitting without postgeneration.

Obviously fission- and fusion-double-formation would be two quite different things, hence twinning could be of a dual nature. It is certain that the above mentioned double-fertilization modifies cleavage in such a way that immediate four-cell formation occurs; this is in support of our position, as shown before.

What forces come into play when the blastula closes? Can perhaps part of this process be understood in physical terms? The cell mass takes the form of a sphere, the form, that is, which possesses minimal surface. Further, why is it, after all, that a strong pulling apart of the half blastomeres without destroying them results in two individuals? These and other questions present themselves, but it were futile to indulge in idle speculation without actual facts.

Summary

If one isolates one of the first two blastomeres of Echinus microtuberculatus it cleaves as if for half-formation but forms a whole individual of half-size which is a part-formation.

Therefore the principle of organ-forming germ-areas is refuted for the observed species while the possibility of artificial production of twins is demonstrated.

Addendum: In proof-reading, I will briefly add that I have just succeeded in killing one cell of the two-cell stage of Spherechinus by shaking and in raising from the other half a small pluteus after half-cleavage.

Naples, October, 1891

REFERENCES

1. Born, Die Furchung des Eies bei Doppelmissbildungen. Breslauer ärztl. Zeitshcrift. 1887. Nr. 15.

2. Boveri, Ein geschlechtlich erzeugter Organismus ohne mütterliche Eigenschaften. Sitz.-Ber. d. Ges. f. Morph. u. Physiol. München 1889.

3. Chabry, Contribution à l'embryologie normale et tératologique des ascidies simples. Journ. de l'anat. et de la physiol.. 1887.

4. Driesch, Die mathematisch-mechanische Betrachtung morphologischer Probleme der Biologie. Jena, Fischer 1891.

5. Fol, Recherches sur la fécondation et le commencement de l'hénogenie. Memoires de la soc. de phys. et d'hist. nat. de Genève. XXVI.

6. Gegenbaur, Beiträge zur Entwicklungsgeschichte der Landpulmonaten. Diese Zeitschr. Bd. III.

7. Hallez, Recherches sur l'embryologie des Nématodes. Paris 1885.

8. O. u. R. Hertwig, Über den Befruchtungs- und Theilungsvorgang des thierischen Eies etc. Jena 1887.

9. O. Hertwig, Experimentelle Studien am thierischen Ei etc. I. Jena 1890.

10. His, Unsere Körperform. Leipzig 1874.

11. Klaussner, Mehrfachbildungen bei Wirbelthieren. München 1890.

12. Kleinenberg, The development of the Earth-Worm. Quarterly Journal, 1879.

13. Korschelt, Zur Bildung des mittleren Keimblattes der Echinodermen. Zool. Jahrb. Bd. IV.

14. Metschnikoff, Über die Bildung der Wanderzellen bei Asteriden und Echiniden. Diese Zeitschr. Bd. XLII.

15. Plateau, Statique des liquides etc. 1873.

16. Rauber, Formbildung und Formstörung in der Entwicklung von Wirbelthieren. Leipzig 1880. Auch Morph Jahrb. Bd. VI.

17. —— Neue Grundlagen zur Kenntnis der Zelle. Morph. Jahrb. VIII.

18. 19. 20. Roux, Beiträge zur Entwicklungsmechanik des Embryo. I. Zeitschr. f. Biol. Bd. XXI. III. Breslauer ärztl. Zeitschr. 1855. V. Virchow's Arch. Bd. CXIV.

21. Selenka, Studien über Entwicklungsgeschichte der Thiere. II. Wiesbaden 1883.

See also references on duplicities (Gegenbaur, Dareste, Lacaze-Duthiers etc.) in Rauber, Klaussner, in Ziegler's Lehrbuch der allgemeinen Pathologie etc.

Induction of Embryonic Primordia by Implantation of Organizers from a Different Species

by HANS SPEMANN and HILDE MANGOLD

I. INTRODUCTION

In a *Triton*[1] embryo, at the beginning of gastrulation, the different areas are not equivalent with respect to their determination.

It is possible to exchange by transplantation parts of the ectoderm at some distance above the blastopore that in the course of further development would have become neural plate and parts that would have become epidermis, without disturbing normal development by this operation. This is feasible not only between embryos of the same age and of the same species but also between embryos of somewhat different age and even between embryos of different species (Spemann 1918, 1921). For instance, presumptive epidermis of *Triton cristatus* transplanted into the forebrain region of *Triton taeniatus* can become brain; and presumptive brain of *Triton taeniatus* transplanted into the epidermal region of *Triton cristatus* can become epidermis. Both pieces develop according to their new position; however they have the species characteristics with which they are endowed according to their origin. O. Mangold (1922, 1923) has extended these findings and has shown that prospective epidermis can furnish not only neural plate but even organs of mesodermal origin, such as somites and pronephric

Abridged from Hans Spemann and Hilde Mangold, "Induction of Embryonic Primordia by Implantation of Organizers from a Different Species," trans. Viktor Hamburger, in *Foundations of Experimental Biology,* ed. Benjamin H. Willier and Jane M. Oppenheimer (Englewood Cliffs, N.J.: Prentice-Hall, 1964), pp. 146–184. Originally published in *Wilhelm Roux' Archiv für Entwicklungsmechanik der Organismen* **100** (1924), 599–638. Reprinted by permission of Springer-Verlag, Heidelberg, Germany.

[1] One genus of salamander, of which *cristatus* and *taeniatus* are two species. [*Eds.*]

tubules. It follows from these experimental facts, on the one hand, that the exchangeable pieces are still relatively indifferent with respect to their future fate; and, on the other hand, that influences of some sort must prevail in the different regions of the embryo that determine the later fate of those pieces that are at first indifferent.

A piece from the upper lip of the blastopore behaves quite differently. If it is transplanted into the region that would later become epidermis, it develops according to its origin; in this region, a small secondary embryonic primordium[2] develops, with neural tube, notochord and somites (Spemann 1918). Such a piece therefore resists the determining influences that impinge on it from its new environment, influences that, for instance, would readily make epidermis out of a piece of presumptive neural plate. Therefore, it must already carry within itself the direction of its development; it must be determined. Lewis (1907) had already found this for a somewhat later developmental stage, when he implanted a small piece from the upper and lateral blastopore lip under the epidermis of a somewhat older embryo and saw it develop there into neural tissue and somites.

It suggested itself from the beginning that effects might emanate from these already determined parts of the embryo that would determine the fate of the still indifferent parts. This could be proved by cutting the embryo in half and shifting the halves with respect to each other; in this case, the determined part proved to be decisive for the direction that subsequent development would take. For instance, the animal half of the gastrula was rotated 90° or 180° with respect to the vegetal half; determination then spread from the lower vegetal piece, that contained just the upper lip, to the upper animal piece. Or two gastrula halves of the same side, for instance two right ones, were fused together. As a result, the half blastoporal lips completed themselves from adjacent material of the fused other half, and in this way, whole neural plates were formed (Spemann 1918).

Thus, the concept of the *organization center* emerged; that is, of a region of the embryo that has preceded the other parts in determination and thereupon emanates determination effects of a certain quantity in certain directions. The experiments to be presented here are the beginning of the analysis of the organization center.

Such a more deeply penetrating analysis presupposes the possibility of subdividing the organization center into separate parts and of testing their organizing capacities in an indifferent region of the embryo. This experiment has already been performed, and it was precisely this experiment that gave the first indication that the parts of the embryo are not equivalent at the beginning of gastrulation (1918). However, this intraspecific, homoplastic transplantation did not make it possible to ascertain how the secondary embryonic anlage[3] that originated at the site of the transplant was constructed, that is, which part of it was derived from the material of the implant and which part had been induced

---

[2] That is, a secondary embryo. [*Eds.*]

[3] "Anlage" is a term used by embryologists, particularly in earlier days, to refer to hereditary determiners. [*Eds.*]

by the implant from the material of the host embryo. The identification of these two components is made possible by heteroplastic transplantation, as for instance by implantation of organizers from *Triton cristatus* into indifferent material of *Triton taeniatus*.[4] . . .

II. EXPERIMENTAL ANALYSIS

. . . Of the species of *Triton* available, *taeniatus* can best tolerate the absence of the egg membrane, from early developmental stages on; and it is the easiest to rear. Hence the organizer that was to be tested for its capacities was always taken from a *cristatus* embryo and usually implanted into the presumptive epidermis of a *taeniatus* embryo. The place of excision was marked by implantation of the piece removed from the *taeniatus* embryo; that is, the pieces were exchanged.

Experiment Triton 1921, Um 8b. The exchange was made between a *cristatus* embryo with distinctly U-shaped blastopore and a *taeniatus* embryo of the same stage. A small circular piece at some distance above the blastopore was removed from the *cristatus* embryo and replaced by a piece of presumptive epidermis of the *taeniatus* embryo. This *taeniatus* implant was found, later on, as a marker in the neural plate of the *cristatus* neurula, between the right neural fold and the midline, and it extended to the blastopore, slightly tapering toward the posterior end (Fig. 1). One could not see in the living embryo whether it continued into the interior, and the sections, which are poor in this region, did not show this either.

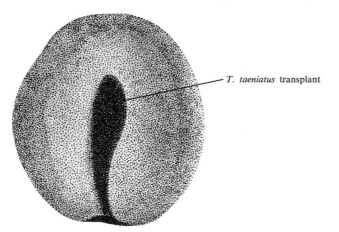

— *T. taeniatus* transplant

Fig. 1. *Um 8 crist. The* cristatus *embryo at the neurula stage. The* taeniatus *transplant is dark and elongated; it is located in the presumptive neural plate. 20 ×.*

The *cristatus* explant (the "organizer") was inserted on the right side of the *taeniatus* embryo, approximately between the blastopore and the animal pole.

---

[4] The important distinction between the cells of the two species (in the early embryonic state) is pigmentation. *T. taeniatus* cells are dark, while *T. cristatus* cells are light. Thus visual examination of a transplanted section shows where host + transplant daughter cells are located. [*Eds.*]

It was found in the neurula stage to the right and ventrally, and drawn out in the shape of a narrow strip (Fig. 2). In its vicinity, at first a slight protrusion was observable; a few hours later, neural folds appeared, indicating the contour of a future neural plate. The implant was still distinctly recognizable in the midline of this plate; it extended forward from the blastopore as a long narrow strip, slightly curved, over about two-thirds of the plate (Fig. 3).

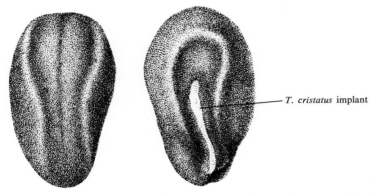

— *T. cristatus* implant

Figs. 2 and 3. *Um 8b. The* taeniatus *embryo at the neurula stage, with primary and secondary neural plate; the elongated white* cristatus *implant is in the median plane of the latter. 20×.*

This secondary neural plate, that developed in combination with the implanted piece, lagged only a little behind the primary plate in its development. When the folds of the primary plate were partly closed, those of the secondary plate also came together. Approximately a day later, both neural tubes were closed. The secondary tube begins, together with the primary tube, at the normal blastopore and extends to the right of the primary tube, rostrad, to approximately the level where the optic vesicles of the latter would form. It is poorly developed at its posterior part, yet well enough that the *cristatus* implant was invisible from the outside. The embryo was fixed at this stage and sectioned as nearly perpendicularly to the axial organs as possible.

The sections disclosed the following:

The neural tube of the primary embryonic anlage is closed through the greater part of its length and detached from the epidermis, except at the anterior end where it is still continuous with it, and where its lumen opens to the exterior through a neuropore. The lateral walls are considerably thickened in front; this is perhaps the first indication of the future primary eye vesicles. The notochord is likewise completely detached, except at its posterior end where it is continuous with the unstructured cell mass of the tail blastema. In the mesoderm, four to five somites are separated from the lateral plates, as far as one can judge from cross sections of such an early stage.

Only the anterior part of the neural tube of the secondary embryonic anlage is closed and detached from the epidermis. Here it is well developed; in fact it is developed almost as far as the primary tube at its largest cross-section: its walls are thick and its lumen is drawn out sideways (Fig. 4). Perhaps we can see here the first indication of optic vesicles. The central canal approaches the surface at its posterior end, and eventually opens to the outside. Then the neural plate rapidly tapers off; its hindmost portion is only a narrow ectodermal thickening (Figs. 5 and 6).

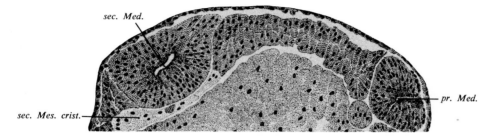

Fig. 4. *Um 8B. Cross section through the anterior third of the embryo (cf. Figs. 2 and 3). pr. Med., primary neural tube; sec. Med., secondary neural tube. The implant (light) is in the mesoderm (sec. Mes. crist.). 100×.*

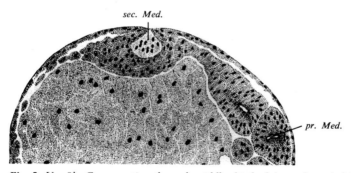

Fig. 5. *Um 8b. Cross section through middle third of the embryo (cf. Figs. 2 and 3). pr. Med., primary neural tube; sec. Med., secondary neural tube. The implant (light) is in the secondary neural tube.*

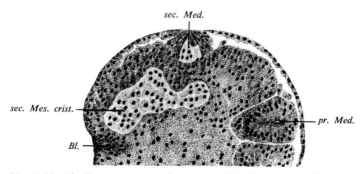

Fig. 6. *Um 8b. Cross section in the region of the blastopore (Bl.) (cf. Figs. 2 and 3). pr. Med., primary neural tube; sec. Med., secondary neural tube. The implant (light) has several cells in the secondary neural tube, with its main mass in the mesoderm (sec. Mes. crist.). 100×.*

Although the overwhelming mass of this secondary neural tube is formed by cells of the *taeniatus* host that can be recognized by the finely dispersed pigment, a long, narrow strip of completely unpigmented cells is intercalated in its floor, in sharp contrast to the adjacent regions. This white strip is part of the *cristatus* implant that was clearly recognizable from the outside in the living embryo before the neural folds closed (Fig. 3). The anterior end of this strip is approximately at the point where the thickness of the neural tube decreases rather abruptly; it opens to the outside shortly thereafter. The strip is wedge-shaped, with the pointed edge toward the outside; as a result, only the tapering ends of the cells reach the surface of the embryo (Figs. 5 and 6) or the central canal at the short stretch where they border it. . . .

Although a piece of presumptive neural plate taken from a region a little anterior to the actual transplant would have become epidermis after transplantation to presumptive epidermis, this implant has resisted the determinative influences of the surroundings and has developed essentially according to its place of origin. Its ectodermal part has become part of the neural plate and the endo-mesodermal part has placed itself beneath it.

Furthermore, not only did the implant assert itself, but it made the indifferent surroundings subservient to it and it has supplemented itself from these surroundings. The host embryo has developed a second neural plate out of its own material, that is continuous with the small strip of *cristatus* cells and underlain by two cell plates of *cristatus* origin. This secondary plate would not have arisen at all without the implant, hence it must have been caused, or induced, by it.

There seems to be no possible doubt about this. However, the question remains open as to the way in which the induction has taken place. In the present case it seems to be particularly plausible to assume a direct influence on the part of the transplant. But even under this assumption, there are still two possibilities open. The ectodermal component of the transplant could have self-differentiated into the strip of neural plate, and could have caused the differentiation of ectoderm anterior and lateral to it progressively to form neural tissue. Or the determination could have emanated from the subjacent parts of the endo-mesoderm and have influenced both the *cristatus* and *taeniatus* components of the overlying ectoderm in the same way. And finally it is conceivable that the subjacent layer is necessary only for the first determination, which thereafter can spread in the ectoderm alone. A decision between these possibilities could be made if it were possible successfully to transplant pure ectoderm and pure endo-mesoderm from the region of the upper lip of the blastopore, and, finally, such ectoderm which had been underlain by the endo-mesoderm. In such experiments, heteroplastic[5] transplantation offers again the inestimable advantage that one can establish afterwards with absolute certainty whether the intended isolation was successful.

In our case, such a separation of the factors under consideration has not been accomplished. Nevertheless it seems noteworthy that the induced neural plate is poorly developed in its posterior part where it is in closest and most extensive

---

[5] Heteroplastic refers to a process in which tissue is formed where it does not normally occur. [*Eds.*]

contact with the ectodermal part of the transplant; and, in contrast, that it is well developed at its anterior end where it is remote from the *cristatus* cell strip, but underlain by the broad *cristatus* cell plate. . . .

Experiment Triton 1922, 132. The organizer was taken from a *cristatus* embryo in advanced gastrulation (medium-sized yolk plug). The median region, directly above the blastopore, was transplanted into a *taeniatus* embryo of the same stage. The implant moved inward in the shape of a shallow cup. The *cristatus* embryo, with the exchange implant from *taeniatus*, developed to a larva with primary optic vesicles; it was lost by accident before sectioning. In the neurula stage, the implant had been located medially in the posterior part of the neural plate and extended to the blastopore. Closure of the neural folds was delayed and not quite complete at the caudal end; it was similar to but not quite as abnormal as that in *Triton* 1922, 131b.

Figs. 7 and 8. *Um. 132. The* taeniatus *embryo at the neurula stage; the secondary neural folds are viewed from the right side (Fig. 7), and from above (Fig. 8)* 20×.

In the *taeniatus* embryo, when this is in the neurula stage, $19\frac{1}{2}$ hours after the operation, the implant is no longer visible. In its place are two short neural folds surrounding a groove. They extend obliquely across the ventral side of the embryo, from left posterior to right anterior in front view. Twenty-five hours later the neural folds have approached each other (Fig. 8). The two folds mentioned above and the groove between them are on the left ventral side of the embryo; they are lengthened, and they approach the anterior ends of the host neural folds at an acute angle (Figs. 7 and 8). After another 22 hours, this secondary embryonic primordium has flattened out anteriorly, but posteriorly it projects considerably above the surface. In this region, somites seem to form. Approximately 28 hours later, the embryo has primary optic vesicles, otic pits and a tail bud. In the secondary embryo, at least on the right side, somites can be quite clearly recognized. After another 20 hours, paired otocysts are seen at its anterior end; they are at the same level as those of the primary embryo. The free posterior end has grown somewhat and is bent toward the primary embryo. Four hours later, a pronephric duct is visible in the induced anlage. The embryo was fixed 6 hours later, when a blister appeared on the dorsal surface; the sections were cut transversely.

Immediately before fixation, the living object showed the following features: The embryo is stretched lengthwise, but its tail is still bent ventrad (Fig. 9).

The optic vesicles are strongly expanded, the otic pits distinct, and a large number of somites is formed. The head is continuously bent to the left, probably due to the secondary embryonic anlage which is on the left side. The latter is rather far ventral, and approximately parallel to the primary axial organs, which it approaches anteriorly at an acute angle. It extends over a considerable part of the length of the primary embryo, from the posterior border of the left optic vesicle to the level of the anus. Its posterior end is lifted up like a tail bud. The central canal of its neural tube is visible through the epidermis, and likewise the lumen of the otic vesicles and of the right somites. The left somites are not recognizable. . . .

Fig. 9. Um 132b. The taeniatus *embryo shown in Figs. 7 and 8, developed further; viewed from the left side. Surface view of the secondary embryo, with tailbud, neural tube, somites, and otocysts. 20 × .*

Of the axial organs of the primary embryonic anlage, the neural tube, notochord and somites are entirely normally developed; so is the right pronephros. The left pronephros, however, which faces the secondary primordium, shows a minor irregularity. In the brain primordium, the primary optic vesicles are already transformed into cups, and the lens primordia are recognizable as slight thickenings of the epidermis. The optic pits have closed to form vesicles, but they are not further differentiated, except for the indication of a *ductus endolymphaticus*. The notochord is separated from the adjacent parts throughout almost its entire length. Between 11 and 13 clearly segregated somites can be counted. Neural tube, notochord and somites pass into undifferentiated tissue at the tip of the tail. The primordium of the pronephros consists on each side of two nephrostomes with associated tubules (Figs. 10 and 11). These open into pronephric ducts, in a normal fashion (Figs. 11 and 12). The left duct has a larger diameter anteriorly than has the right one. The pronephric duct can be traced far posteriorly, but not to their opening to the outside.

The secondary embryonic enlage also possesses all the axial organs; they are in part very well formed. The neural tube is closed in its entire length and detached from the epidermis. It is sharply delimited except for its caudal end where it becomes continuous with the undifferentiated mass of the secondary tail bud. In its middle part, the right side is somewhat more strongly developed than the left side (Fig. 12). Toward its anterior end, the diameter increases, and the roof becomes broader and thinner, as in a normal medulla (Fig. 10). At this level,

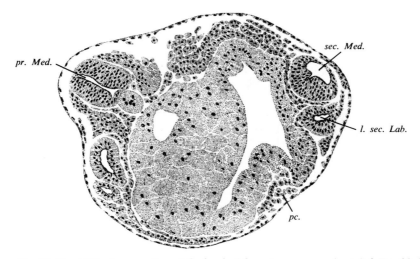

Fig. 10. *Um 132b. Cross section at the level of the primary pronephros (cf. Fig. 9). The primary axial organs are at the upper left of the figure and the secondary axial organs at the right. l. sec. Lab., left secondary otocyst; pc., pericardium. 100 ×.*

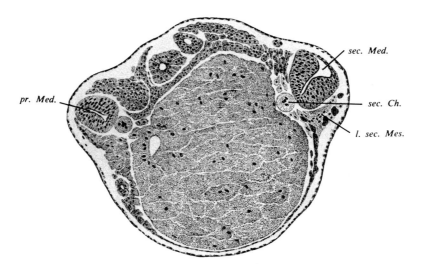

Fig. 11. *Um 132b. Cross section in the anterior third of the embryo (cf. Fig. 9). The primary axial organs are at the left of the figure and the secondary axial organs at the right. The implant (light) has differentiated notochord and left secondary somite. 100 ×.*

two otocysts are adjacent to it. The right otocyst is shifted forward; it lies at the level of the anterior end (compare the surface view, Fig. 9), and the left one is slightly more posterior (Fig. 10). They are still attached to the epidermis, and the formation of the endolymphatic duct seems indicated. The notochord extends less far craniad than normally. It is not yet found at the level of the posterior octocyst (Fig. 10); it does not begin until 90 μ behind this section. Otherwise it is well formed, and sharply delimited all the way to its posteriormost part in the tail bud. Somites are formed on both sides; there are more (4 to 6) on the right side facing the primary embryo than on the left side (2 to 3). On the right side, they extend farther forwards (Fig. 12). A pronephric duct is formed on both sides; again, the left one is longer (about 300 μ) than the right one (about 500 μ) [figures probably erroneously reversed]. Caudally they are not yet separated from the mesoderm, and anteriorly, tubules and funnels are not formed, or not yet. The two adjacent ducts, namely the left one of the primary embryo and the right one of the secondary embryo, are in communication with each other directly behind the second pronephric tubule.

Both embryos share the intestine which is primarily directed toward the primary embryo. It cannot be ascertained with certainty to what extent the secondary embryo has a share in it in all regions. In the pharynx, primordia of visceral pouches may belong to the secondary embryo (Fig. 10); however, they could also belong to the primary embryo and merely be shifted slightly by the secondary embryo. This holds, at any rate, for the heart primordium (Fig. 10 pc, in section through the posterior end of the pericardium). In contrast, a secondary intestinal lumen is distinctly induced beneath the axial organs of the induced anlage, although it can be traced for only a very short distance (about 60 μ; Fig. 12). The anus is somewhat expanded, so that the endoderm is exposed; it is also shifted toward the left side.

The secondary embryonic anlage is again a chimera formed by cells of the host and of the implanted organizer. The two posterior thirds of the neural tube have a ventral strip of *cristatus* cells (Figs. 12 and 13). The notochord is formed entirely of *cristatus* cells. In the somites, the *cristatus* contribution is in the anterior and posterior sections of the left row (Figs. 11 and 13, right) and in the middle part of the right row (Fig. 12, left); there are no somites at all in the middle of the left row (Fig. 12, right). The implant has remained in one place, throughout its length (Figs. 11–13).

All the other structures of the secondary embryo that are not formed by *cristatus* cells have been undoubtedly induced in *taeniatus* material by the organizer.

Hence, in the case the two embryonic anlagen have interfered with each other only to the extent that some of the organ primordia are somewhat more strongly developed on the inner side than on the outer side, and that the pronephric ducts are connected with each other. In other respects, the induced embryonic primordium is entirely independent. This is perhaps one of the main conditions for its complete development. . . .

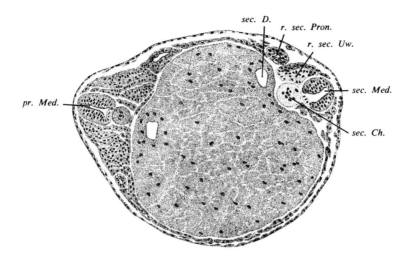

Fig. 12. *Um 132b. Cross section through the middle of the embryo (cf. Fig. 9). The primary axial organs are at the left of the figure and the secondary axial organs at the right. r. sec. Pron., right secondary pronephric duct. The implant (light) has formed notochord and part of the right secondary somite. 100×.*

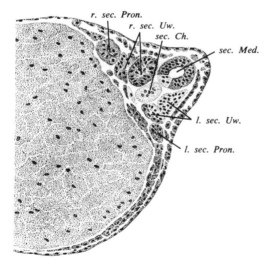

Fig. 13. *Um 132b. Cross section through the secondary axial organs, slightly anterior to the secondary tailbud (cf. Fig. 9). The implant (light) is in the floor of the secondary neural tube and in the left secondary somite and has formed notochord. 100×.*

III. SUMMARY OF RESULTS

A piece taken from the upper blastopore lip of a gastrulating amphibian embryo exerts an organizing effect on its environment in such a way that, following its transplantation to an indifferent region of another embryo, it there causes the formation of a secondary embryo. Such a piece can therefore be designated as an organizer.

If the organizer is implanted within the normal zone of invagination, then it participates in the gastrulation of the host embryo and, afterwards, shares the blastopore with it; if transplanted outside the zone of invagination, it invaginates autonomously. In this case, part of it may remain on the surface and there participate in the formation of the ectoderm and, specifically, of the neural plate; or it may move altogether into the interior and become endo-mesoderm entirely. In this event it is likely that cells of the host embryo can also be invaginated along with the transplant. Indeed, this might be considered already as a determinative effect of the implant on its environment.

In the host embryo, a secondary embryo originates in connection with the implant; it can show different degrees of differentiation. This depends, in part, on whether it interferes with the primary axial organs, or whether it remains completely independent. In one case in the latter category, a neural tube without brain and eyes, but with otic vesicles, and also notochord, somites, and pronephric ducts developed.

These secondary embryonic primordia are always of mixed origin; they are formed partly of cells of the implant and partly of cells of the host embryo. If, in the experiment under discussion, an organizer of another species is used for induction, then the chimeric composition can be established with certainty and great accuracy. It was demonstrated for most organs, for neural tube, somites, and even for the notochord.

There can be no doubt but that these secondary embryonic primordia have somehow been induced by the organizer; but it cannot yet be decided in what manner this occurs and, above all, when and in what way. The inductive effect could be limited to a stimulation to gastrulation, whereupon all else would follow, as in normal development. In this event, the different parts of the secondary zone of gastrulation would be subjected to the determination without regard to their origin. But the induction by the implant could also continue beyond the stage of gastrulation. In this case, the organizer, by virtue of its intrinsic developmental tendencies, would essentially continue its development along the course which it had already started and it would supplement itself from the adjacent indifferent material. This might also hold for the determination of the neural plate; but it is more likely that the latter is determined by the underlying endo-mesoderm. But the development of the implant could not be pure self-differentiation; otherwise it could not have been harmoniously integrated with the secondary embryonic primordium which is smaller than the primary primordium. Apparently the inducing part, while in action, was subjected to a counter-action by the induced part. Such reciprocal interactions may play a large role, in general, in the development of harmonious equi-potential systems.

IV. REFERENCES

Boveri, Th., Über die Polarität des Seeigeleies. Verhandl. d. Phys.-Med. Ges. zu Würzburg. N. F. Bd. 34. 1901.

Braus, H., Ist die Bildung des Skelettes von den Muskelanlagen abhängig? Morphol. Jarhb. Bd. 35, S. 38 bis 110. 1906.

Lewis, W. H., Transplantation of the lips of the blastopore in *Rana palustris*. Americ. Journ. of Anat. Vol. 7. S. 137–143. 1907.

Mangold, O., Transplantationsversuche zur Ermittelung der Eigenart der Keimblätter. Verhandl. d. dtsch. zool. Ges. Bd. 27, S. 51–52. 1922.

——, Transplantationsversuche zur Frage der Spezifität und Bildung der Keimblätter bei *Triton*. Arch. f. mikrosk. Anat. u. Entwicklungsmech. Bd. 100. S. 198–301. 1923.

Ruud, G. and Spemann, H., Die Entwicklung isolierter dorsaler und lateraler Gastrulahälften von *Triton taeniatus* und *alpestris,* ihre Regulation und Postgeneration. Arch. f. Entwicklungs-mech. d. Organismen. Bd. 52, S. 95–165. 1923.

Spemann, H., Über die Determination der ersten Organanlagen des Amphibienembryo I–IV. Ibid. Bd. 43, S. 448–555. 1918.

——, Mikrochirurgische Operationstechnik. *Abderhaldens* Handb. d. biol. Arbeitsmethoden, 2. Aufl., S. 1–30. 1920.

——, Über die Erzeugung tierischer Chimären durch heteroplastische embryonale Trans-plantation zwischen *Triton cristatus* und *Triton taeniatus*. Arch. f. Entwicklungsmech. d. Organismen Bd. 48, S. 533–570. 1921.

v. Ubisch, L., Das Differenzierungsgefälle des Amphibienkörpers und seine Auswirkungen. Ibid. Bd. 52, S. 641–670. 1923.

Vogt, W., Die Einrollung und Streckung der Urmundlippen bei *Triton* nach Versuchen mit einer neuen Methode embryonaler Transplantation. Verhandl. d. dtsch, zool. Ges. Bd. 27, S. 49–51. 1922.

Evidence for the Formation of Cell Aggregates by Chemotaxis in the Development of the Slime Mold Dictyostelium Discoideum

by JOHN TYLER BONNER

INTRODUCTION

Dictyostelium discoideum is a member of that curious group of amoeboid slime molds, the Acrasiales, which forms one of numerous bridges between unicellular

Abridged from John Tyler Bonner, "Evidence for the Formation of Cell Aggregates by Chemotaxis in the Development of the Slime Mold *Dictyostelium Discoideum*," *Journal of Experimental Zoology* **106** (October 1947), 1–26. Reprinted by permission.

organisms and multicellular organisms. In its life cycle (see Raper, '35, '40a, '40b, '41, and Bonner, '44 for descriptive details) there is both a unicellular stage which subsequently develops by the aggregation of cells to central collection points into a differentiated multicellular organism.

So far as is known the life cycle is completely asexual. Individual capsule-shaped spore cells germinate by splitting down the side and liberating a single, uninucleate myxamoeba. This myxamoeba feeds on bacteria by phagocytosis and divides by binary fission to form many of its own kind, but each daughter myxamoeba remains a separate, independent individual. At the end of this so-called *vegetative stage,* the myxamoebae cease to feed or multiply, thus having a natural separation in their own life histories between growth processes, and purely formative, morphogenetic processes. The myxamoebae subsequently enter the *aggregation stage* and stream in together to form a mass of cells known as a *pseudoplasmodium* (see Figs. 1, 2). The psudoplasmodium then crawls as a body for variable distances during the *migration stage.* Finally the pseudoplasmodium rights itself and rises up into the air, forming a delicate tapering stalk set at its large basal end in a small *basal disk,* and holding at its apex the *sorus* which is a spherical mass of encapsulated spores. This rise in height and differentiation of the mature fruiting body or sorocarp comprises the *culmination stage.*

The problem that concerns us at the moment is the mechanism by which aggre-gation occurs; how can great numbers of independent myxamoebae be drawn together to form one unified organism.

In a number of papers Raper ('40a, '40b, '41) reviews the past work done on aggregation and his discussions of the subject will be briefly summarized. There are 2 aspects that he has considered: the external factors affecting aggregation, and the cause of aggregation.

Many authors believe that the primary external factor involved in the stimulation of the initiation of aggregation is food shortage (Potts, '02; Oehler, '22; von Schuckmann, '24; Arndt, '37; Raper, '40b). Raper ('40b) found that the time of initiation of aggregation was shortened and the resulting patterns were made smaller by the following agents: decreased humidity, increased temperature, and light. Potts ('02) and Harper ('32) also noticed that smaller fruiting bodies were obtained in light.

Concerning the cause of aggregation, Olive ('02) and Potts ('02) independently suggested that there were chemotactic stimuli arising from the central mass of aggregating myxamoebae. Neither investigator offered any evidence for this hypothesis but believed that the general appearance indicated such a mechanism. Olive actually tried to influence aggregating myxamoebae with malic acid and sugar solutions, placed in a sealed-off capillary tube, following the work of Pfeffer on the chemotaxis of spermatozoids of ferns, but with no encouraging results. The only other suggestion was that of von Schuckmann ('25) and Harper ('26) that aggregation is caused by a negative hygrotropic response, but Raper ('41) effectively proved that such a mechanism cannot be seriously considered.

There has been one more recent important contribution: that of Runyon ('42). He showed that, if a semi-permeable membrane of cellophane (regenerated cellulose) was placed over an aggregating pattern, and additional myxamoebae were placed on the upper side of the membrane, the upper myxamoebae would follow the myxamoebae below. The streams of incoming myxamoebae and the central collecting points would coincide above and below the cellophane sheet. Thus Runyon showed that the aggregation stimulus could pass through a semipermeable membrane. From this he concluded that aggregation is caused by the chemotactic response of myxamoebae to a dialyzable substance.

It was thought, in the beginning of this work, that there was no real evidence that the theory of Olive, Potts and Runyon was correct for they gave no supporting evidence at all, and Runyon's ingenious experiment is hardly conclusive. A variety of physical agents besides a diffusing substance could conceivably be responsible for the orientation of the myxamoebae and could also pass through a semipermeable membrane. But it is clear from the experimental evidence that will be presented in the following pages that the only mechanism that was supported was that of diffusion of a substance to which the myxamoebae respond chemotactically.

METHODS

A large part of the experimental work described here was made possible by the development of new techniques for the study of Dictyostelium. The principal of such innovations is the discovery that, contrary to Runyon's ('42) statement, aggregation will occur under water. This can be achieved by *D. discoideum, D. giganteum, D. mucoroides, D. purpureum, Polysphondylium violaceum* or *Polysphondylium pallidum* on a water-glass interface in depths of water up to 10 cm. Depths greater than this have not been tested because there seem to be no practical or theoretical reasons for so doing. Figures 1 and 2 illustrate the appearance of this under-water aggregation. Development, however, does not proceed any further, leaving a rounded or irregular shaped mass of cells (see Fig. 1, D). Further development (migration and culmination) can only be attained by bringing the mass into contact with an air-water or mineral oil-water interface.

Before discussing the details of this under-water technique, the standard culture technique will be described, followed by a description of the method of preparing the myxamoebae for under-water aggregation.

Culture Technique

A large supply of myxamoebae are required for experiments on aggregation. As Dictystelium feeds on bacteria, a large supply must be obtained and this is done by using a rich medium such as Raper ('40b) describes: (Raper's medium has been slightly modified by adding a buffer to insure a pH of about 6.0.) Peptone, 10 gm; dextrose, 10 gm; $Na_2HPO_4 .12H_2O$, 0.96 gm; K_2HPO_4, 1.45 gm; agar, 20 gm; distilled H_2O, 1000 ml.

The inoculum of Dictyostelium spores and *Escherichia coli* (which is used as a source of food for the myxamoebae) is placed on the nutrient agar in a petri dish (90 mm diameter). The inoculum is spread over the entire surface of the

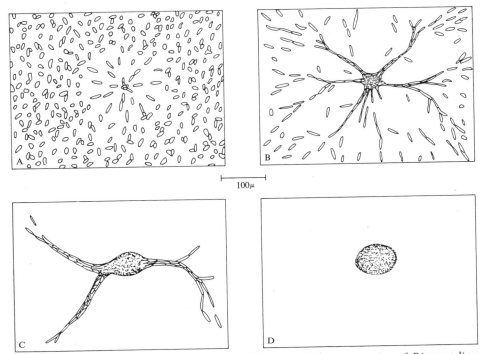

100μ

Fig. 1. *A semi-diagrammatic representation of 4 stages of the aggregation of Dictyostelium taking place under water on the bottom of a glass dish. A, the beginning of aggregation showing the formation of a small center; B, C, successive stages of aggregation showing the thickening of the streams and the enlargement of the center; D, the final pseudoplasmodium.*

agar by adding a few drops of sterile water and smearing with a sterile glass rod. The culture is incubated at room temperature for 2 days, by which time there is a thick growth of vegetative myxamoebae.

Centrifuge Technique

In a culture which has been incubated for 2 days the myxamoebae are found spread out over the whole surface of the agar and surrounded by large numbers of bacteria. For the under-water technique the myxamoebae must be concentrated and freed from bacteria. A simple method is to wash them by centrifugation as was done by Runyon ('42), but since the details of his method have not to my knowledge, been published, the exact procedure used in this study will be described.

No sterile precautions are necessary in the centrifuge method since all nutrients are largely eliminated and there never has been any evidence of deleterious effects of contamination. The 2-day-old petri dish culture is now flooded with distilled water and thoroughly mixed with a glass rod. The suspension of myxamoebae and bacteria is placed in a centrifuge tube and centrifuged gently for 3 minutes. The force of centrifugation is regulated by a few trial experiments so that the

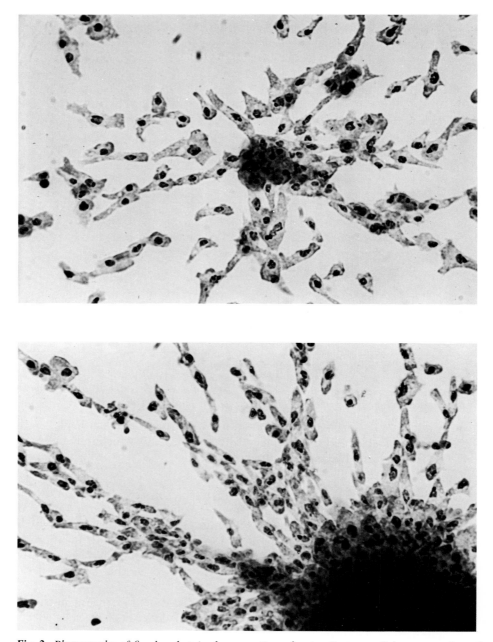

Fig. 2. *Photographs of fixed and stained preparations showing 2 stages of the aggregation of Dictyostelium taking place under water on the surface of a coverslip. (Fixed in Shaudin's solution and stained by Bodian's silver impregnation method.) The upper photograph shows the beginning of aggregation with the formation of a small center; the lower photograph shows a middle stage of aggregation with a larger center in the lower right-hand corner.*

myxamoebae will be separated from the bacteria, and thrown down to the bottom of the tube. The liquid containing bacteria is poured off, distilled water added, and the process repeated. A concentrated mass of myxamoebae relatively free of bacteria is finally left in the tube to which a small amount of distilled water is again added.

Under-Water Technique

The supension of myxamoebae is placed with a pipette directly into a syracuse or other suitable flat dish containing water. The myxamoebae soon settle to the bottom of the vessel where they subsequently aggregate. At room temperature, with optimum myxamoeba concentrations, aggregation will start in 6 to 8 hours but may be delayed by placing the dish in a cooler environment. In distilled water the myxamoebae lack adhesiveness and the slightest agitation causes them to become detached from the bottom of the dish, but if suitable electrolytes are added the myxamoebae adhere firmly to the glass substratum. This method is based on that of Mast ('29) who showed a similar effect of electrolytes on the adhesiveness of *Amoeba proteus,* and from his data the following standard salt solution (henceforth referred to as "standard solution") was devised and regularly used: NaCl, 0.60 gm; KCl, 0.75 gm; $CaCl_2$, 0.30 gm; distilled H_2O, 1000 ml. It is interesting to note that Mast showed that this is not a case of salt antagonism, for the effect of the various anions is slightly additive.

Thin Film of Water Technique

In a few of the experiments the myxamoebae were placed on a thin film of water on the underside of a coverslip. The procedure follows: a no. 1, 22×22 mm coverslip which has been carefully cleaned in 95 % ethyl alcohol and wiped dry, is sealed with a mixture of approximately 2 parts vaseline and 1 part beeswax onto a van Tieghem cell (10 mm deep, 20 mm in diameter). This van Tieghem cell cup with the sealed-on coverslip serving as the bottom is filled about $\frac{1}{3}$ full with standard solution and the myxamoebae, prepared in the fashion already described, are added. A microscope slide is then sealed over the open end of the van Tieghem cell. In 20 minutes time all the myxamoebae will have settled to the bottom and adhered to the coverslip. The slide is then gently turned over so that the coverslip is on the upper surface. Since the myxamoebae are in a thin film of water in contact with moist air, the organism will go through its complete life cycle producing abundant sorocarps on the underside of the coverslip.

RESULTS

The Attraction of Myxamoebae at a Distance

That contact between myxamoebae is not a controlling factor in aggregation was first emphasized by Raper ('41). It can readily be seen in observing aggregation that isolated individual myxamoebae or groups of myxamoebae will move directly towards one of the radiating streams of incoming myxamoebae (henceforth referred to as "stream") or to the central mass of cells (henceforth referred to as "center").

With the under-water technique it was possible to get a clearer and more quantitative picture of this attraction at a distance. If one removes the center of an aggregation pattern at either of the 2 stages illustrated in Fig. 1, C and D, and places it beside the stream, in 3 to 5 minutes each myxamoeba in the stream will independently turn and start to move toward the center at its new location. They will continue to move toward the center until they reach it and become incorporated into it in the normal fashion. An attempt was made to measure the maximum distance at which the center could influence the myxamoebae, care being taken to have no myxamoebae between the center and the myxamoebae under observation in order to eliminate the possibility that intermediate myxamoebae might affect the attractive power in some way. Some of the results of this type of experiment are given in Table 1.

Table showing the ability of the centers to attract myxamoebae across various distances.

Distance between center and myxamoebae	Attraction
770 μ	None
423 μ	None
358 μ	Weak
214 μ	Strong
180 μ	Strong
128 μ	Strong
98 μ	Strong

It is clear that myxamoebae up to 200 μ distant will become, in 3 to 5 minutes, oriented toward the center. If the diameter of a rounded myxamoeba is considered to be about 15 μ, then the distance between the myxamoebae and the center can be represented as over 13 myxamoeba diameters. In a slightly modified type of experiment discussed later even larger gaps are bridged. In fact it was possible to obtain weak but definite orienting effect at a distance of 800 μ or 53 myxamoeba diameters.

The Inability of an Electric Field to Affect Aggregation

Both vegetative and aggregating myxamoebae were subjected to electrical currents of various densities. The type of chamber and the electrical circuit were essentially similar to those used by Hahnert ('32) on *Amoeba proteus*. Briefly the chamber is a small, rectangular cell (30 × 10 mm), in which the small ends are completely walled off with 2 platinum ribbon electrodes. To guard the center of the cell from harmful electrolytic products, a piece of porous material (porcelain or cellulose sponge) is placed directly in front of and parallel to each electrode. The experiments on Dictyostelium were done in tap water and distilled water with the same result in both cases. Parallel observations were made on *Amoeba proteus* (in tap water). The results are given in Table 2. As can be seen from the table *A. proteus* shows the characteristic migration toward the cathode, while the myxamoebae of Dictyostelium showed no response whatever to the electrical current.

Table 2. *Table showing the effect of 3 different current densities on* Amoeba proteus *and on the myxamoebae of* D. discoideum

Current density in μamp/mm^2	Effect on *A. proteus*	Effect on myxamoebae of *D. discoideum*
5	Possible slight orientation	Death
20	Streams towards cathode	No effect
70	Immediate death	No effect

The Inability of a Magnetic Field to Affect Aggregation

Some very cursory experiments, which are reported here for the sake of record, were done with an Alnico magnet (1 cm^2 pole face) at various angles to aggregation patterns of Dictyostelium. No effect was observed.

The Inability of a Conducting Metal (Tantalum) to Affect Aggregation

This experiment is basically similar to the previously described experiment of Runyon ('42), but instead of separating the center from the myxamoebae by a semi-permeable membrane, they were separated by a thin sheet of tantalum (about 12 μ thick). A 1 cm^2 sheet of the tantalum was placed in a syracuse dish containing standard solution. Myxamoebae free from bacteria were allowed to settle on one side of the tantalum, using the standard technique previously described. When the myxamoebae had just started to aggregate, which they did normally, the sheet was turned upside down and set on a small stand (a van Tieghem cell 5 mm deep, 20 mm in diameter) so that it was not touching the bottom of the dish and yet was completely submerged in the standard solution. A large active center from another dish was taken in a micro-pipette and placed on the upper surface of the tantalum.

In no case was the effect of the upper center transmitted through the sheet, and the myxamoebae below, while they aggregated normally, bore no relation in their pattern to the strong center above.

The Impermeability of Glass, Mica, and Quartz to the Aggregation Stimulus

By using the same technique as described immediately above, coverslip glass (120 μ thick), mica (100–150 μ thick), and quartz glass (50–100 μ thick) were tested. Again, in no case was there any visible orienting effect transmitted through these materials although aggregation appeared normal in each instance.

The Attraction of Myxamoebae Around Corners

This experiment was designed to see if a center could orient myxamoebae that were not in a direct line with the center, but were separated by an impermeable substance that could be circumvented. Some myxamoebae free of bacteria were spread on a no. 1 coverslip (22 × 22 mm, approximately 160 μ thick) which had been placed in the bottom of a syracuse dish full of standard solution. When the myxamoebae had just begun to aggregate the coverslip was turned upside down and held in such a position so that it formed a shelf, completely surrounded by standard solution. This is represented diagrammatically in Fig. 3, A. An active, strongly attractive center was placed approximately 60 μ from the edge of the coverslip, on the upper surface. Very shortly afterwards, the separate myxamoebae on the underneath surface became oriented towards the point on the edge nearest the center above and moved up around the edge to join the center (see Fig. 3, A). In other words the center exerted its influence around the corner, from the upper surface to the lower surface.

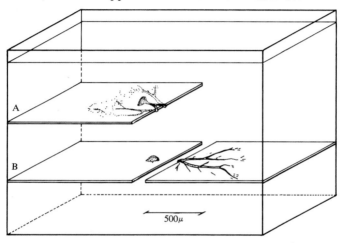

Fig. 3. *A semi-diagrammatic representation of 2 experiments done on aggregation in Dictyostelium using coverslip shelves held under water. A, the myxamoebae previously at random under the coverslip are attracted around the edge to the center on the upper surface; B, the myxamoebae previously at random on the right-hand coverslip are attracted to the center on the left-hand coverslip, across the substratum gap.*

The Inability of the Orientation of the Substratum to Affect Aggregation

The following experiments involve using the techniques of Weiss ('45) who obtained oriented growth of fibroblasts of chick embryos by placing them on specific types of substrata. Myxamoebae were placed on a sheet of mica in which shallow grooves had been scratched with a fine steel needle (see Weiss, '45 for the details of the preparation of the mica). Neither the aggregating myxamoebae, nor the wandering vegetative myxamoebae showed any preference for the grooves, but would pass across them as though completely unaffected by their existence. Glass fibers (from glass wool) lying in a heap under water in a syracuse dish were also covered with myxamoebae and again the myxamoebae showed no more tendency to adhere to the fibers than to the glass bottom of the dish.

Attempts to Observe Structural Connections Between Aggregating Myxamoebae

It is not possible in a living preparation, even using an oil immersion (1.8 mm) objective and preparing the material with the thin film of water technique, to see any connections between the aggregating myxamoebae except when the cells are half a cell diameter or less from one another. Then they often are attached by definite filopodia. To examine this point further, aggregation stages were stained with silver using the technique of Bodian. Aggregation was allowed to occur on coverslips under water and at the desired stages they were removed, fixed in Shaudin's solution, and stained. The gold toning was not used. Photographs of such a preparation are shown in Fig. 2. As can be seen from the photographs, and also from careful oil immersion examination of the slides, there is no evidence of any filopodia extending any great distances. Nor is there any evidence of any material, exudate, or ground mat such as Weiss ('45) describes for oriented chick fibroblasts, which he stained in the same fashion.

An Attempt to Reveal a Deposit Made by Aggregating Myxamoebae That Might Orient Other Myxamoebae

It was possible to show by experiment that an aggregation pattern leaves behind no structure on the substratum that can orient myxamoebae. The standard solution was poured off a syracuse dish in which the aggregation was complete or nearly so for all the pseudoplasmodia. The dish was then placed in the ice compartment of an electric refrigerator and allowed to freeze. After removal from the refrigerator more standard solution and fresh myxamoebae were added. The old centers that had been killed by freezing could still be seen. Care was taken to observe if the live myxamoebae were affected in any way by any type of structure that the previous aggregation patterns might have created. No such effect was demonstrated; the new patterns bore no relation to the previous ones.

The Importance of an Interface Connecting the Center and the Myxamoebae

It was found that a center could attract myxamoebae to which it was not directly connected by an interface. This fact was first realized in an accidental observation. A hanging drop preparation had been made with myxamoebae free from bacteria in standard solution and a clear aggregation pattern formed at the base of the drop, at the air-water interface. I noticed that above this pattern, on the glass-water interface, a few myxamoebae were aggregating to a center directly above the center of the aggregation pattern below. Since the upper center formed at the nearest point to the lower center, one can reason that this was caused either by the fact that the positions of both the upper and lower centers were determined by similar tensions in the drop, or that the lower center, which was the farthest advanced of the two, directly influenced the upper myxamoebae without being directly connected to them by an interface.

In an effort to rule out the possible effect of the tensions in a hanging drop, an experiment was designed in which 2 no. 1 coverslips (22 × 22 mm) were prepared in standard solution, one with many myxamoebae just starting to aggregate, and the other with one large center. One was then turned over and placed on top of the other, taking care to prevent their surfaces from touching by placing 2 wedges between them, one on each side. The myxamoebae were than facing the center, separated by a thin layer of standard solution. Again an immediate response was obtained and the myxamoebae formed a pattern so that their center was directly opposite, that is the shortest distance from, the strong center on the opposite coverslip. Numerous attempts were made to determine how far apart the plates could be and still obtain an orienting influence of the center on the myxamoebae. If the plates were 500 μ apart the effect was obvious and strong. At 800 μ there was a weak and diffuse, but still discernible orienting effect. Thus without the disturbing surface tension effects of a hanging drop, a center again affected distant myxamoebae to which it was not directly connected by an interface.

This was done in another striking way illustrated in Fig. 3, B. Two coverslips were prepared as above and placed side by side in a dish to form 2 shelves, surrounded by standard solution, and separated by a small gap. The center was placed fairly near the edge, and it immediately affected the myxamoebae on the opposite shelf so they all streamed to the nearest point on the edge (see Fig. 3, B). Again the effect of a center was transmitted across a gap which possessed no interface but merely a layer of water.

A few observations on this experiment should be mentioned. The first myxamoebae that got to the edge appeared to be reaching out into the gap between the coverslips with a sort of hopeless pseudopodial waving. Later when they became more numerous, they formed their own center directly opposite the original center on the other coverslip. However, if the coverslips were closer together so that the gap was very small (about 20–30 μ) then the myxamoebae formed a stream, a bridge right across the gap and joined the center on the opposite side.

The Effect of Water Flowering over Aggregation Patterns

A flow of water was created over myxamoebae that were about to aggregate or that were in the process of aggregating and a distinct modification of the aggregation pattern was obtained. The flow of water was achieved 2 different ways. In one a glass rod (4 mm in diameter) bent into an "L" shape was attached to a shaft of a 6 rpm electric motor, and held over the center of a syracuse dish (containing bacteria-free myxamoebae) so that the lower bar of the "L" was just submerged in the water, forming a radius to the circular dish. In this way the water was slowly swirled in a circular fashion, creating a fairly linear flow at any spot in the dish other than near the center. The other method of creating a flow involved drawing water through a channel between 2 coverslips (approximately 100 μ apart). A controlled rate of flow was obtained by leading the water from a reservoir to the coverslips through a fine glass capillary tube.

If the myxamoebae were about to aggregate when placed in this current, they continued to do so, but the aggregation patterns, as shown in Fig. 4, A, were atypical. Each possessed only one unusually long stream which always approached the center from the downstream side. If the myxamoebae had already started normal aggregation before being subjected to the flow, they would quickly assume a similar form as shown in Fig. 4, B. The streams that had existed on the upstream side would break up rapidly, and although the downstream and lateral streams remained, they would continue to form only in line with the direction of the flow of water. In both cases the most striking fact was that the myxamoebae, upstream of the center, even those almost touching it, showed no effect of any stimulus from the center and moved in a random fashion. Yet judging from the length of the streams, the stimulus from the center apparently had extended an abnormally long distance downstream. If vegetative myxamoebae were placed under such a current no effect was observed whatsoever, but they continued their random locomotion.

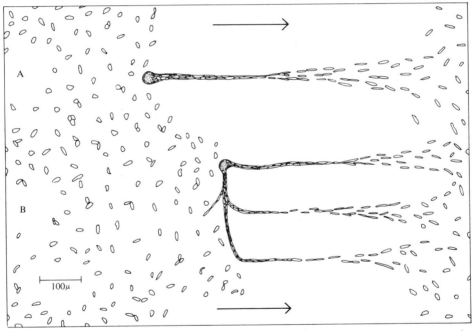

Fig. 4. *A semi-diagrammatic drawing showing the effect of a moving stream of water (the arrows indicate the direction of movement) over an aggregation pattern in Dictyostelium. A, an aggregation pattern that formed while the water was in motion; B, an aggregation pattern that formed in still water and was subsequently subjected to a stream of moving water.*

DISCUSSION

If the facts that have been obtained from the experiments described above, and those from the literature are summarized, the following statements can be made of the aggregation process in Dictyostelium: (1) the attraction can operate across a semi-permeable membrane (Runyon, '42); (2) the center will attract myxamoebae at considerable distances; (3) it has been impossible to date to show any effect of an electric field or (4) of a magnetic field on the aggregation pattern; (5) aggregation occurs on the surface of a conducting metal (tantalum), but (6) a center will not attract myxamoebae when separated from the myxamoebae by a sheet of tantalum; (7) nor can a center attract myxamoebae through glass, (8) mica, or (9) quartz; (10) a center can attract myxamoebae around a corner of some impermeable substance; (11) the structure of the substratum does not appear to affect the aggregation pattern; (12) it has been impossible to demonstrate any sort of bridge or connection between a center and distant myxamoebae; (13) there is no evidence of any myxamoeba-orienting substance deposited on the substratum; (14) a center does not have to be directly connected to myxamoebae by an interface in order to attract them; (15) aggregation patterns forming under flowing water are deformed so that only the myxamoebae directly downstream of the center will show any orientation.

In our search for the immediate cause of aggregation in Dictyostelium, the first fundamental question that arises is, does the center pull in the myxamoebae by force or does it merely orient the myxamoebae by stimulation? There is every indication that the energy of locomotion is contributed by each individual myxamoeba, and that the center orients them by a different stimulation.

The problem might be approached by examining various reasonable possible mechanisms suggested by investigations on other forms in the light of the facts known about aggregation in Dictyostelium. For instance one might consider the likelihood of aggregation to be: (1) an agglutination process; (2) in some way controlled by an electric or (3) magnetic field; (4) or by some form of radiation; (5) controlled by some type of orienting structure deposited on the substratum; (6) or by the oriented molecules in a molecular surface film; (7) or, finally, controlled by the gradient of a substance to which the myxamoebae respond chemotactically.

Agglutination Hypothesis

Some actual immunological work has been done on *D. mucoroides* by von Schuckmann ('25) who showed that when rabbit antiserum to vegetative myxamoebae is added to a culture of similar myxamoebae, they will agglutinate into clumps in an irreversible fashion. Unfortunately von Schuckmann does not describe the details either of the process or of further development, if any, of the clumps; but it is notable that he does not attempt to interpret normal aggregation in terms of agglutination. In some work that will be reported in detail at a future date, I have been able to obtain pseudoplasmodium formation by what is apparently agglutination, and these pseudoplasmodia develop into complete sorocarps. But in such an instance the normal aggregation process has been completely circumvented and the pseudoplasmodium has been achieved by an unnatural means.

There are a number of strong evidences against the "clumping" of myxamoebae found in normal aggregation being an agglutination process. In the first place the fact that a center can attract myxamoebae across great distances is inconsistent with agglutination. A basic property of all agglutination processes is that the cells come together by chance collision; for example as a result of active random motion or brownian motion, followed by a firm adhesion of the collided cells.

Another evidence comes from the fact that the myxamoebae which are in contact can and do normally separate readily from one another. A striking example of this is the case mentioned where a center is removed and placed laterally to its stream. The compacted mass of myxamoebae forming the stream will break up, each myxamoeba becoming unattached and going independently to the new location of the center. Such a phenomenon is never seen in agglutination processes. The nearest they approach it is in the case of reverse agglutination, but then up to the point of reversal the cells are solidly stuck to one another. In Dictyostelium the myxamoebae can be separated at all times.

A final evidence that aggregation is not achieved by agglutination comes from the fact that attraction between the center and the myxamoebae is obtained through a semi-permeable membrane as previously described in the experiment of Runyon ('42). Proteins or complex polysaccharides are the important molecules in immunological reactions, and even the smallest proteins will not (except possibly at an extremely slow rate) pass through the regenerated cellulose dialyzing membranes used. I have repeated Runyon's experiments many times with different types of membranes all presumably impermeable to proteins, and always obtained the same sort of rapid (3 to 5 minute) response of the myxamoebae to the center on the opposite side of the membrane. From these arguments it may be concluded that aggregation in Dictyostelium is not an agglutination process. This does not exclude the possibility that antigen-antibody reactions are factors in development at a later stage. But some other factor must be responsible for initiating the normal "clumping" of the Dictyostelium myxamoebae.

Electrical Hypothesis

The evidence weighs against the possibility that aggregation can be explained in terms of an electric field. Consider first the fact that an electric field surrounding aggregation patterns will not affect them. While it is true that such negative evidence is in no way conclusive, it is nevertheless indicative.

Perhaps better evidence comes from the tantalum experiment, where normal aggregation was found to occur on the surface of a conducting metal, but the attraction could not take place through a thin sheet of the metal. If the aggregation mechanism were electrical then the metal would most likely have created a short circuit preventing aggregation, which is not the case. Even granting that aggregation could occur on the surface of the metal, one would further expect the attraction to be conducted through the tantalum sheet.

Magnetic Hypothesis

Magnetism is also an unlikely possibility for reasons very similar to those mentioned for electricity. Not only was the aggregation pattern not affected by a magnetic field (which again is only indicative evidence) but also the attraction could not pass through a tantalum sheet, which could be readily achieved by a magnetic force.

Radiation Hypothesis

Rays emitted from the center of Dictyostelium could conceivably guide the myxamoebae, but the evidence does not support this view. First, if such a ray exists, it can penetrate water, and cellophane, but is stopped by glass, quartz and mica. This certainly does not eliminate the hypothesis but it narrows the possibilities.

Stronger evidence against a radiation phenomenon comes from the experiment in which a center on the upper surface of a coverslip attracted myxamoebae on the lower surface, around the edge (Fig. 3, A). It is difficult for me to see how a ray mechanism could operate here, for if the coverslip were permeable to the ray one would expect the underneath myxamoebae to aggregate to the point nearest the above center, which would be directly below the center on the underside of the glass. If the coverslip were impermeable to the hypothetical ray, then one would expect no effect whatsoever of the upper center on the myxamoebae underneath. But this is not the case; the myxamoebae go around the edge. Rays travel in straight lines and can hardly be expected to pass from one side of an impermeable barrier to the other.

Contact Guidance Hypothesis

"Contact guidance" designates the idea that the amoeboid processes of cells are oriented by being mechanically guided by either the ultra-structure of the substratum or the direction of flow of an exudate given off by the cell. The concept of contact guidance is that of Weiss ('29, '34, '45) who studied the causes of orientation in cell growth and movement of cells of higher animals in tissue culture.

There is no evidence to indicate that contact guidance plays a part in aggregation, for it has been impossible to demonstrate any guiding structure deposited on the substratum, or even that the orientation of the substratum itself has any orienting effect.

Molecular Surface Film Hypothesis

It was thought, since aggregation only occurs at an interface, that a molecular surface film might be involved in orienting the aggregating myxamoebae. But this hypothesis was invalidated by showing that it is quite possible for a center to attract myxamoebae when the center is not connected directly to the myxamoebae by an interface.

CONCLUSION

Diffusion Hypothesis

Good evidence that aggregation is achieved by the center producing a substance to which the myxamoebae respond chemotactically[1] comes from the experiment

---

[1] A note should be made here concerning the use of the word chemotaxis in this paper. As Blum ('35) points out there are 2 separate factors to consider in oriented movements: (1) the orientation of the organism, in this case to the diffusion field of a chemical substance and (2) the movement of the organism which may quite possibly be in no way affected by the chemical substance (since there is movement in the absence of the substance).

in which the aggregation patterns are deformed by flowing water. In fact the following deductions can be made from this experiment: (1) No mechanical explanation, such as the direct effect of the current on the myxamoebae, could explain the patterns obtained under flowing water because vegetative cells in the current continued normal random movement. That is, the pattern was not imposed on the myxamoebae by the external moving water, but it arose in the normal fashion as a result of the activities of the myxamoebae themselves. (2) Under the flow of water the center remained the source of production of the stimulating agent for the myxamoebae were attracted to it. (3) The agent was washed downstream—the myxamoebae upstream were not attracted in any way by the center, whereas the myxamoebae downstream were attracted to it from great distances. (4) The only reasonable type of agent that could be carried along in such a fashion by a slow current is a free-diffusing chemical substance. (5) The fact mentioned previously that a substance can only be effective in orienting the myxamoebae when it is in a gradient helps interpret a number of phenomena. For instance: the myxamoebae upstream must have been surrounded by the substance which came from the other centers (and let us assume it is in a high enough concentration to be able to obtain a response), but they showed no orientation because the substance in that region became, by diffusion, more evenly distributed and not in a sufficient concentration gradient to cause orientation. (6) Also the only method in which a gradient could be maintained during aggregation would be by a constant production of the substance of the center. Since diffusion would tend always to obliterate the gradient, and the maintenance of a steady state is necessary, it must be assumed that the substance is produced either continuously or at frequent intervals by the center.

Therefore in summarizing we have deduced from this flowing water experiment that during the aggregation of Dictyostelium there is some type of chemical substance (which is not necessarily homogeneous but might consist of a group of compounds) produced continuously or at frequent intervals by the center, which freely diffuses, and the myxamoebae move in the resulting gradient of this substance towards the point of its highest concentration. The final proof of the existence of the substance (and an important problem for future research) must be its isolation *in vitro*. But considering the present weight of evidence, it seems fitting to propose tentatively a name for the substance. The term *acrasin* is suggested, and it can be defined for the moment as a type of substance consisting either of one or numerous compounds which is responsible for stimulating and directing aggregation in certain members of the Acrasiales. It also may perform other duties in the development of these organisms but such considerations are not within the scope of this article. Also at a later date I plan to present an examination of the formation of streams during aggregation, a process which may appear puzzling in the light of the present discussion.

One of the most difficult factors to understand in any chemotaxis hypothesis is how it is possible for a single small amorphous amoeboid cell to be sensitive to gradients of diffusing substances. The concentrations of these substances in a great many of these cases must be small, and of course, the molecules in diffusion move at random in all directions. Thus the cell must detect very small concentration differences between one end of the cell and the other. . . .

SUMMARY

Dictyostelium discoideum is a member of that group of amoeboid slime molds (Acrasiales) characterized by forming the fruiting structure from a compacted mass of uninucleate myxamoebae known as a pseudoplasmodium. The pseudo-plasmodium arises by the aggregation of many myxamoebae which were previously completely independent and separate from one another. In this so-called aggregation stage radial streams of elongate myxamoebae move towards a central point by means of pseudopodial locomotion. Attempts to discover the immediate cause of this centripetal streaming of myxamoebae revealed that it is not an agglutination process; that a spreading molecular surface film phenomenon is not responsible; that an electrical or magnetic force is improbable; that any form of directing ray is not involved; and that no type of predetermined structural matrix exists that could guide the myxamoebae to the center. However, evidence was obtained for a substance diffusing from a central mass of myxamoebae through the liquid medium and the incoming myxamoebae orienting themselves in the diffusion field, moving towards the point of highest concentration. This was shown by inducing a gentle stream of water to flow over an aggregation pattern, causing in the usually radial pattern of incoming myxamoebae an asymmetry that can only be interpreted as the warping of the diffusion field of a substance to which the myxamoebae are sensitive. This type of substance has been tentatively called *acrasin*. . . .

LITERATURE CITED

Arndt, A.   1937   Untersuchungen über Dictyostelium mucoroides Brefeld. Roux' Arch. Entwmech., *136:* 681–747.

Bonner, J. T.   1944   A descriptive study of the development of the slime mold Dictyo-stelium discoideum. Amer. Jour. Bot., *31:* 175–182.

Blum, H. F.   1935   An analysis of oriented movements of animals in light fields. Cold Spring Harbor Symposia on Quantitative Biology, *3:* 210–223.

Hahnert, W. F.   1932   A quantitative study of reactions to electricity in Amoeba proteus. Physiol. Zool., *5:* 491–526.

Harper, R. A.   1926   Morphogenesis in Dictyostelium. Bull Torrey Bot. Club., *53:* 229–268.

——   1932   Organization and light relations in Polysphondylium. Bull Torrey Bot. Club., *59:* 49–84.

Mast, S. O.   1929   Mechanism of locomotion in Amoeba proteus with special reference to the factors involved in attachment to the substratum. Protoplasma, *8:* 344–377.

Oehler, R.   1922   Dictyostelium mucoroides (Brefeld). Centbl. Bakt. (etc.), *89:* 155–156.

Olive, E. W.   1902   Monograph of the Acrasieae. Proc. Boston Soc. Nat. Hist., *30:* 451–513.

Potts, G.   1902   Zur Physiologie des Dictyostelium mucoroides. Flora (Jena), *21:* 281–347. (Jena), *21:* 281–347.

Raper, K. B.   1935   Dictyostelium discoideum, a new species of slime mold from decaying forest leaves. Jour. Agric. Res., *50:* 135–147.

——   1940a   The communal nature of the fruiting process in the Acrasieae. Amer. Jour. Bot., *27:* 436–448.

——   1940b   Pseudoplasmodium formation and organization in Dictyostelium discoideum. Jour. Elisha Mitchell. Sci. Soc., *56:* 241–282.

——   1941   Developmental patterns in simple slime molds. Growth (third Growth Symposium), *5:* 41–76.

Rashevsky, N.   1938   Mathematical Biophysics. Chicago.

Runyon, E. H.   1942   Aggregation of separate cells of Dictyostelium to form a multicellular body. Collecting Net, *17:* 88.

Schuckmann, W. von   1924   Zur Biologie von Dictyostelium mucoroides Bref. Centbl. Bakt. (etc.) (I), *91:* 302–309.

——   1925   Zur Morphologie und Biologie von Dictyostelium mucoroides Bref. Arch. Protistenk., *51:* 495–529.

Weiss, P.   1929   Erzwingung elementarer Strukturverschiedenheiten am in vitro wachsenden Gewebe. Die Wirkung mechanischer Spannung auf Richtung und Intensität des Gewebewachstums und ihre Analyse. Roux' Arch. Entwmech., *116:* 438–554.

——   1934   In vitro experiments on the factors determining the course of the outgrowing nerve fiber. J. Exp. Zool., *68:* 393–448.

——   1945   Experiments on cell and axon orientation in vitro; the role of colloidal exudates in tissue organization. J. Exp. Zool., *100:* 353–386.

Serial Transplantation of Embryonic Nuclei

by THOMAS J. KING and ROBERT BRIGGS

Over the past many years genetical research has revealed large numbers of gene effects on cell differentiation. These are usually effects on the final phases of differentiation, but may also be manifested at early developmental stages (Gluecksohn-Waelsch, 1954; Hadorn, 1948, 1956; Poulson, 1945; and others). In principle,

Abridged from Thomas J. King and Robert Briggs, "Serial Transplantation of Embryonic Nuclei," *Cold Spring Harbor Symposium on Quantitative Biology* **21** (1956), 271–290. Reprinted by permission.

the analysis of these effects depends upon the permanent alteration or deletion of a chromosome segment, and the subsequent detection of a change in differentiation—usually a deficiency. The evidence so obtained permits the conclusion that a particular gene or gene set is required for a particular type of differentiation to proceed normally. However, in general it leaves unanswered the questions which are of greatest concern to students of development. First, the genetic evidence as yet provides no explanation of the orderly segregation of cell types during development—of the fact that a given gene comes to have one effect in one part of the organism while in another part it has no effect or a different one. This must, of course, involve interactions of the geneticist's nucleus with the embryologist's cytoplasmic localizations, but the nature of this inter-action is unknown. Second, the available evidence fails to account for the stability or irreversibility of differentiation. In other words, while genes have particular functions in differentiation, in general, it is not known how they acquire them, nor whether they are themselves altered in the performance of these functions in such a way as to confer stability on the differentiated cells.

It has been apparent for some time that in order to obtain answers to the questions posed above it would be necessary to devise new methods for detecting changes in gene function in somatic cells. Essentially, such methods should yield recombinations of nucleus and cytoplasm and of different types of nuclei of somatic cells, comparable with the natural recombinations of germ cells from which most genetic information is obtained.

Experiments of the type mentioned above, involving artificial transfer of cytoplasm or nucleus, were accomplished with unicellular organisms some years ago. Hämmerling (1934, 1953), using the unicellular uninucleate alga, *Aceta-bularia,* grafted stalk pieces from one species to the nucleated rhizoidal ends of another and demonstrated that the form of the cap that regenerated from the grafted stalk was controlled by the nucleus. Later Hämmerling (1953) produced heterokaryons and showed that the form of the regenerated cap was intermediate between the forms characteristic of the species contributing the nuclei. This and other evidence led to the conclusion that the nucleus produces specific morpho-genetic substances which pass into the cytoplasm and there control the differentia-tion of the cap. . . .

To the best of our knowledge, the transfer of nuclei (by pricking frog's eggs coated with embryonic brei) was first attempted by Rostand in 1943, with uncertain success. A few years later, we began to work on the problem, and after a considerable number of failures devised a different procedure for the trans-plantation of living nuclei from embryonic cells into enucleated eggs of the frog, *Rana pipiens* (Briggs and King, 1952). More recently transfers of embryonic nuclei have also been made by Waddington and Pantelouris (1953), Lehman (1955, 1956), Markert (referred to in Lehman, 1956) and Subtelny (1956). The method used is not without its difficulties and complications, but it appears to represent the most direct experimental approach for obtaining evidence of the genetic condition of nuclei in differentiating embryonic cells.

NOTE ON METHODS

. . . The transplantation operation is carried out in two main steps. First, the recipient eggs *(Rana pipiens)* are activated with a glass needle and subsequently enucleated, following Porter's (1939) technique. With practice and care, the enucleation operation is 100 per cent successful. The second part of the procedure involves the isolation of the donor cells and the nuclear transfer itself. Free donor cells may be obtained by the appropriate use of Versene (Ethylene diamine tetra acetic acid, Na salt) alone or in combination with trypsin, as previously described (King and Briggs, 1955). A given cell, in Niu-Twitty (1953) solution, is then drawn into the tip of a micropipette, the inner diameter of which is somewhat smaller than that of the cell. When this is properly done the cell surface is broken but the contents are not dispersed. In this way the nucleus is protected by its own cytoplasm until the pipette is inserted into the recipient egg and the broken cell ejected, liberating the nucleus into the egg cytoplasm. The technique sounds deceptively simple, but it takes practice to perform these operations consistently well.

Two features of the method that bear on the interpretation of results are first the inclusion of donor cell cytoplasm along with the injected nucleus, and second, the possibility of inadvertently damaging the nucleus in the course of the operation. Nuclear damage can be appraised by a study of control eggs injected with undifferentiated blastula nuclei, and by observations on cleavage patterns and chromosomes of test eggs. With reference to the donor cell cytoplasm, it should be mentioned that it represents in volume only 1/40,000 to 1/500,000 the volume of cytoplasm of the recipient egg. Still, the possibility that it might contain self-replicating units controlling differentiation must be considered, and where necessary, control transfers of cytoplasm from differentiating cells must be carried out—as will be mentioned in a subsequent section of this paper.

TRANSPLANTATION TESTS OF BLASTULA NUCLEI

The first successful transplantations were carried out with nuclei of mid- to late blastulae. The donor blastulae were 18 to 24 hours old (at 18°C) and consisted of approximately 8,000 to 16,000 cells (estimates of cell number based on Sze's (1953) determinations). Only nuclei of undetermined animal hemisphere cells were used. In the first set of experiments, about one-third of the transfers led to normal cleavage and blastula formation on the part of the recipient eggs, and the majority of these blastulae, some 75 per cent, developed into complete embryos. Half of the embryos appeared to be perfectly normal while the remainder displayed minor abnormalities (Briggs and King, 1952). In more recent experiments, the number of transfers of this type leading to normal cleavage has been larger (40% to 80%) and the majority (ca. 80%) of the resulting embryos develop normally to larval or later stages (King and Briggs, 1955 and unpub.).

The proof that the nuclear transfers are successful, and that the test eggs contain only the transplanted nuclei, consists of the following:

1. Control operations for removal of the egg nucleus, performed on normally fertilized eggs, show that all eggs develop as androgenetic haploids. Failures would lead to the development of diploids, of which there were none in control series of more than 500 embryos during the past two years.

2. Sections of eggs which cleave following enucleation and nuclear transplantation reveal the egg nucleus outside the egg, in the enucleation exovate, while the blastomeres contain nuclei derived from the transferred nucleus (Briggs and King, 1952).

3. Enucleated eggs which were injected with diploid nuclei and which begin cleavage at the normal time after activation, develop into diploid embryos, ploidy being determined by cell size, nucleolar number, and chromosome counts (see Table 2 of this paper for chromosome counts). If the first cleavage is initiated one cleavage interval late, the resulting embryos are tetraploids.

4. Enucleated eggs injected with haploid nuclei develop into haploid embryos unless there is a delayed initiation of cleavage—in which case the embryos become diploids (Subtelny, unpub.).

5. When enucleated *Rana pipiens* eggs are injected with *R. catesbeiana* nuclei the resulting development duplicates exactly that of the normally produced lethal hybrid between these two species (King and Briggs, 1953).

The results summarized above proved that late blastula nuclei could be transplanted in undamaged condition, and since the test eggs developed normally it was further demonstrated that the nuclei were unchanged, that is, equivalent to the nucleus at the beginning of the development. . . .

NUCLEI OF EARLY GASTRULAE

As has been appreciated for a long time, the beginning of gastrulation is a crucial phase of development. At this time the regional localization of materials present from the beginning in the egg cytoplasm have their first morphogenetic expression. For example, in the amphibian egg the gray crescent material, localized on the dorsal side of the egg shortly after fertilization, is known to determine the position of the dorsal lip of the blastopore, and consequently the point of origin of the chorda mesoderm and the whole axial organization of the embryo. While the position of the dorsal lip is thus determined by the gray crescent cytoplasm, it is also known that in order for it to invaginate and form chorda mesoderm, it must be provided with a "normal" set of chromosomes. Prior to gastrulation, cleavage and blastula formation may proceed with nuclei containing variable numbers of chromosomes (Fankhauser, 1934b), no chromosomes (Fankhauser, 1934a; Stauffer, 1945; Briggs, Green and King, 1951); or with various foreign genomes (see review by Moore, 1955). However, in all these cases development stops at or before the beginning of gastrulation, from which it is concluded that gastrulation and later phases of development require the participation of a balanced chromosome set. Furthermore, nucleus and cytoplasm must be of the same or closely related species. This and other information indicates that the nuclei come to have specific essential functions at the beginning of gastrulation. Whether they undergo irreversible or quasi-irreversible changes, and whether these are the same or different in different parts of the early gastrula, are questions we have approached by means of nuclear transplantation. The work is not quite finished yet, and will be described in full elsewhere. Here we may give only a brief account to provide a background for the following portions of this paper.

Nuclei from the following portions of the early gastrula were tested: 1) animal hemisphere, near the pole, 2) dorsal lip region, 3) endoderm including the floor of the blastocoel, and a region between the vegetal pole and the dorsal lip. The nuclei were transplanted to enucleated eggs in the usual way, giving the following results:

1. Animal hemisphere nuclei—39 per cent of 33 test eggs formed complete blastulae, 69 per cent of the blastulae developed into tadpoles.

2. Dorsal lip nuclei—25 per cent of 77 test eggs formed complete blastulae, of which 74 per cent developed into tadpoles.

3. Endoderm nuclei—54 per cent of 107 recipient eggs cleaved normally, 66 per cent of the blastulae so produced developed into tadpoles.

These preliminary experiments provide no definite evidence of differences among the nuclei from the various regions of the gastrula. The proportion of recipient eggs forming complete blastulae was smaller in the case of animal hemisphere and dorsal lip nuclear transfers than it was in the case of the endoderm transfers, but this is probably due to differences in donor cell size and ease of isolation. With respect to the development of the complete blastulae, there was some indication (in one experiment) that blastulae containing endoderm nuclei were more frequently arrested in gastrula or post-neurula stages. However, in the majority of experiments endoderm, dorsal lip, and animal hemisphere nuclei appeared equally capable of promoting normal development to the early larval stage, at least.

This result, indicating equivalence of early gastrula nuclei, is to some extent to be expected. One of the donor regions, the animal pole, is definitely undetermined and would not be expected to contain differentiated nuclei. The dorsal lip area is, of course, determined to form chordamesoderm. However, the determination is on a regional and not a cell basis, for if parts of the region are explanted they are found to be capable of differentiating into neural and endodermal as well as mesodermal structures (Holtfreter, 1938). The endoderm, on the other hand, gives evidence of being already determined in the early gastrula (Holtfreter, 1938). Whether the individual cells are irreversibly set in their path of differentiation appears uncertain, but the endoderm cell mass and portions of it are apparently determined to form gut and gut derivatives. Yet the endoderm nuclei, along with nuclei of other regions, give no definite evidence of differentiation in the transplantation experiments. This could mean either that the individual endoderm cells are not irreversibly determined, or that if they are, the determination does not involve irreversible nuclear changes. Since our experiments involve the transfer of donor cell cytoplasm along with the nuclei, the results also indicate that there are no genetic units in the cytoplasm which are capable of directing the differentiation of the recipient eggs.

The nuclear transplantation work summarized above emphasizes a point which has been familiar to embryologists for some time; namely, that the morphogenetic events in the early gastrula depend on the regional localization of cytoplasmic materials present in the egg at the beginning of development. Normal nuclei are essential for morphogenesis to proceed, but neither the nuclei nor the individual cells (except possibly endoderm cells) are irreversibly specialized at this stage. In other words, the intrinsic properties of the individual cells provide no explanation of the morphogenetic events, which are directed by the afore-mentioned cytoplasmic localizations. Thus, the role of the nucleus in this early phase of development will eventually have to be studied prior to fertilization, when these materials are being laid down in the oocyte.

NUCLEI OF LATE GASTRULAE

During gastrulation the germ layers are established, and by the late gastrula stage are determined in the sense that they cannot be transformed, one into the other, by grafting to inductive sites. In order to see if the determination of the layers involves detectable changes in the nuclei, we have made transplantation tests of nuclei from chorda mesoderm, presumptive medullary plate, and endoderm. The first tests were done on nuclei of the presumptive plate and the chorda mesoderm. These nuclei elicited normal cleavage in a considerably smaller proportion of the test eggs than had been the case with the blastula nuclei. Further-more, about half the normally cleaved eggs were arrested in blastula and gastrula stages, and of the ones completing gastrulation the majority displayed abnormalities later in development (King and Briggs, 1954). However, a few embryos did develop normally, indicating that at least some of the chorda mesoderm and medullary plate nuclei were undifferentiated. The significance of the cases in which development was arrested or abnormal remained in doubt because of the technical problems in handling the small donor cells. At the time, these cells were being isolated with glass needles with some risk of injury; and being small they were difficult to handle in the micropipette without some dilution of the cytoplasm with the Niu-Twitty medium and consequent damage to the nucleus. In order to circumvent these problems, we began to use trypsin as an aid in separating embryonic layers, and Versene to dissociate the cells (King and Briggs, 1955). In addition, it was decided to concentrate on the endoderm since this tissue appears to be definitely determined in the late gastrula, and still consists of large cells which are as readily managed in the transfer procedure as are those of mid- to late blastulae.

Late gastrula endoderm nuclei. In view of the considerations mentioned above, an extensive series of transfers of late gastrula endoderm nuclei has been made, the donor cells being taken usually from the presumptive anterior midgut region (King and Briggs, 1955 and unpub.). These nuclei elicited normal cleavage and blastula formation in about 40 per cent of the test eggs, and were therefore equivalent to undifferentiated blastula nuclei in this respect. However, the later development of the "endoderm blastulae" differed from that of the controls. Approximately 80 per cent of the control blastulae, containing transplanted blastula nuclei, developed into normal larvae. By contrast, the majority of the endoderm blastulae displayed pronounced abnormalities in their development. About one-third were arrested in late blastula or gastrula stages, one-half gastrulated normally but later displayed deficiencies, while the remaining minority developed normally into tadpoles. . . .

Endoderm nuclei from later stages. Nuclei from the anterior midgut region of mid-neurulae elicited normal cleavage and blastula formation in only 16 per cent of the test eggs, compared with 40 per cent or more in the case of the late gastrula nuclei. Of the blastulae obtained, a larger proportion (70%) were arrested early, in blastula or gastrula stages. The remaining embryos gastrulated, but the large majority later displayed the abnormalities mentioned above. Endoderm nuclei from the same region of tail bud embryos displayed a still further reduced capacity to promote cleavage of recipient eggs. Only seven per cent of the test eggs developed into complete blastulae 9 in number. Seven of these blastulae were arrested in late blastula or early gastrula stages, and two were abnormal "endoderm embryos."

These results on endoderm nuclear transfers indicate that the nuclei are going through definite changes. Nuclei from the late gastrula show an undiminished ability to promote cleavage and blastula formation. However, in their subsequent development the endoderm blastulae fall into three general classes— (a) embryos which are arrested before or during the formation of chorda mesoderm, (b) embryos which complete gastrulation but later show deficiencies, especially in ectodermal derivatives, and (c) normal embryos. This suggests that in the late gastrula some endoderm nuclei are unchanged; others are limited in their capacity to promote ectodermal differentiation; and still others are incapable of participating in chorda mesoderm formation. Results of transfers of midneurula and tail bund endoderm nuclei indicate that as differentiation proceeds the number of unchanged nuclei decreases, and that some nuclei may lose their capacity even to promote cleavage of recipient eggs.

That the changes described above occur in the nucleus or some nucleus-associated structure is indicated by the fact that endoderm cytoplasm, injected into normally nucleated eggs, has no influence on their development. This does not exclude cytoplasmic participation in the effects observed, but does indicate that cytoplasmic factors would be nucleus-dependent in their activity. In what follows, we shall refer to the changes detected by the transplantation procedure as nuclear changes, with the understanding that these changes may actually involve either the nucleus itself or some perinuclear organelle, or both.

SERIAL TRANSPLANTATION OF ENDODERM NUCLEI

From the experiments described above, it looks very much as if there is, during development, a progressive restriction of the capacity of endoderm nuclei to promote the coordinated differentiation of the various cell types required for the formation of a normal embryo. The two most pressing questions concerning these nuclear changes are 1) are they specific? and 2) are they stable or irreversible? For various reasons it seemed that the question of specificity could be solved more readily if that of irreversibility were first settled. A method of doing this is illustrated in Figure 1.

The experiment consists of first making transfers of a series of endoderm nuclei to enucleated eggs. Each egg receives one nucleus as usual, and a sizable proportion of the eggs then cleave and form complete blastulae. Each blastula will be, so to speak, populated by descendants of a single endoderm nucleus. Different blastulae contain nuclei derived from different endoderm cells, and develop in the different ways shown in the figure. Now, in order to test the descendants of any given endoderm nucleus we may sacrifice one of the original recipient eggs at the blastula stage, and make from it a new series of nuclear transfers. All of the new group of recipient eggs will contain descendants of one original endoderm nucleus. If the expression of the nucleus with respect to differentiation is uniform and not much affected by vagaries of experimentation all of this new generation of test eggs (called the 1st blastula generation) should develop in the same fashion. It will, in effect, represent the first generation of a clone of embryos all containing descendants of a single nucleus, and is referred to as a nuclear clone. The characteristics of the clone may be studied further by sacrificing an individual of the first blastula generation to provide nuclei for another group of test eggs, referred to as the second blastula generation. The development of this group of eggs will tell us not only how uniform is the differentiation-promoting activity of the nucleus but also, by comparison with the preceding generation, how stable.

The actual experiments were carried out in the following way. In any given experiment we first transferred approximately 15 endoderm nuclei to the same number of enucleated eggs. Anywhere from 6 to 12 of these eggs cleaved and formed complete blastulae. The first two or three cleavages were observed and recorded, and the eggs were then placed in a water bath at 14°C. On the following day (*ca.* 24 hours later) the blastulae were removed from the 14° tank to the 18° room, three donors were selected, and the remaining embryos were set aside for observation. The donors were always blastulae of perfectly normal appearance which had records of having initiated cleavage at the normal time. . . . Nuclei from each of the three donors were transferred to ten enucleated eggs to give the first blastula generation of three nuclear clones. Again cleavages were observed and on the following day one of the resulting blastulae in each clone was selected as the donor for the second blastula generation, while the remaining blastulae were allowed to develop. Usually the experiments were not carried beyond the second blastula generation, and as outlined above, each such experiment, producing three nuclear clones, required at least 75 nuclear transfers. The work reported below on 27 nuclear clones (9 control nuclei, 18 endoderm nuclei) is based on a total of about 850 nuclear transfers.

RESULTS

Results of serial transplantation of nuclei are given in the form of actual records of representative experiments and in a summary table and chart (Figs. 1–8 and Table 1). The experimental records reproduced here include only the test eggs that cleaved completely forming normal blastulae. Not included are eggs that failed to cleave, or cleaved abnormally or partially, since for one reason or another these provide no test of the capacity of the transferred nuclei to promote differentiation.

Figure 1, illustrating the principle of the experimental procedure, is also an accurate record of the development of one nuclear clone. In this experiment, the original transfers of endoderm nuclei as usual led to quite different types of development, ranging from arrested gastrulae to normal embryos, as illustrated by the camera lucida drawings. One blastula was sacrificed to provide nuclei for transfer to a new group of enucleated eggs, giving rise to a nuclear clone which, in the first blastula generation, displayed a quite uniform type of development— in contrast to the wide variety of developmental types seen among the original recipients of the different endoderm nuclei. The embryos of this generation gastrulated normally, but later showed marked deficiencies, particularly in the ectodermal derivatives. One of the blastulae of this generation was sacrificed to provide nuclei for the second blastula generation, which also developed fairly uniformly and in a manner nearly identical with that of the first generation.

Figure 2 is a camera lucida record of another experiment in which three different original donors were used. Endoderm nuclei from each of these donors were transferred to ten enucleated eggs, which then showed the usual range of developmental types, as illustrated in the three groups of drawings in the upper part of Figure 2. One blastula from each group of embryos was sacrificed to provide nuclei for the first blastula generation. Endoderm nuclei from blastula "A" promoted completely normal development in practically all of the recipient eggs that showed complete cleavage, in both the first and second blastula generations. Nuclei from blastula "C" also promoted uniform development, stopping in late blastula or early gastrula stage. Nuclei from blastula "B", on the other hand, elicited normal blastula formation in only three of the test eggs, of which one developed normally, one arrested in neurulation, while one was sacrificed at blastula stage to provide nuclei for the second blastula generation. The second generation developed abnormally and displayed somewhat greater variability than usual. The variable development of this clone poses a problem of interpretation. Possibly some nuclei, chosen by chance at the time when they are beginning to undergo a change, will continue to change following transfer to egg

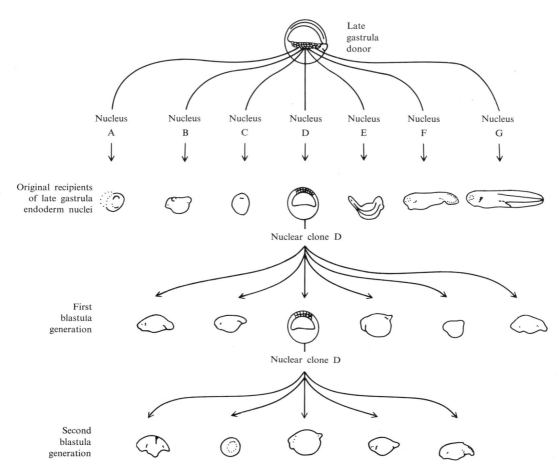

Fig. 1. *Diagram illustrating serial transplantation of endoderm nuclei. Donor nuclei are actually taken from the presumptive anterior midgut region of the late gastrula. Transferred to enucleated eggs they promote the various types of development shown for the "original recipients" in the diagram. One of the original recipients, sacrificed at the blastula stage, provides nuclei for a single clone which shows the more uniform development illustrated for the first and second blastula generations. In this and subsequent figures the illustrations of embryos are in the form of either camera lucida drawings or photographs.*

cytoplasm. An alternative explanation would be that the variations in development within clone "B" are accidentally induced.

Another serial transplantation experiment is summarized in Figure 3. In this experiment all three nuclear clones were derived from a single donor. Descendants of nucleus "A" promoted development only to gastrula stages, in both the first and second blastula generations. Descendants of nucleus "B" promoted development of abnormal post-neurula embryos. The abnormalities were similar to those described in the previous section of this paper, being most pronounced in the

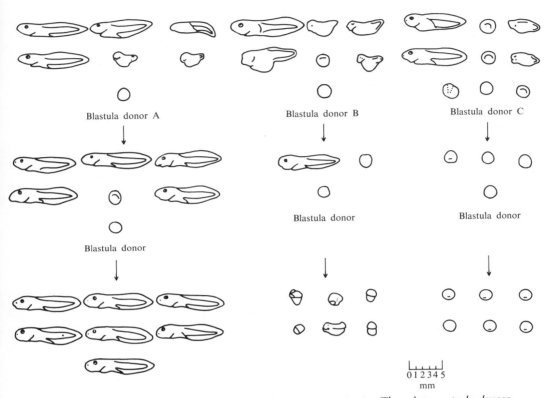

Fig. 2. *Camera lucida record of serial transplantation experiment. Three late gastrula donors were used (not diagrammed in above record). Nuclei from these donors were transferred to 3 groups of enucleated eggs, which developed in the various ways illustrated in the upper part of the figure. The derived clones developed much more uniformly.*

ectodermal derivatives, and were quite uniformly expressed in the first blastula generation. The majority of embryos of the second generation were similar to those of the first, but two out of the eight embryos were arrested earlier, at gastrula stage. Embryos of nuclear clone "C" also developed to an abnormal post-neurula stage. In the first blastula generation they were uniformly somewhat better developed than individuals in clone "B," but none the less displayed typical characteristics of endoderm embryos. In the second generation two of the five individuals were apparently identical with the embryos of the first generation while the remainder showed more marked deficiencies, as shown in Figure 3.

The actual appearance of the embryos is shown in the photographic record of another experiment. Figure 4 consists of photographs of living embryos and illustrates clearly how uniform are the individuals within a given clone, and how distinct the clones are from each other. Some of the internal morphology of these embryos is illustrated in Figure 5. Figure 5 shows sections through the eye region. In clone "A" the brain is poorly developed, the eye is in the form of a small vesicle,

Serial Transplantation of Endoderm Nuclei

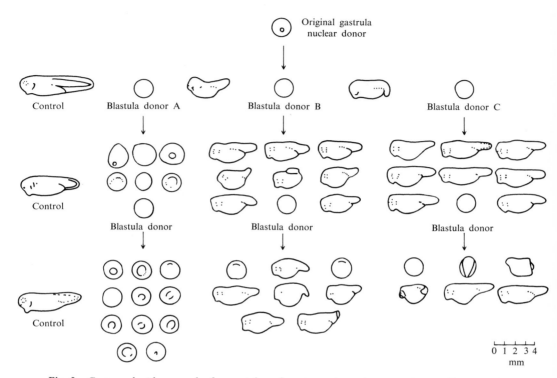

Fig. 3. *Camera lucida record of a serial nuclear transplantation experiment. See text for description.*

there is no lens, head mesenchyme is poorly formed, and the development of the foregut is retarded. Although it is not visible in the low power photographs, there is pycnosis in the nuclei of the brain, eye, and dorsal mesenchyme, but not significantly in the ventral mesenchyme and foregut. Sections through the trunk show the notochord well formed and of about the same diameter as the notochord in the controls. Somites are also present, although abnormal in form. On the other hand, both the spinal cord and the dorsal mesenchyme are very poorly developed and contain pycnotic nuclei. The midgut is still in the form of a large endoderm mass in controls and experimental embryos at this stage. In clone "A" it is distorted by swelling of the coelomic space, but does not contain pycnotic nuclei.

Clone "B" displays more advanced differentiation than clone "A" but is still deficient compared with the controls. The deficiencies, although less pronounced, are of the same general character as those in clone "A". Brain and dorsal head mesenchyme contain numerous pycnotic nuclei. The eye cup has induced a lens which is still in the form of a simple vesicle whereas in the controls

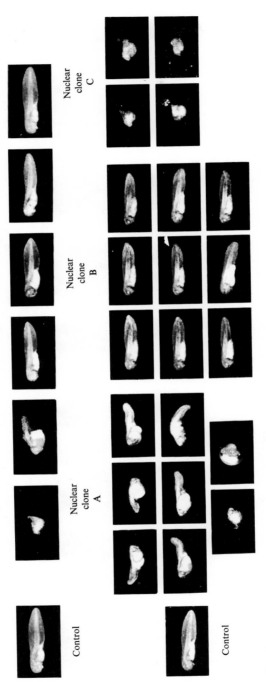

Retransplantation of Endoderm Nuclei

Original recipients of late gastrula endoderm nuclei

Fig. 4.

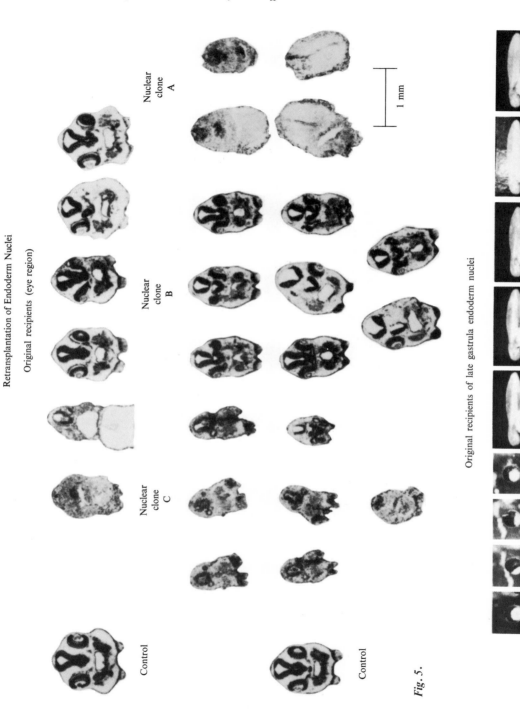

Retransplantation of Endoderm Nuclei

Original recipients (eye region)

Nuclear clone A

Nuclear clone B

Nuclear clone C

Control

Control

1 mm

Original recipients of late gastrula endoderm nuclei

Fig. 5.

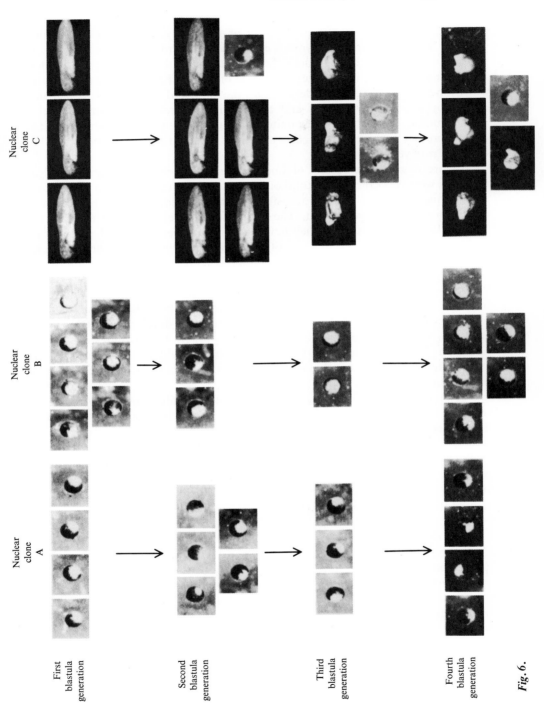

Fig. 6.

it has differentiated into the main body of the lens and the lens epithelium. Foregut and ventral mesenchyme are somewhat retarded but contain no significant number of pycnotic nuclei. Sections through the trunk show a modest but definite reduction in the size and degree of differentiation of the spinal cord.

Clone "C" shows extreme deficiencies, the brain and head mesenchyme being absent or very poorly formed and containing numerous degenerating nuclei. In the trunk the notochord and somite material is present. A rudimentary spinal cord is present in three of four cases examined. The gut is poorly developed, but contains no pycnotic nuclei.

Figure 6 gives the results of one experiment in which the serial nuclear transfers were carried on for a total of four blastula generations. The experiment was unique in that the original transfers of late gastrula endoderm nuclei led to only two types of development. The recipient eggs were either arrested in the very early gastrula stage, or they developed into perfectly normal postneurula embryos, as shown in the top line of photographs of Figure 6. There were no embryos of intermediate type. Correspondingly, clones derived from this group of embryos also expressed at first only the two types of development. Clones "A" and "B" showed uniformly an arrest of development in early gastrula stage, and even though the transfers were carried on for four blastula generations there was no evidence of reversal to a more normal type of development. Clone "C" embryos, on the other hand, developed normally for the first two blastula generations, but in the third and fourth generations the development changed, giving rise to abnormal post-neurula embryos of the type commonly seen in the other endoderm experiments.

A summary of the serial transplantation tests of endoderm embryos is given in Table I and Figure 7. The main point to be emphasized concerning the data in Table 1 is that the same types of embryos occur in about the same proportions in both the original population of endoderm embryos and in the derived clones. Each clone displays a fairly uniform type of development and as a clone corresponds to one or another of the individual embryos in the original population. In other words, in the process of deriving the clones we obtain a faithful representation of the original types.

We have included also in Table 1 the data on serial transfers of undifferentiated blastula nuclei, for the purpose of showing that in the majority of experiments these give rise to clones of normal embryos. A detailed record of one of these experiments is given in Figure 8.

Figure 7 gives a comparison of the development of the endoderm clones in the successive blastula generations. Each generation of each clone is represented in the figure by a single typical embryo. The important fact emerging from this summary is that in no case so far studied is there a reversal to a more normal type of development in the second (or later) blastula generation compared with the first. In other words, the nuclear condition responsible for given deficiencies in differentiation is irreversible under the conditions of these experiments. However, it is possible that nuclear changes leading to more restricted development

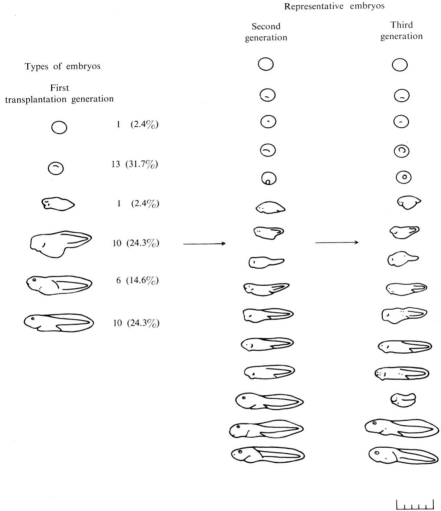

Summary
Serial Transplantation of Endoderm Nuclei

Fig. 7. Summary of serial transplantation experiments including all endodem clones except the ones shown in Fig. 4 (not included because the experiment was carried on for only 2 generations). The row of drawings on the left illustrates the types of embryos developing from the original recipient eggs injected with endoderm nuclei. The middle row shows typical embryos from the clones in the second generation (referred to in text as the first blastula generation). Each embryo represents a single clone. The same clones in the third generation are represented in the right hand row of drawings. Note that in general the development in the third generation is similar to that in the second, with no evidence of change to a more normal type of differentiation.

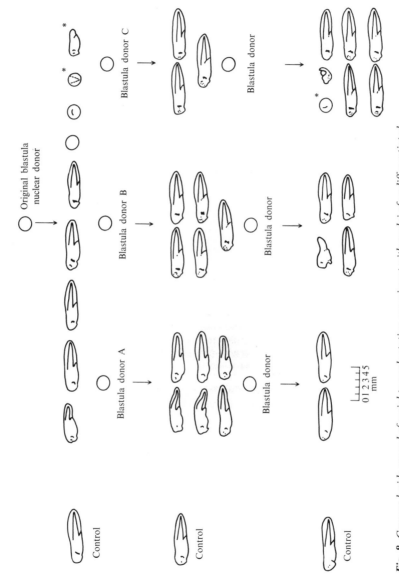

Fig. 8. *Camera lucida record of serial transplantation experiment with nuclei of undifferentiated blastula cells. Embryos marked * died from some infectious or toxic process after developing normally to the stages shown.*

Table 1. *Development of original recipients of endoderm nuclei compared with development of endoderm clones*

Source of nuclei	Total No. complete blastulae	Development		
		Blastulae and gastrulae	Abnormal post-neurulae	Normal larvae
Endoderm (late gastrula)				
Original recipients (individual eggs)	44	14 (32%)	20 (45%)	10 (23%)
Clones	18	5 (28%)	8 (44%)	5 (28%)
Control (blastulae)				
Original recipients (individual eggs)	22	2 (9%)	2 (9%)	18 (82%)
Clones	9	0	2 (22%)	7 (78%)

may sometimes progress in the course of repeated transfers. Two instances of a more restricted development in the later generations have been noted (Figs. 2 and 6) and it is possible, though far from certain, that endoderm nuclei may continue "differentiating" in egg cytoplasm.

CHROMOSOME STUDIES

Since it is known that embryos with unbalanced chromosome sets develop abnormally and are frequently arrested at early developmental stages (Fank-hauser, 1934b), it was important to determine the condition of the chromosomes in the endoderm embryos described above. This was done as follows:

In each experiment portions of the original donor gastrula and of the blastula donor for each transplant generation were handed over to Miss Marie Di-Berardino, who immediately prepared acetic-orcein squashes of the material. All the subsequent work on the chromosomes was done by Miss DiBerardino.

The preparation of satisfactory squashes of blastula chromosomes posed some problems. If the cells are squashed directly from the Niu-Twitty medium it is very difficult to obtain adequate separation of the chromosomes. A photo-graph of a typical metaphase plate is reproduced in Figure 9A, showing the long blastula chromosomes intertwined and impossible to count accurately. Adequate separation of chromosomes can be produced by pre-treating the cells with hypotonic medium and colchicine (Hungerford, 1955), but still better results can be obtained by pre-treatment for 30 minutes with a Niu-Twitty medium lacking Ca^{++} and Mg^{++}, and buffered to pH 7.5 with phosphate. A photograph of a plate from such a preparation is given in Figure 9B. The effect of pre-treatment with the modified Niu-Twitty medium is immediately reversed if the

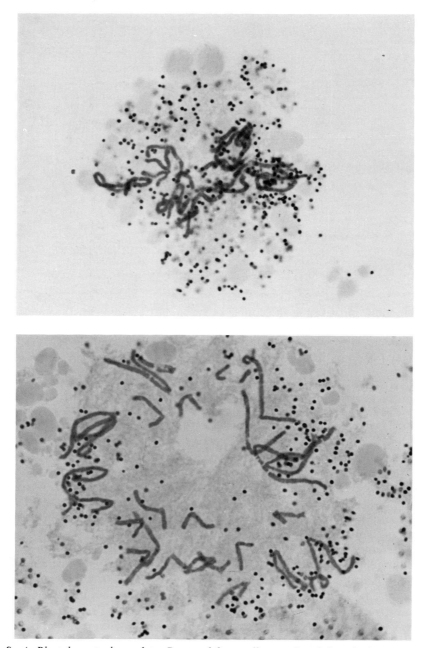

Fig. 9. *A. Blastula metaphase plate. Prepared from cells transferred directly from Niu-Twitty solution to acetic-orcein stain-fixative. B. Blastula metaphase plate showing increased spreading of chromosomes resulting from pretreatment of cells with modified Niu-Twitty solution (lacking Ca^{++} and Mg^{++}). Black spots are pigment granules. Magnification, $\times$ 1370. Photographs by David A. Hungerford.*

cells are returned to the normal medium before squashing. The effect is also different for tissues from more advanced stages of development. These and other phenomena are being studied by Hungerford and DiBerardino and will be described elsewhere.

The results of the chromosome studies are presented in Table 2 and Figures 10 and 11. With respect to chromosome number the results are clear. In the majority of cases, the normal diploid number (26) was found, regardless of the type of development promoted by the nuclei. In one clone there was a shift from diploidy to a triploid or near triploid number between the first and second blastula generations. Otherwise the numbers remained at the diploid value throughout.

With respect to chromosome morphology there was also no detectable change in the majority of donors. However, in three clones the donor nuclei contained a few small ring chromosomes (see Figure 10) similar to those noted by Fankhauser (1934a) in one merogonic fragment of a salamander egg. These clones developed only to the late blastula or very early gastrula stage. In a fourth clone, displaying development to a mid-gastrula stage, ring chromosomes were present in the first blastula generation but not in the second. In the remaining eleven clones studied chromosome morphology appeared to be normal even though the different clones developed in quite different ways.

Even though there were, for the majority of clones, no variations in chromosome number or morphology that could be correlated with type of development, it was still possible that deletions or translocations might have occurred that would have escaped detection. A rough attempt to detect such alterations was made in the following way. The lengths of the camera lucida drawings of chromosomes were measured with a Keuffel and Esser map reader. In order to put chromosome lengths in different figures and squashes on a comparable basis we calculated the relative length as the ratio: individual chromosome length/total length of all 26 chromosomes (L/Total L). The relative lengths of the chromosomes in any given figure were then plotted in the manner shown in Figure 11. From a comparison of such plots one can determine whether the distribution of chromosome lengths is the same or different in the different clones. The results of this analysis are illustrated in Figure 11. In general, the distribution of chromosome lengths did not appear to differ in the different types of clones. One of the clones containing ring chromosomes did differ from the others in displaying a wider range of chromosome lengths (Figure 11). Otherwise, there were no differences that could be definitely related to type of development. This does not eliminate the possibility that deletions, etc. may have occurred, but does suggest that they would have to be on a relatively small scale. It also does not mean that more subtle types of chromosomal (or other) changes may not be occurring as a regular concomitant of differentiation (for example, see Beermann, this volume).

DISCUSSION

The serial transplantation experiments described above show that the changes occurring in endoderm nuclei during differentiation are highly stabilized, in the

Table 2. Chromosome numbers of donor embryos used in serial transplantation experiments.

Type of donor	Dev. of test eggs	No. of embryos	No. of metaphase plates	Exact chromosome counts								Approximate counts		
				12	13	20	23	24	25	26	27	13–14	21–28	35–45
Endoderm nuclei														
Original donor (last gast.)	Variable	8	33		4					17			12	
Clonal donors (blastulae)	Normal	10	43	1	3				2	29			8	
	Abnormal postneurula	14	55		2		1			34		13		5
	Arrested blast. and gast.	14	73		1	1		2	2	44	1	5	16	
	Arrested blast. and gast.*	7	26							26				
Blastula nuclei														
Original and clonal donors	Normal	20	75					1		59			15	
(blastulae)	Abnormal postneurula	2	15		2							8	5	

Original donors—late gastrulae: Donor cells taken from presumptive anterior mid-gut. For reasons of technical convenience chromosome counts were done on squashes of archenteron roof.

Clonal donors: Embryos derived from eggs injected with endoderm nuclei, sacrificed at blastula stage to provide nuclei (animal hemisphere) for establishment of clones. Counts done on part of animal hemisphere of these donors. In the table donors are grouped according to type of development observed in the derived clones. Listed separately (*) are 7 blastulae which were not used as donors. They were taken from the 4th blastula generation of two clones which consistently showed arrest in late blastula or early gastrula stage.

Controls: Original donors and clonal donors, both in blastula stage, grouped together.
For further description see text and Figs. 10 and 11.

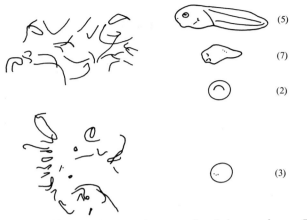

Fig. 10. *Chromosome complements of endoderm embryos. Types and numbers of endoderm nuclear clones are illustrated by the drawings of representative embryos. The corresponding chromosome complements are shown in the form of camera lucida drawings of typical metaphase plates. Rings were present in clones displaying arrest of development in late blastula or early gastrula stage. Of two clones arresting at about mid-gastrula stage (*) one displayed rings in the first blastula generation but not in the second. Otherwise the chromosome complements appeared normal regardless of type of development.*

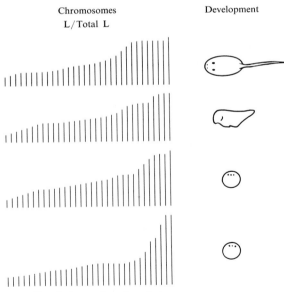

Fig. 11. *Relative lengths of chromosomes were measured on a total of 78 metaphase plates from 14 endoderm embryos and 6 controls. The results shown above for endoderm embryos are representative. Differences in relative lengths, from embryo to embryo, are not significant being within the range observed in different plates from single embryos. The one exception, in which the range in relative lengths is greater than normal, is plotted at the bottom of the figure.*

sense that they are not reversed in egg cytoplasm. Each transfer is followed by cleavage of the recipient egg to produce a donor blastula consisting of approximately 8,000 cells, requiring about 13 divisions (or generations) of the original nucleus. In the majority of experiments, three such transfers were done serially and therefore involved about 39 nuclear generations. In the most extensive experiments (5 serial transfers) there would have been 65 reproductions of the original endoderm nucleus, with still no evidence of reversal. Thus, regardless of its exact character and mode of origin, we are dealing with a heritable change in the capacity of the nucleus to promote differentiation. At the least, it could be a change induced in the original endoderm nuclei accidentally during the transfer operation. At the most, it would represent a specific genetic change elicited somehow by particular cytoplasmic localizations, and responsible in turn for the stabilization of differentiation of individual cells.

The idea that nuclear changes such as we see in endoderm cells might be accidentally induced cannot be ignored. The hazard of nuclear damage is always present in this kind of experimentation. The arguments against it are as follows:

1. The technical problems of making nuclear transfers from endoderm cells are no greater than they are for blastula cells. Yet, the blastula nuclei promote normal differentiation of recipient eggs while the endoderm nuclei generally do not.

2. Although the original transfers of endoderm nuclei give a variety of types of development, subsequent transfers of descendants of a particular nucleus lead to fairly uniform development of the recipient eggs. If the variation were accidentally induced one would expect to find it in the clones as well as in the recipients of the original nuclei. (Unless, of course, endoderm nuclei are somehow much more sensitive to damage in their own cytoplasm than they are in egg cytoplasm.)

3. While the original endoderm transfers usually lead to a variety of types of development, this is not always so. In one experiment (Figure 6) we observed only two classes of embryos, which would be hard to account for on the basis of chance injury to the nuclei.

4. In the majority of clones there was no evidence of chromosome changes such as might be expected to result from nuclear damage.

On the basis of this evidence we may assume that the restrictions in the capacity of endoderm nuclei to promote differentiation are real and not artificially induced. Other points about which definite statements can be made are: 1) that the nuclear changes are highly stabilized, as shown by the serial transplantation experiments, and 2) that they do not occur in all cells at once. Rather it appears that in the late gastrula the endoderm nuclei fall into three general classes: 1) undifferentiated nuclei, 2) nuclei restricted to varying degrees in their capacity to promote normal post-gastrula development, particularly of ectodermal derivatives, and 3) nuclei incapable of participating in the formation of chorda mesoderm, resulting in arrest at gastrulation. In later stages of development the number of nuclei in class 1 (undifferentiated) decreases while those showing restrictions of differentiation-promoting capacity increase. This indicates that a progressive and "irreversible" nuclear change occurs during differentiation. Whether in any given cell this restriction in differentiating-promoting ability occurs slowly or rapidly, continuously or in distinct steps, we do not know, although a study of nuclear changes during the post-blastula development of the clones might eventually give answers to some of these questions. Also, it is unknown which of the nuclear or peri-nuclear structures are involved. Control experiments have shown that the endoderm cytoplasm by itself is incapable of modifying the differentiation of normally nucleated eggs. However, we cannot yet determine whether it is the nucleus itself or some replicating perinuclear organelle which is responsible for the restricted developmental potencies.

Finally, we should consider briefly the question of the specificity of the nuclear changes in endoderm cells. We have seen that these changes result first in a loss of the capacity to promote normal differentiation of ectodermal derivatives, and presumably later the ability to promote differentiation of chorda mesoderm is also lost. Thus, the nuclear changes are consistent with the fact that the nuclei are derived from endoderm. But whether they are specific for endoderm is uncertain. In order to settle this point it would be necessary to explore the capacity for various types of differentiation by appropriate grafting experiments with parts of the arrested endoderm embryos, and the same sort of analysis would have to be done on embryos containing other types of nuclei. Now that the nuclear changes in endoderm cells are known to be highly stabilized and to give a fairly uniform type of development in the clones, this central problem of specificity may be attacked.

SUMMARY

Nuclei of late gastrula endoderm, transplanted to enucleated eggs *(Rana pipiens)* promote the following general types of development: 1) arrest at gastrula stages, 2) normal gastrulation followed by deficient development in later stages, especially in the ectodermal derivatives, 3) normal development throughout.

In order to determine if the nuclear changes responsible for the deficient development are stable, serial transfers of endoderm nuclei were carried out. Individual nuclei were transplanted to enucleated eggs, which cleaved and produced blastulae. In a given test, one of these blastulae was sacrificed to provide nuclei for transfer to a new group of eggs. Such a group represents a clone, all members of which are nucleated by descendants of one original endoderm nucleus. One member of such a clone may be sacrificed at the blastula stage to provide nuclei for transfer to a new group of enucleated eggs, giving in effect a second blastula generation of the clone. The same process may be repeated to provide several generations.

Analysis of the development of 18 clones revealed the following: Whereas test eggs containing different endoderm nuclei developed in the different ways mentioned above, eggs within one clone developed much more uniformly. In some clones all embryos were arrested at gastrula stage, in others they displayed a fairly uniform set of deficiencies in post-gastrula development, and in a few clones almost all embryos developed normally throughout. Furthermore, within any given clone the development in the second and later generations were generally of the same type as that observed in the first generation. In a few clones the deficiencies became more severe in the later generations, but no case of reversal to a more normal type of development was noted.

Chromosome studies on donor embryos in the clonal experiments showed that chromosome number generally remained unchanged at the diploid value (26). In three clones, all consisting of embryos arresting at early gastrula stage, a few small ring chromosomes were present. Otherwise, no chromosome changes were detected even though the clones exhibited quite different types of development.

These experiments show that descendants of individual endoderm nuclei have a fairly uniform expression with respect to differentiation, which does not reverse to a more normal expression in the course of the serial transfers. In other words, compared with nuclei of undifferentiated cells, the endoderm nuclei show stabilized changes in capacity to promote differentiation. How these changes arise, whether they are specific, and which of the nuclear or peri-nuclear structures are involved, are problems remaining to be worked out.

ACKNOWLEDGEMENTS

We wish to thank Dr. Jack Schultz for the benefit derived from many discussions we have had with him on problems of differentiation. We also wish to acknowledge the assistance of Miss Marie DiBerardino, who carried out the chromosome studies described in this paper and provided valuable assistance in many other ways as well.

REFERENCES

Beermann, W., 1956, Nuclear differentiation and functional morphology of chromosomes. Cold Spr. Harb. Symp. Quant. Biol. *21:* 217–232.

Briggs, R., Green, E. U., and King, T. J., 1951, An investigation of the capacity for cleavage and differentiation in *Rana pipiens* eggs lacking "functional" chromosomes. J. Exp. Zool. *116:* 455–500.

Briggs, R., and King, T. J., 1952, Transplantation of living nuclei from blastula cells into enucleated frogs' eggs. Proc. Nat. Acad. Sci. Wash. *38:* 455–463.

——, 1953, Factors affecting the transplantability of nuclei of frog embryonic cells. J. Exp. Zool. *122:* 485–506.

Comandon, J. and De Fonbrune, P., 1939, Greffe nucleaire totale, simple ou multiple, chez une Amibo Compt. rend. soc. biol. *130:* 744–748.

Danielli, J. F., Lorch, I. J., Ord, M. J., and Wilson, E. C., 1955, Nucleus and cytoplasm in cellular inheritance. Nature, Lond. *176:* 1114–1115.

Ephrussi, B., 1951, Remarks on cell heredity. In: Genetics in the 20th Century. New York, Macmillan Company, pp. 241–262.

——, 1953, Nucleo-cytoplasmic relations in microorganisms. Oxford, Clarendon Press.
Fankhauser, G., 1934a, Cytological studies on egg fragments of the salamander *Triton*, IV. The cleavage of egg fragments without the egg nucleus. J. Exp. Zool. *67:* 349–394.

——, 1934b, Cytological studies on egg fragments of the salamander *Triton*. V. Chromosome number and chromosome individuality in the cleavage mitoses of merogonic fragments. J. Exp. Zool. *68:* 1–57.

Gluecksohn-Waelsch, S., 1954, Some genetic aspects of development. Cold Spr. Harb. Symp. Quant. Biol. *19:* 41–49.

Grobstein, C., 1952. Effects of fragmentation of mouse embryonic shields on their differentiative behavior after culturing. J. Exp. Zool. *120:* 437–456.

Grobstein, C., and Zwilling, E., 1953, Modification of growth and differentiation of chorioallantoic grafts of chick blastoderm pieces after cultivation at a glass-clot interface. J. Exp. Zool. *122:* 259–284.

Hadorn, E., 1948, Gene action in growth and differentiation of lethal mutants of *Drosophila*. Symposia Soc. Exp. Biol. *2:* 177–195.

——, 1956, Patterns of biochemical and developmental pleiotropy. Cold Spr. Harb. Symp. Quant. Biol. *21:* 255–382.
Hämmerling, J., 1934, Uber genomwirkungen und Formbildungsfähigkeit bei *Acetabularia*. Arch. Entwickmech. Org. *132:* 424–462.

——, 1953, Nucleo-cytoplasmic relationships in the development of *Acetabularia*. Intern. Rev. Cytol. *2:*475–498.

Holtfreter, J., 1933, Die totale Exogastrulation, eine Selbstablösung des Ektoderms vom Entomesoderm. Entwicklung und funktionelles Verhalten nervenloser Organe. Arch. Entwick-meck. Org. *129:* 669–793.

——, 1938, Differenzierungspotenzen isolierter Teile der Anurengastrula. Arch. Entwick-mech. Org. *138:*657–738.

Hungerford, D. A., 1955, Chromosome numbers of ten-day fetal mouse cells. J. Morph. *97:* 497–510.

King, T. J., and Briggs, R., 1954, Transplantation of living nuclei of late gastrulae into enucleated eggs of *Rana pipiens*. J. Embryol. Exp. Morph. *2:*73–80.

——, 1955, Changes in the nuclei of differentiating gastrula cells, as demonstrated by nuclear transplantation. Proc. Nat. Acad. Sci. Wash. *41:* 321–325.

Lederberg, J., 1956, Infection and heredity. Growth Symp. *13:* 101–124. Princeton Univ. Press.

Lehman, H. E., 1955, On the development of enucleated *Triton* eggs with an injected blastula nucleus. Biol. Bull. *108:* 138–150.

——, 1956, Nuclear transplantation, a tool for the study of nuclear differentiation. AAAS Symp. (In press).

Loeb, J., 1894, Über eine einfache Methode, zwei oder mehr zusammengewachsene Embryonen aus einem Ei hervorzubringen. Pflüger's Arch. *55:* 525–530.

Lorch, I. J., and Danielli, J. F., 1950, Transplantation of nuclei from cell to cell. Nature, Lond. *166:* 329–333.

Moore, J. A., 1955, Abnormal combinations of nuclear and cytoplasmic systems in frogs and toads. Adv. Genet. *7:* 139–182.

Niu, M. C., and Twitty, V. C., 1953, The differentiation of gastrula ectoderm in medium conditioned by axial mesoderm. Proc. Nat. Acad. Sci. Wash. *39:* 985–989.

Porter, K. R., 1939, Androgenetic development of the egg of *Rana pipiens*. Biol. Bull. *77:* 233–257.

Poulson, D. F., 1945, Chromosomal control of embryogenesis in *Drosophila*. Amer. Nat. *79:* 340–363.

Rostand, J., 1943, Essai d'inoculation de noyaux embryonnaires dans l'oeuf vierge de grenouille. Rev. sci. *81:* 454–456.

Schultz, J., 1952, Interrelations between nucleus and cytoplasm: problems at the biological level. Exp. Cell Res. Suppl. *2:* 17–43.

Sonneborn, T. M., 1954, Patterns of nucleocytoplasmic integration in *Paramecium*. Proc. 9th Intern. Congress Genetics. Caryologia, suppl. 1954: 307–325.

Spemann, H., 1914, Über verzögerte Kernversorgung von Keimteilen. Vergandl. deut. zool. Ges., 1914: 16–221.

——, 1938, Embryonic Development and Induction. New Haven, Yale Univ. Press, pp. 211.

Stauffer, E., 1945, Versuche zur experimentallen Herstellung haploider Axolotl-Merogone. Rev. suisse zool. *52:* 231–327.

Subtelny, S. S., 1956, Personal communication.

Sze, L. C., 1953, Changes in the amount of desoxyribonucleic acid in the development of *Rana pipiens*. J. Exp. Zool. *122:* 577–601.

Tartar, V., 1953, Chimeras and nuclear transplantations in ciliates, *Stentor coeruleus* × *S. polymorphus*. J. Exp. Zool. *124:* 63–103.

Waddington, C. H., and Pantelouris, E. M., 1953, Transplantation of nuclei in newt's eggs. Nature, Lond. *172:* 1050.

Weisz, Paul B., 1951, A general mechanism of differentiation based on morphogenetic studies in ciliates. Amer. Nat. *85:* 293–311.

Wilson, E. B., 1925, The Cell in Development and Heredity. 3rd ed. New York, Macmillan Company.

The Developmental Capacity of Nuclei Taken from Intestinal Epithelium Cells of Feeding Tadpoles

by J. B. GURDON

INTRODUCTION

An important problem in embryology is whether the differentiation of cells depends upon a stable restriction of the genetic information contained in their nuclei. The technique of nuclear transplantation has shown to what extent the nuclei of differentiating cells can promote the formation of different cell types (e.g. King & Briggs, 1956; Gurdon, 1960c). Yet no experiments have so far been published on the transplantation of nuclei from fully differentiated normal cells. This is partly because it is difficult to obtain meaningful results from such experiments. The small amount of cytoplasm in differentiated cells renders their nuclei susceptible to damage through exposure to the saline medium, and this makes it difficult to assess the significance of the abnormalities resulting from their transplantation. It is, however, very desirable to know the developmental capacity of such nuclei, since any nuclear changes which are necessarily involved in cellular differentiation must have already taken place in cells of this kind.

The experiments described below are some attempts to transplant nuclei from fully differentiated cells. Many of these nuclei gave abnormal results after transplantation, and several different kinds of experiments have been carried out to determine the cause and significance of these abnormalities.

The donor cells used for these experiments were intestinal epithelium cells of feeding tadpoles. This is the final stage of differentiation of many of the endoderm cells whose nuclei have already been studied by means of nuclear transplantation experiments in *Xenopus*. The results to be described here may therefore be regarded as an extension of those previously obtained from differentiating endoderm cells (Gurdon, 1960c).

MATERIAL AND METHODS

The animals used for these experiments belong to the subspecies *Xenopus laevis laevis*. The transplantation technique has been carried out as described previously (Elsdale *et al.,* 1960), except that the donor tissue was exposed to the dissociating Versene solution (5×10^{-4} M) for 30–40 minutes. The *Xenopus* nuclear marker

J. B. Gurdon, "The Developmental Capacity of Nuclei Taken from Intestinal Epithelium, *Journal of Embryology and Experimental Morphology* **10** (December 1962), 127–147. Reprinted by permission of The Company of Biologists Limited.

was used (Elsdale *et al.*, 1960), and marked donor nuclei were transplanted into unmarked recipient eggs. Among the transplant-embryos described below, all those which developed beyond the blastula stage contained marked nuclei, thus proving that they were derived from the transplanted nucleus and not from the egg nucleus. The nuclear marker can only be seen in embryos which have passed the blastula stage.

Donor Cells

The differentiated cells used to provide donor nuclei were intestinal epithelium cells from the mid-intestine of feeding tadpoles (stages 46–48 of Nieuwkoop & Faber, 1956). These cells (plate) have the following features characteristic of their differentiated state: a tall columnar shape with basally situated nuclei; pigment granules inside the surface exposed to the gut lumen; and, most important, the striated border typical of cells having an absorptive function. Some of these cells contain a few yolk platelets, but these are rapidly absorbed at about this stage. All the epithelium cells in the part of the intestine used for these experiments are of this kind except for less than 1 percent which are typical gland cells; there are no undifferentiated cells in the epithelium at this stage. The epithelium cells are larger than the other cell types present in the mid-intestine, and so can be easily recognized in the dissociated cell preparations.

Controls

Owing to the variable quality of the *Xenopus* recipient eggs laid in the laboratory (Gurdon, 1960*b*), the transplantation of intestinal epithelium cell nuclei has been accompanied by control transplantations of blastula or gastrula nuclei. Since no change in developmental capacity has been detected in Xenopus nuclei until after the late gastrula stage, either blastula or gastrula nuclei have been used as controls according to convenience.

RESULTS

Six experiments involving the transplantation of intestinal epithelium cell nuclei (referred to as intestin nuclei) gave similar results, and these have been combined in Table 1. In each experiment control transfers from blastulae or gastruiae (referred to as embryonic nuclei) were interspersed with transfers of intestine nuclei.

Normal Tadpoles

Altogether 10 normal feeding tadpoles have been obtained from the transplantation of intestinal epithelium cell nuclei. These tadpoles have diploid nuclei carrying the nuclear marker referred to above. They therefore provide a clear demonstration that at least a few differentiated intestine cells contain nuclei which are capable of giving rise to all the cell types necessary for the formation of a feeding tadpole.

These normal tadpoles constitute only $1\frac{1}{2}$ percent of the 726 transplanted intestine nuclei, and all the remaining transfers resulted in various degrees of

Table 1. *The development resulting from the transplantation of nuclei from differentiated and embryonic cells of Xenopus laevis.*

Donor stage (Nieuwkoop & Faber, 1956)	Total transfers	No cleavage	Total transfers resulting in cleavage	Development resulting from transplanted nuclei								
				Abortive cleavage	Partial cleavage	Complete blastulae	Arrested blastulae	Abnormal gastrulae	Abnormal post-neurulae	Stunted tadpoles	Died as swimming tadpoles	Normal feeding tadpoles
Intestinal epithelium cell nuclei (stage 46-48)	726 100%	347 48%	379 52%	175 24%	156 21.5%	48 6.5%	18	8	5	6	1	10 1.5%
Blastula or gastrula endoderm nuclei (stage 8-12)	279 100%	66 24%	213 76%	8 3%	32 11%	173 62%	4	17	19	27	6	100 36%

abnormality ranging from a complete lack of cleavage to nearly normal tadpoles (Table 1). Some experiments have been carried out in order to determine the significance of these abnormalities and, in particular, whether the abnormalities are due to a limited developmental capacity of the transplanted nuclei or to other factors such as variation in technique. The two methods used were first, the cytological analysis of eggs fixed soon after they had been injected with nuclei, and secondly, the serial transplantation of nuclei from abnormal transplant-embryos.

The Cytological Analysis of Eggs Fixed Soon After Receiving Transplanted Nuclei

The procedure followed in this analysis was to transplant nuclei from one donor embryo into eggs laid by one frog. Soon after transplantation some of the eggs were taken at random and fixed while the remainder were allowed to develop as far as they were able. The fixed eggs were then serially sectioned and stained. Subsequent microscopic examination of the sections often revealed abnormalities of the transplanted nucleus and achromatic apparatus. The eggs which were not fixed served as exact controls since they were laid by the same frog as the fixed eggs and contained transplanted nuclei from the same donor embryo. These showed how the sectioned eggs would have developed if they had not been fixed. In this way a certain cytological abnormality could be associated with a particular developmental abnormality, thus indicating the cause of the latter. This analysis was carried out on eggs with transplanted intestine nuclei as well as on those with transplanted embryonic nuclei.

The total lack of cleavage following nuclear transfer

Forty-eight percent of the intestine nuclei and 24 percent of the embryonic nuclei failed to promote cleavage of any kind after transplantation (Table 1). The following results show that this can be attributed to a failure in the technique such that the transplanted nucleus was not effectively exposed to the recipient egg cytoplasm. The eggs fixed about 40 minutes after receiving transplanted nuclei fell into two distinct categories. First there were those with distinct regions of cytoplasm; these had an almost yolk-free area in the animal half of the egg, containing the developing transplanted nucleus, and close to it the dying irradiated egg nucleus (Gurdon, 1960a. Fig. 1). This is the typical condition of irradiated recipient eggs which have been fertilized or in which a successful nuclear transfer has been made. The other fixed eggs revealed an entirely different situation. These had a relatively homogeneous cytoplasm just as in newly laid unfertilized eggs, and the irradiated egg nucleus was found in the vegetal half. There was no yolk-free area in the animal half of the egg and the transplanted nucleus was either entirely absent or else could be seen inside an intact donor cell.

The total absence of the transplanted nucleus from a recipient egg is probably due to the donor cell sticking to the injection pipette and so being withdrawn from the egg with the pipette. This would not be observed in the course of an experiment unless looked for carefully. The presence of a whole donor cell in the

Table 2. *The cytological analysis of eggs fixed 60–80 minutes after transplantation.*

	Number of eggs fixed	Eggs with no developing nucleus	Chromosomes clumped at first mitosis	3–4 polar spindle at first mitosis	Normal at first mitosis
(a) Tadpole nuclei from intestinal epithelium cells	70	22 out of 70 31.5%	3 out of 11[1] 27%	4 out of 11[1] 36%	—
(b) Nuclei from blastulae and gastrulae	59	8 out of 59 13.5%	0 out of 30[1] 0%	4 out of 30[1] 13%	20 out of 30[1] 67%

The cleavage of control transfers which were allowed to develop as far as they were able

	Numbers of transfers	Uncleaved	Abortive cleavage	Partial blastulae	Complete blastulae
(c) Tadpole nuclei from intestinal epithelium cells	60	18 30%	16 26.5%	21 35%	5 8.5%
(d) Nuclei from blastulae and gastrulae	95	12 12.5%	2 2%	11 14%	67 70.5%

[1] Only these eggs were fixed at the time of the first nuclear division.

egg clearly results from a failure to break the wall of the donor cell when it is sucked into the injection pipette. The successful breaking of the cell wall depends upon the extent to which the cell is distorted in the pipette. A very close correlation has been found between the degree of donor cell distortion and the proportion of transfers which result in normal cleavage (Gurdon, 1960b). It was found that if the cell wall is very little distorted, the great majority of transfers fail to cleave, while strong distortion results in many developmental abnormalities probably through exposure of the nucleus to the saline medium. It is very difficult to distort intestine cells to an ideal degree, and in order to avoid damage to the nuclei these cells were distorted rather little. Transplanted intestine nuclei would therefore be expected to result in a total lack of cleavage much more often than the nuclei of the larger embryonic cells.

The results of the cytological analysis of fixed eggs are compared with the development of their controls in Table 2. There is a very close correspondence between the proportion of developing eggs which failed to cleave and the proportion of fixed eggs in which the transplanted nucleus was either lacking or was present in an intact donor cell. This applies to the results of transplanting intestine as well as embryonic nuclei, and justifies the conclusion that the total lack of cleavage following nuclear transplantation can be attributed to the technical difficulty described above. The developmental capacity of nuclei which fail to promote any cleavage at all after transplantation has not therefore been tested.

Abortive cleavage

This term refers to eggs which consist only of abnormal blastomeres and uncleaved regions of cytoplasm. The blastomeres are of irregular size and shape, and contain no normal nuclei though sometimes asters and chromatin can be seen. Such eggs usually die after a few irregular cleavages. Many of the eggs which receive intestine develop in this way, but very few of those with embryonic nuclei do so (Table 1). Useful information regarding the cause of this abnormality is provided by the cytological examination of eggs fixed during metaphase of the first division of the transplanted nucleus. Only 11 eggs with intestine nuclei were found to have been fixed at exactly this time, and in 3 of these the chromosomes were clumped and pycnotic. In some cases the spindle also seemed abnormal. It is clear that these eggs could not have cleaved normally; the chromosomes would probably have broken up into pycnotic lumps and have been distributed to abnormal blastomeres. As shown in Table 2, the percentage of fixed eggs with clumped chromosomes was very close to the percentage of control transfers which resulted in abortive cleavage. It can be concluded that abortive cleavage results from the incapacity of the transplanted nucleus to divide normally at its first division.

It is not known why some nuclei divide abnormally after transplantation, but it is possibly because their chromosomes have not replicated by the time they enter mitosis. The nuclei of intestinal epithelium cells divide infrequently and have a relatively long interphase period between mitoses. Since chromosome replication takes place during interphase, some nuclei would by chance be transplanted when at the beginning of interphase and so would have unreplicated chromosomes. The time at which a transplanted nucleus enters division is determined by the egg cytoplasm, and except in nuclei which become tetraploid, this division takes place at about 80 minutes after transplantation. Thus the situation may arise in which an intestine nucleus is forced to enter mitosis even though its chromosomes are unreplicated. This would be expected to lead to the abnormal chromosome condition described above. Embryonic nuclei, on the other hand, divide at frequent intervals during cleavage. The interphase period in which their chromosomes are unreplicated is short, and embryonic nuclei are therefore generally transplanted with already replicated chromosomes. This would explain why intestine nuclei give abortive cleavage much more often than embryonic nuclei. An hypothesis of this general kind has also been suggested by Briggs, King, & DiBerardino (1960) to account for abnormal cleavage in their experiments.

It can be concluded that transplanted nuclei which promote abortive cleavage do so through their inability to divide normally. This prevents them showing the range of cell types that they are genetically capable of giving rise to.

Partial cleavage

A blastula is described as partially cleaved when part of it consists of normal blastomeres, and the rest is uncleaved or abortively cleaved. Blastulae of this kind usually die before gastrulation commences, but if the uncleaved portion is very small they may form abnormal gastrulae. Transplanted intestine nuclei result in partial cleavage more commonly than embryonic nuclei (Table 1). Eleven eggs with transplanted intestine nuclei were fixed during the first nuclear division, and 4 of these had apparently normal chromosomes but an abnormal achromatic apparatus with 3- or 4-polar spindles (Table 2). At least some chromosomes were present on each of the three or four metaphase plates. It is possible that a normal set of chromosomes might be distributed to one of the poles of such a spindle, leaving an aneuploid number of chromosomes at the other poles. In this way a partial blastula could be formed with the aneuploid blastomeres giving rise to the abnormally cleaved part of the egg. Whatever the cause of this condition, there is agreement between the proportion of fixed eggs with an abnormal mitotic apparatus but apparently normal chromosomes, and the proportion of the developing controls which became partial blastulae (Table 2). The significance of partial cleavage has been directly determined by the serial transplantation experiments described below.

Development Abnormalities Following the Transplantation of Nuclei from a Foreign Genus

Experiments involving the transfer of nuclei from different genera to eggs of the same species show that genetically very different nuclei may give rise to the same percentages of abnormal cleavage. These experiments therefore show that the frequency of cleavage abnormalities does not necessarily represent the degree of genetic difference between transplanted nuclei. Blastula nuclei from *Hymenochirus curtipes* and *X. laevis* were transplanted to recipient eggs of *X. laevis*, and the results are given in Table 3. The genetic difference between *Hymenochirus* and *Xenopus* is demonstrated by the early arrest in development of all *Xenopus* eggs which received *Hymenochirus* nuclei in contrast to the normal development of many of the *Xenopus* to *Xenopus* transfers. However, in spite of this, the percentage of transfers which resulted in partial, abortive, or entirely deficient cleavage was the same in both cases. These results show that the post-blastula development of transplant-embryos can indicate a genetic difference between the nuclear and cytoplasmic species, while this is not necessarily so of cleavage. Since genetically very different nuclei give the same frequency and severity of abnormal cleavage, this provides an additional reason for believing that the abnormal cleavage resulting from transplanted intestine nuclei does not indicate any genetic difference between the nuclei of intestine and embryonic cells.

Table 3. *The transplantation of nuclei from* Hymenochirus *and* Xenopus *into recipient eggs of* Xenopus

Donor nuclei	Total number of transplantations	Uncleaved	Abortive cleavage	Partial blastulae	Complete blastulae	Neural folds	Normal swimming tadpoles
Hymenochirus curtipes early gastrula	169 100%	62 37%	1 1%	22 12%	84 50%	0 —	0 —
Xenopus laevis early gastrula	78 100%	22 28%	3 4%	11 14%	42 54%	35 —	20 —

The Transplantation of Nuclei from Abnormal Nuclear Transplant-Embryos

Information on the cause and significance of partial blastulae and of abnormal post-blastulae has been obtained by means of serial nuclear transfers. The basic design of the experiments was as follows. Nuclear transfers were made using original intestine or embryonic donor cells. When the resulting "first-transfer" embryos had differentiated as far as they were able, some of their endoderm nuclei were used for serial transfers, giving rise to the "first serial-transfer" generation. As a result of experience, the best differentiation that will be achieved by an abnormal transplant-embryo can be judged to within narrow limits, before developmental arrest takes place and cell death sets in. For instance, partial blastulae in which an appreciable part of the surface area is uncleaved, never develop beyond the late blastula or very early gastrula stage. Similarly, it has been found that embryos in which part of the yolk-plug protrudes during gastrulation will never form normal late gastrulae or neurulae, and that embryos which do not elongate properly will remain as stunted postneurulae with a belly oedema. The furthest differentiation to be expected can with practice be judged to within much narrower limits than these. By this type of experiment the differentiation of the most normal serial-transfer embryos can be directly compared with that of the first-transfer embryo from whose nuclei they were derived.

Original donor nuclei were taken from 31 abnormal first-transfer embryos (11 from original gastrula nuclei and 20 from feeding tadpole intestine nuclei). These abnormal embryos were selected arbitrarily and are a random sample of the partial blastulae and abnormal post-blastulae included in Table 1. The nuclei from each first-transfer embryo gave rise to a wide range of abnormal embryos, and sometimes to normal tadpoles, as shown in Table 4 (p. 236). The differentiation of each first-transfer embryo is compared with that of the serial-transfer embryos derived from its nuclei in Text-Figs. 1 and 2. In these diagrams the stage of differentiation attained by each first-transfer embryo is shown by a solid line; the dotted continuation of this line represents the most normal differentiation achieved by any of the resulting serial-transfer embryos. It can be seen that in all 31 cases some of the serial-transfer embryos differentiated more normally than the first-transfer embryo from whose nuclei they were derived. It is interesting that the nuclei of partial blastulae can sometimes promote the development of a normal or nearly normal tadpole. This is of some importance since a large proportion of transplanted intestine nuclei result in partial blastulae.

There are two possible explanations for these results. First, the developmental capacity of a nucleus might increase as a result of nuclear transplantation so that serial-transfer embryos are more normal than first-transfer embryos. Second, the abnormality of the first-transfer embryo might be due to some nongenetic cause such as poor egg quality. In the latter case the developmental capacity of the transplanted nucleus would not increase, but would not always be fully expressed owing to the effect of factors such as poor egg quality.

Evidence has already been obtained from different kinds of experiments that the developmental capacity of a nucleus does not increase as a result of transplantation (Gurdon, 1960c). Confirmation of this has been obtained in the present experiments by making further serial-transfers in the same way as described above. Nuclei from an abnormal first-transfer embryo gave rise to the embryos of the first serial-transfer generation; the most normal of these embryos

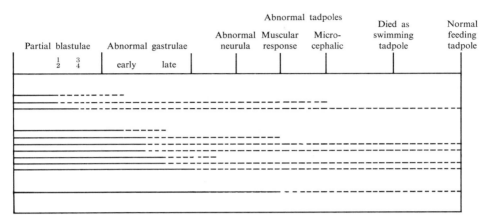

Fig. 1. *Serial nuclear transfers from abnormal first-transfer embryos. Original gastrula donor nuclei (embryonic nuclei). Furthest differentiation attained by each first-transfer embryo (solid line) and by the most normal of the serial-transfer embryos derived from its nuclei (dotted line).*

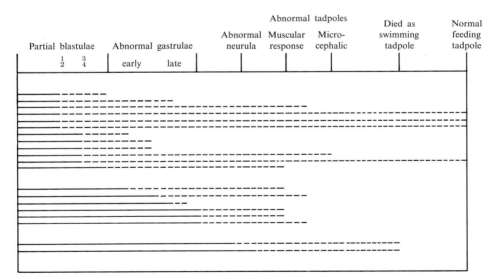

Fig. 2. *Serial nuclear transfers from abnormal first-transfer embryos. Original tadpole intestine nuclei. Furthest differentiation attained by each first-transfer embryo (solid line) and by the most normal of the serial-transfer embryos derived from its nuclei (dotted line).*

Table 4. *Some typical examples of the development promoted by nuclei from abnormal nuclear transplant-embryos.*

Original donor	Abnormal transplant-embryos used as donors	Total transfers	Partial and complete blastulae	Complete blastulae	Post-neurulae	Heart-beat tadpoles	Normal feeding tadpoles
Gastrula endo-derm cells; stages 11–13 of Nieuwkoop & Faber, 1956	½ cleaved blastula	36	8	2 (died as gastrulae)	—	—	—
	½ cleaved blastula	36	13	11	7	4	—
	¾ cleaved blastula	36	13	6	5	4	4
	Total exo-gastrula	35	—	9 (3 developed further than the donor)	—	—	—
	Abnormal mid gastrula	26	—	24	18	8	4
	Abnormal late gastrula	32	—	12	8	3	3
Control	Normal gastrula	57	—	14	4	3	3

was then used to provide nuclei for a further transfer generation. In each case the most normal embryo of one transfer generation was used to provide nuclei for the next. If the development capacity of nuclei increases as a result of transplantation, this kind of selective serial-transfer experiment should lead to more normal development in each successive transfer generation. About ten such experiments have been carried out, and in some of these, four serial-transfer generations were made from the nuclei of one abnormal first-transfer embryo. In every experiment, the development of the embryos in each serial-transfer generation was about the same, and the later transfer generations did not contain more normal embryos than the first serial-transfer generation. These results show that the developmental capacity of a nucleus does not increase as a result of serial transplantation. It can therefore be concluded from these experiments that the minimum developmental capacity of a nucleus is shown by the most

Table 4. (cont.)

Original donor	Abnormal transplant-embryos used as donors	Total transfers	Partial and complete blastulae	Complete blastulae	Post-neurulae	Heart-beat tadpoles	Normal feeding tadpoles
Intestinal cells of feeding tadpoles; stages 46–48 of Nieuwkoop & Faber, 1946	½ cleaved blastula	36	4	4	3	3	—
	½ cleaved blastula	36	10	10	4	4	2
	¾ cleaved blastula	36	15	6 (died as gastrulae)	—	—	—
	Abnormal mid gastrula	48	—	17	4	—	—
	Abnormal late gastrula	54	—	17	4	1	—
	Abnormal early neurula	72	—	20	12	9	4
Control:	Normal neurula	58	—	14	4	4	3

normal transplant-embryo to which it gives rise. Thus the presence of a feeding tadpole among any of the transplant-embryos derived from a nucleus shows that the nucleus had the genetic information required for this before transplantation, even though the first-transfer embryo as well as most of the serial-transfer embryos may have been abnormal.

The more normal development of the first serial-transfers embryos compared to the first-transfer embryos can be satisfactorily explained by attributing the abnormalities of the first-transfer embryos to a nongenetic cause. It is known that the quality of eggs laid by *Xenopus* in the laboratory is variable, and that poor egg quality sometimes causes abnormal development of transplant-embryos (Gurdon, 1960b). If the quality of some recipient eggs is variable, only a certain proportion of the transplant-embryos resulting from these eggs will develop as normally as the developmental capacity of their nuclei will allow. The effect of making serial transfers is to transplant the mitotic products of a nucleus into several different recipient eggs, so that at least some of these are of good quality and therefore demonstrate the real developmental capacity of the original somatic nucleus. So long as a sufficient number of transfers are made in the first serial-transfer generation for at least some eggs to be of good quality, the later serial-transfer generations would not be expected to contain more normal embryos than the first-transfer generation. As pointed out above, the most normal embryo that can be obtained from an original donor nucleus is generally contained in the first serial-transfer generation. The effects of poor egg quality therefore account for all the results reported here.

It has now been shown that the developmental capacity of a nucleus and of its mitotic products does not increase from one transfer generation to the next, but that the serial-transfer embryos may differentiate more normally than the first-transfer embryo derived from the same original donor nucleus. These two observations together show that the abnormality of many transplant-embryos must be due to non-genetic factors such as poor egg quality. This is true of all abnormal transplant-embryos which contain some nuclei capable of giving rise to more normal differentiation than they showed themselves, and this includes all 31 first-transfer embryos used in these experiments.

The Developmental Capacity of Original Donor Nuclei from which Abnormal First-Transfer Embryos Were Obtained

It has been established above that the developmental capacity of a somatic nucleus is generally shown by the most normal embryos of the first serial-transfer generation. The right-hand end of each dotted line in Text-Figs. 1 and 2 therefore represents the developmental capacity of one original somatic nucleus. The developmental capacity of the original intestine nuclei used in these experiments can now be compared with that of the original embryonic nuclei. The capacity of embryonic and intestine nuclei to give rise to normal feeding tadpoles is shown by the number of dotted lines which reach the right-hand extremity of Text-Figs. 1 and 2. It can be seen that 6 out of 11 (55 percent) of the original embryonic nuclei and 4 out of 20 (20 percent) of the original intestine nuclei were able to promote the differentiation of a normal feeding tadpole.

The following conclusions can be drawn for these results: (i) Of the original intestine nuclei which gave rise to partial blastulae and abnormal post-blastulae after first-transfer, 20 percent contained the genetic information required for the formation of feeding tadpoles. The equivalent figure for original gastrula nuclei was 55 percent. The numbers on which these figures are based are too small to show whether they indicate a significant difference in developmental capacity between intestine and embryonic nuclei. (ii) Of the original intestine nuclei which gave rise to partial blastulae and abnormal gastrulae after first-transfer, 12 out of 18 (67 percent) were capable of giving rise to *muscular-response stage tadpoles* with functional nerve and muscle cells. The comparable figure for original gastrula nuclei was 7 out of 10 (70 percent). Both of these values are obtained from the results given in Text-Figs. 1 and 2.

DISCUSSION

The Genetic Information Contained in the Nuclei of Differential Cells

The genetic information contained in a nucleus before transplantation is shown by the range of cell types that its mitotic products can form after its transplantation so long as the genetic information carried by a nucleus does not change as a result of transplantation itself. It will be assumed in this discussion that the developmental capacity of a nucleus and of its daughter nuclei does not increase as a result of transplantation. There is no evidence that any increase does take place, and the evidence that it does not comes from the serial transplantation of nuclei between different species and subspecies (Gurdon, 1926*b*) and of nuclei from abnormal transplant-embryos within the same sub-species. Thus, if a transplanted nucleus supports the development of a feeding tadpole, this is regarded as showing that it possessed the genetic information required for this when it was present in the donor cell, and did not acquire this information only after transplantation. This applies to the results of serial transfers just as much as to the results of first transfers, since apart from variation in donor stage, exactly the same procedure is involved in both kinds of experiment. Thus the genetic information contained in a nucleus is regarded as equal to or greater than that required to form the most normal of the transplant-embryos derived from it, whether by first or serial transfer. This is so even when the first-transfer embryo is abnormal and when only a few of the serial-transfers form feeding tadpoles.

The minimum genetic information contained in the nuclei of intestinal epithelium cells can be determined by combining the results of first transfers and serial transfers. The first transfers showed that $1\frac{1}{2}$ percent of the intestine nuclei can give rise to feeding tadpoles. Serial transfers have shown that a further $5\frac{1}{2}$ percent of the intestine nuclei also have this capacity. This figure of $5\frac{1}{2}$ percent represents the proportion of intestine nuclei which gave partial blastulae and abnormal post-blastulae after first-transfer, but which could give rise to some feeding tadpoles after serial transfer. This figure is calculated as follows. It was found that 27 percent of the original intestine nuclei formed partial blastulae and abnormal embryos after the first transfer (Table 1). About 20 percent of these, or $5\frac{1}{2}$ percent of the original intestine nuclei, gave rise to feeding tadpoles after serial transfer. Combining the results of first and serial transfers, at least 7 percent of intestinal epithelium cell nuclei contain the genetic information required to form all cell types of a feeding tadpole, except perhaps for the germ cells whose presence has not yet been looked for.

This figure of 7 percent is expressed in terms of the total number of transplanted intestine nuclei. However, the developmental capacity of many of these nuclei was not in effect tested, and the percentage of intestine nuclei capable of promoting the formation of feeding tadpoles is increased if this is taken into account. The cytological examination of fixed eggs showed that the total lack of cleavage after transplantation can be wholly attributed to technical difficulties. The transfers which result in no cleavage are a random sample of the total transfers made and can be discounted from the results. The intestine nuclei capable of promoting the formation of feeding tadpoles then constitute 13 percent of the remaining successful transfers (Table 5).

It can be inferred from the cytological analysis of fixed eggs that abortive cleavage results from nuclei which happen to have been taken for transplantation at an unsuitable stage in their mitotic cycle. If this is so, then the nuclei which give rise to abortive cleavage are a random sample of those transplanted, and can be excluded from the total number of transfers. The remaining nuclei are those which were transplanted successfully as well as at a suitable stage in their mitotic cycle for their developmental capacity to be tested; the intestine nuclei capable of supporting the development of feeding tadpoles then constitute 24 percent of these (Table 5).

The main conclusions from these results are the following, though the evidence for each is not equally strong.

Table 5. *Summary of conclusions reached regarding the developmental capacity of nuclei taken from differentiated and embryonic cells of* Xenopus laevis.

Donor nuclei	Developmental capacity of nuclei. Stages of Nieuwkoop & Faber, 1956	Results of first-transfers only as percentage of total transfers	Combined results of first and serial transfers		
			As percentage of total transfers	As percentage of total transfers, less those resulting in no cleavage	As percentage of total transfers, less those resulting in no cleavage or abortive cleavage
Intestinal epithelium cell nuclei	Capable of forming feeding tadpoles; stage 50	1.5% (10)	7% (49)	13% (49)	24% (49)
Blastula or gastrula cell nuclei		36% (100)	57% (158)	74% (158)	77% (158)
Intestinal epithelium cell nuclei	Capable of forming muscular response tadpoles; stage 26	2.3% (17)	20% (142)	37% (142)	70% (142)
Blastula or gastrula cell nuclei		48% (133)	65% (181)	85% (181)	88% (181)

The figures in brackets represent the number of individuals.
The figures for serial transfers were calculated as described [above].

a) It has been clearly shown that about 7 percent of the total number of transplanted intestine nuclei have the genetic information required to form
normal feeding tadpoles. This figure represents the combined results of first
and serial transfers expressed as a percentage of total transfers.

b) Thirteen percent of the eggs receiving *successfully* transplanted intestine
nuclei can give rise to feeding tadpoles. This figure represents the combined
results of first and serial transfers expressed as a percentage of those transfers
which resulted in some kind of cleavage. There is good evidence that the
transfers which result in no cleavage do so for technical reasons and are a
random sample of the total transfers.

c) The formation of normal feeding tadpoles can be promoted by 24 percent
of the intestine nuclei which were transplanted successfully as well as at a
suitable stage in their mitotic cycle. This figure is the combined results of
first and serial transfers expressed as a percentage of the total transfers
excluding those which resulted in no cleavage or abortive cleavage.

If the capacity of a transplanted nucleus to give rise to muscular response
tadpoles with functional nerve- and muscle-cells is considered, then a greater
percentage of intestine nuclei fall into the three categories above. These percentages
as well as the equivalent figures for embryonic nuclei are given in Table 5.

The Differentiation of Cells and the Developmental Capacity of Their Nuclei

The results so far obtained from nuclear transplantation experiments in Amphibia
have contributed in two ways to the question of whether stable nuclear changes
are causally connected with cellular differentiation. Some experiments have shown
that different kinds of cells may have unchanged nuclei, while others have
demonstrated a stable restriction of developmental capacity in the nuclei of
differentiating cells.

The following results have demonstrated the wide range of genetic information contained in the nuclei of cells which are approaching, or which have actually
attained, the differentiated state. The experiments described above are of this
kind; they show that at least 7 percent of the nuclei of intestinal epithelium cells
can promote the formation of normal feeding tadpoles, and that at least 20 percent
can promote the formation of muscular response tadpoles with functional muscle-
and nerve-cells (Table 5). Evidence of this kind has also been described by King
& McKinnell (1960). From 142 eggs of *Rana pipiens* injected with 10–20 adeno-
carcinoma cell nuclei they obtained one post-neurula embryo showing a certain
degree of tissue differentiation.

It can be argued that some cells may become differentiated under the influence
of nuclei from neighboring cells, and hence that a few cells in a differentiated
tissue may have nuclei capable of forming normal tadpoles while the majority of
cells have nuclei which do not possess the capacity to form other cell types.
Such an argument seems to be excluded by the experiments with intestine nuclei
in *Xenopus*, since it was found that at least 20 percent, and probably 70 percent

(Table 5), of these nuclei could give rise to muscle- and nerve-cells after trans-plantation. These experiments therefore show that a nucleus can be responsible for the formation of an intestinal epithelium cell and at the same time possess the capacity to form other kinds of differentiated cells.

Other experiments have clearly shown that some of the nuclei derived from somatic cells have undergone a stable change restricting their developmental capacity. The clearest evidence for these changes comes from serial nuclear transplantation experiments in *R. pipiens* (King & Briggs, 1956) and in *Xenopus* (Gurdon, 1960c). These experiments have not shown that the nuclear changes took place during the normal development of the donor embryos from which the nuclei were taken. If this should prove to be the case, it still remains to be deter-mined whether these nuclear changes are necessary for cellular differentiation to take place, or whether they are only a result of this.

Until the significance of stable nuclear changes is known, the results of nuclear transplantation experiments seem to be consistent with the view that stable changes restricting the developmental capacity of nuclei are not essential for cellular differentiation to take place. This conclusion can now be related to different theories of differentiation.

Cellular differentiation is most probably initiated by the effect of the cyto-plasmic environment on a nucleus, so that the nucleus provides specific genetic information which promotes the formation of a particular cell type (recent discussion by Fischberg & Blackler, 1961). Three possible ways in which this could happen are the following. First, nuclei might undergo a progressive loss of genetic material, so that cellular differentiation would result from the genetic material that is retained in different nuclei. Secondly, an inactivation of certain parts of the genetic material might take place, so that specific genetic information would be provided by the non-inactivated parts of a genome. This kind of inactivation would be stable under the normal conditions of cell mitosis. A theory of differentiation along these lines is suggested by various reports of stable nuclear changes in somatic cells (e.g. Brink, 1960). The third possibility is that the genetic information provided by a nucleus is entirely dependent on its cytoplasmic environment at any one time; in this case a nucleus would never undergo any stable changes having a qualitative effect on its function. This kind of system is suggested by the reversible appearance of puffs in the polytene chromosomes of insects (e.g. Breuer & Pavan, 1955) and by cases of metaplasia (e.g. Reyer, 1954). The first of these three possibilities is rendered very improbable by the results of the experiments reported in this article; these have shown that a nucleus may be responsible for the differentiation of one cell type while still possessing the capacity to form all other types of somatic cell in a feeding tadpole. It has previously been found that most of the normal feeding tadpoles resulting from transplanted nuclei of *Xenopus* will eventually form adult frogs (Gurdon, 1962a). However, the possibility still exists that intestine nuclei may have undergone stable changes restricting their capacity to form adult frogs and normal germ cells, since intestine nuclei have not yet been tested in these respects. The results are therefore consistent with any theory of cell differentiation which does not require that the nucleus of a differentiated cell has lost the genetic information required for the formation of other differentiated somatic cell types.

SUMMARY

1. Nuclei from differentiated intestinal epithelium cells of feeding tadpoles and from control blastulae of *Xenopus* have been transplanted into enucleated recipient eggs. The differentiated state of the intestinal epithelium cells was shown by their possession of a striated border.
2. The cleavage and embryonic development resulting from the intestinal epithelium cell nuclei was much more abnormal than that resulting from control blastula transfers.
3. $1\frac{1}{2}$ percent (10 out of 726) of the first transfers of intestine nuclei resulted in normal feeding tadpoles.
4. The serial transplantation of nuclei and of their mitotic products showed that some of the intestine nuclei which promoted abnormal development after first transfer could nevertheless promote the formation of normal feeding tadpoles after serial transfer. The combined results of first transfers and of serial transfers demonstrated that at least 7 percent of the intestine nuclei possessed the genetic information required for the formation of normal feeding tadpoles.
5. The cytological examination of eggs fixed soon after receiving transplanted nuclei indicated that the lack of cleavage and abortive cleavage following transplantation result from nuclei which were not effectively exposed to the recipient egg cytoplasm or which were transplanted at an unsuitable stage in their mitotic cycle. If these cases are excluded from the results, the intestine nuclei capable of promoting the formation of feeding tadpoles then constitute 24 percent of the remaining successful transfers.
6. A similar interpretation of the experimental results shows that 70 percent of the successfully transplanted intestine nuclei have the genetic information required to form muscular response stage tadpoles with functional muscle- and nerve-cells.
7. These results show that a nucleus can promote the formation of a differentiated intestine cell and at the same time contain the genetic information necessary for the formation of all other types of differentiated somatic cell in a normal feeding tadpole. It is concluded that the differentiation of a cell cannot be dependent upon the incapacity of its nucleus to give rise to other types of differentiated cell.

ACKNOWLEDGEMENT

The author wishes to express his gratitude to Professor M. Fischberg for his interest in this work, and for his help in obtaining the animals and facilities required.

REFERENCES

Breuer, M. E., & Pavan, C., 1955, Behaviour of polytene chromosomes of *Rhynchosciara angelae* at different stages of larval development. *Chromosoma,* **7**, 371–86.

Briggs, R., King, T. J., & Di Berardino, M., 1960, Development of nuclear-transplant embryos of known chromosome complement following parabiosis with normal embryos. *Symposium on Germ Cells and Development,* Inst. Int. d'Emb., pp. 441–77.

Brink, R. A., 1960, Paramutation and chromosome organization. *Quart. Rev. Biol.,* **35**, 120–37.

Elsdale, T. R., Gurdon, J. B., & Fischberg, M., 1960, A description of the technique for nuclear transplantation in *Xenopus laevis. J. Embryol. exp. Morph.,* **8**, 437–44.

Fischberg, M., & Blackler, A. W., 1961, How cells specialize. *Sci. Amer.,* **205**, 124–40.

Gurdon, J. B., 1960a, The effects of ultraviolet irradiation on the uncleaved eggs of *Xenopus laevis. Quart. J. micr. Sci.,* **101**, 299–312.

——, 1960b, Factors affecting the abnormal development of transplant-embryos in *Xenopus laevis. J. Embryol, exp. Morph.,* **8**, 327–40.

——, 1960c, The developmental capacity of nuclei taken from differentiating endoderm cells of *Xenopus laevis. J. Embryol, exp. Morph.,* **8**, 505–26.

——, 1962a, Adult frogs derived from the nuclei of single somatic cells. *Devel. Biol.,* **4**, 256–73.

——, 1962b, The transplantation of nuclei between two species of *Xenopus. Devel. Biol.,* **5**, 68–83.

King, T. J., & Briggs, R., 1956, Serial transplantation of embryonic nuclei. *Cold Spr. Harb. Symp. quant. Biol.,* **21**, 271–90.

King, T. J., & McKinnell, R. G., 1960, An attempt to determine the developmental potentialities of the cancer cell nucleus by means of transplantation. *Cell Physiology Neoplasia,* PP. 591–617. University of Texas Press.

Nieuwkoop, P. D., & Faber, J., 1956, *Normal Table of* Xenopus laevis (Daudin). Amsterdam: North Holland Publishing Company.

Reyer, R. W., 1954, Regeneration of the lens in the Amphibian eye. *Quart. Rev. Biol.,* **29**, 1–46.

EXPLANATION OF PLATE

Sections of the mid-intestin of a feeding tadpole of *X. laevis*. Owing to the coiling of the intestine the sections are only transversely cut in some places. By serial sections it could be seen that some part of each cell reaches the gut lumen and constitutes part of the striated border. The striated border and underlying pigment granules can be most clearly seen in Fig. C.

Figs. A and B. Stage 46 of Nieuwkoop & Faber (1956).

Fig. C. Stage 47. Most of the donor cells used in these experiments were taken from tadpoles at this stage.

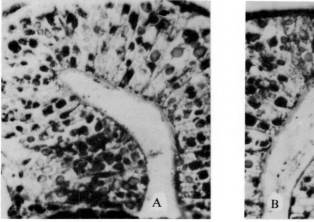
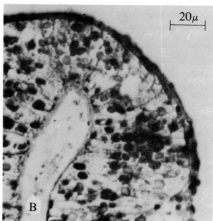

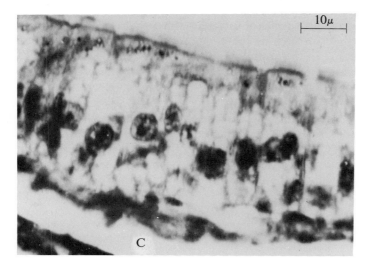

General Conclusions:
Teleonomic Mechanisms
in Cellular Metabolism, Growth,
and Differentiation

by JACQUES MONOD and FRANCOIS JACOB

I. INTRODUCTION

Before attempting to draw the conclusions, or some of the conclusions, which emerge from the discussions of the past eight days, we would like to express the unanimous feeling of the participants that the choice of the subject and the timing of this conference were excellent, as shown by the exceptional and sustained interest of the sessions. For this we are deeply indebted to our host Dr. Chovnick, Director of the Long Island Biological Laboratory, and to Dr. Umbarger who had a major share in the planning of the conference.

We shall not attempt here to summarize the proceedings of a meeting where such an abundance of observations, pertaining to a wide variety of systems, were presented. We would rather try to reconsider the problem of cellular regulation as a whole, in perspective so to say, as it appears to us as a result of this confrontation.

One conclusion which was repeatedly emphasized is the wide-spread occurrence and the extreme importance of regulatory mechanisms in cellular physiology. Since this aspect has been treated, with characteristic elegance and insight by Dr. B. Davis, in his introductory paper, we shall not dwell on it here. Let us however recall, for instance, the systems described by Dr. Kornberg (see this Symposium, page 257) which illustrate the fact that essential enzymes of intermediary metabolism, such as the condensing enzyme (a typical "amphibolic" enzyme according to the useful terminology proposed by Davis), are submitted to wide regulatory variations, depending on the substrates present in the medium. The idea, often expressed in the past, that adaptive effects are limited to "unessential" enzymes is thus evidently incorrect. Let us also recall that the genetic breakdown of a regulatory mechanism has repeatedly been found (cf. the cases of β-galactosidase, alkaline phosphatase, aspartate and ornithine transcarbamylase) to lead to enormous overproduction of the enzyme concerned; it is evident that no cell could survive the breakdown of more than two or three, at most, such systems. Finally, let us also point to the wide variations observed, in relation to different diets, in the level of liver enzymes, and to the significant observation

Jacques Monad and Francois Jacob, "General Conclusions: Teleonomic Mechanisms in Cellular Metabolism, Growth, and Differentiation," *Cold Spring Harbor Symposium on Quantitative Biology* **26** (1961), 389–401. Reprinted by permission.

that, in certain hepatic tumors, the same enzymes appear to obey altogether different rules of conduct (see Van Potter, this Symposium, page 355).

In the present discussion, we wish to center attention on the mechanisms, rather than on the physiological significance, of the different regulatory effects. It is clear that great progress has been accomplished in this respect, allowing us now clearly to distinguish between different types of mechanisms, and also to recognize that certain systems which appeared entirely different from one another a few years ago, are in fact submitted to similar, if not identical, controls. This is particularly striking in the case of inducible and repressible enzyme systems and of lysogenic systems, all three of which would seem to obey fundamentally similar controlling elements, merely organized into different circuits.

The major part of this paper will then be devoted to the discussion of mechanisms. However, the analysis of these mechanisms has been, so far, largely restricted to microbiological objects. A constantly recurring question is: to what extent are the mechanisms found to operate in bacteria also present in tissues of higher organisms; what functions may such mechanisms perform in this different context; and may the new concepts and experimental approaches derived from the study of microorganisms be transferred to the analysis and interpretation of the far more complex controls involved in the functioning and differentiation of tissue cells? We shall consider this question in the last section of this paper.

II. REGULATORY MECHANISMS

A. Possible, Plausible, and Actual Cellular Control Mechanisms

To begin with, we might try to classify and define *a priori* the main types of cellular regulatory mechanisms, including any likely or plausible mechanism which may or may not have been actually observed, or discussed during the present conference.

1. *Mass action*

Since many, if not most, metabolic reactions are largely reversible, mass action might have a significant share in regulation. However most pathways involve one or several irreversible steps which could not be controlled by mass action. Moreover, it is a general observation that the intracellular concentration of most intermediary metabolites in the cell is vanishingly small, indicating that mass action only plays a limited role, and also suggesting that other mechanisms must intervene in metabolic regulation. Mass action effects were, in fact, not discussed during this conference.

2. *Enzyme activity*

By virtue of the buffering effect implied by Henri-Michaelis kinetics, an enzyme constitutes, by itself, a controlling element. The rate of the reaction which it catalyzes depends upon its characteristic kinetic constants, in particular on its relative affinity for substrate and product. It is worth noting that these constants are related to the equilibrium constant, i.e., to the free energy change of the reaction itself, by the Haldane equation, thus reintroducing mass action as one of the controlling factors in any enzyme-catalyzed reaction. The relative values of the forward and backward reaction constants in the Haldane equation may be supposed to present, in some systems at least, a physiological, controlling significance. For instance, the fact that alkaline phosphatase, which catalyzes a virtually irreversible reaction, has a very high affinity for orthophosphate may result in control of this reaction by the product, in spite of irreversibility. The "teleonomic" significance of this correlation, where it obtains, is emphasized by the fact that in other irreversible systems, the enzyme shows very low affinity for the products. This is the case, for instance, for the β-galactosidase reaction. Thus, intracellular phosphate esters may be protected by intracellular orthophosphate, while galactosides would not be so protected by galactose. The products of an enzyme necessarily are *analogues* of the substrate, and competitive inhibition is expected in any case: whether it is physiologically significant or not depends upon the specific construction of the enzyme site.

Competitive inhibition of enzymes by organic substances other than steric analogues of the substrate (including product) is not observed, in general. But the specific construction of enzyme sites offers yet other regulatory possibilities, as revealed by the discovery of the "feedback" or "endproduct" inhibition effect. As we have seen, this type of effect actually turns out to be extremely wide-spread and physiologically highly significant. We shall discuss it at some length.

3. *Enzyme activation and "molecular conversion"*

The well-known conversion of zymogens into active proteases evidently plays an important regulatory and protective role. On this basis, one might expect various types of alteration of molecular structure ("molecular conversion") to occur in the regulation of activity of intracellular enzymes. Actually, relatively few observations of such effects have been reported. However, the mechanisms described by Tompkins and Rall and Sutherland may be considered as "molecular conversions" and this may also be true of the effects reported by Hagerman. We shall discuss the possible implications of these mechanisms in a later section.

4. *Specific control of enzyme synthesis*

Since it is well known that cells of different tissues within the same organism do not exhibit the same enzyme (or protein) patterns, while all these cells presumably contain the same genome; and since the same may be said of bacteria from a single clone grown in different media, it is evident that specific mechanisms exist, which control the expression of genetic potentialities with respect to specific protein synthesis. In bacteria, adaptive enzyme systems have been the subject of much work, and we shall discuss these systems at some length. The occurrence of similar mechanisms in differentiated organisms is highly probable, although, as the discussions here have shown, not conclusively demonstrated in any single case. It would appear that some of the "adaptive" effects observed in tissue cells are due to enzyme stabilization rather than to control of enzyme synthesis. This will be discussed in the last section of this paper.

From this brief review and classification of the main plausible and/or actually observed mechanisms of cellular control, it is apparent that *all* these mechanisms —except mass action—are directly related to the specific molecular structure of the enzymes, or other proteins, concerned. The fundamental problem of specific determinism in protein synthesis is, therefore, coextensive to our field of investigation. This would be the justification, if any were needed, for the fact that a major part of this conference was devoted to this problem. We shall discuss it in connection with enzymatic adaptation since, as we have seen, induction and repression are directly related to the mechanisms of information transfer from genes to proteins.

B. The Novick-Szilard-Umbarger Effect: Endproduct or "Allosteric" Inhibition

In 1954, Novick and Szilard discovered that the synthesis of a tryptophan precursor (later identified as indol-3-glycerol-phosphate) in *E. coli* was inhibited by tryptophan. They formulated the hypothesis that tryptophan specifically inhibited the activity of an *early* enzyme in tryptophan biosynthesis and that this effect had regulatory significance. Observations of the Carnegie group on isotopic competition (Roberts *et al.,* 1955) between endogeneous and exogeneous metabolites suggested the occurrence of similar effects in the synthesis of several amino acids. The work of Umbarger (see this Symposium, page 301), directly at the enzyme level, indeed demonstrated that, in many pathways, an early enzyme is so constructed as to be strongly and specifically inhibited by the metabolic endproduct of the pathway.

As the reports here have shown, endproduct inhibition is extremely widespread in bacteria, insuring immediate and sensitive control of the rate of metabolite biosynthesis in most, if not all, pathways. From the point of view of mechanisms, the most remarkable feature of the Novick-Szilard-Umbarger effect is that the inhibitor *is not a steric analogue of the substrate*. We propose therefore to designate this mechanism as "allosteric inhibition." Since it is well known that competitive behavior toward an enzyme is, as a rule, restricted to steric analogues, it might be argued that an enzyme's concept of steric analogy need not be the same as ours, and that proteins may see analogies where we cannot discern any. That this interpretation is inadequate is proved by many observations which were reported here. Umbarger and others have shown that in general, only *one* enzyme, the first one in the specific pathway concerned, is highly sensitive to inhibition by the endproduct. If steric analogy were involved, the different enzymes of the pathway would then be considered to hold private and dissenting opinions about stereochemistry. And the same would have to be said of two different enzymes catalyzing an *identical* reaction in the *same* organism, as in the remarkable case of β-aspartokinase, reported by Cohen and Stadtman (see this Symposium, page 319).

Such observations leave no doubt that the construction of the binding site of enzymes subject to allosteric inhibition is exceptional and highly specialized. The findings of Changeux (see this Symposium, page 313) actually show that the groups involved in the binding of inhibitor, in the case of threonine-deaminase, may be inactivated without parallel inactivation of the enzyme. They show, moreover, that the abnormal reaction kinetics of this enzyme (already noted by Umbarger) are directly related to its competence as a regulatory enzyme, and may be experimentally normalized by inactivation of the inhibitor binding groups. This leads to the conclusion that two distinct, albeit interacting, binding sites exist on native threonine deaminase. Competitive inhibition in this system, therefore, is not due to *mutually exclusive* binding of inhibitor and substrate, as in the classical case of steric analogues.

Closely similar observations have been made independently and simultaneously by Pardee (private communication) on another enzyme sensitive to endproduct (aspartate-carbamyl-transferase). This situation may therefore be a general one for enzymes subject to allosteric inhibition and these findings raise several interesting new problems of enzyme chemistry. Studies of the structure of the two sites and of their interaction, using analogues of the substrate and inhibitor, might conceivably lead to interpretations in terms of the "induced-fit" theory of Koshland (1959). In any case, one may predict that "allosteric enzymes" will become a favorite object of research, in the hands of students of the mechanisms of enzyme action.

Since the allosteric effect is not *inherently* related to any particular structural feature common to substrate and inhibitor, the enzymes subject to this effect must be considered as pure products of selection for efficient regulatory devices. This raises a question concerning the genetic determinism of allosteric enzymes. If indeed these enzymes generally possess two different binding groups, they might be supposed to represent the association, favored by selection, of two originally independent enzyme-proteins. If such were the case, one might expect the structural gene corresponding to such an enzyme to be, as a rule, composed of two cistrons, governing respectively the structure of each of the two components of the molecule. In vitro dissociation and reassociation of the two components might also be observed, and would help greatly in the analysis of the effect itself.

A particularly interesting possibility is suggested by this discussion. Namely that, since again there is no obligatory correlation between specific substrates and inhibitors of allosteric enzymes, the effect *need not be restricted to "endproduct" inhibition*. (This in fact is the main reason for avoiding the term "endproduct inhibition" in a general discussion of this mechanism. We feel that endproduct inhibition may turn out to constitute only *one class* of allosteric effects.) It is conceivable that in some situations a cell might find a regulatory advantage in being able to control the rate of reaction along a given pathway through the level of a metabolite synthesized in another pathway. Wherever favorable, such "cross inhibition" might have become established through selection. In other words, *any* physiologically useful regulatory connection, between any two or more pathways, might become established by adequate selective construction of the interacting sites on an allosteric enzyme. This, we feel, may be a very important point, to which we shall return later.

Another aspect should be mentioned. As is well known, the principle of steric analogy has been widely used in attempts to rationalize the design of synthetic drugs, particularly in the case of antibacterial and antitumoral agents. The results have been rewarding, although not as much, perhaps, as one might have anticipated. Yet the principle is evidently valid. But it may prove even more rewarding to look for analogues of the natural controlling agent, rather than for analogues of the substrate of the reaction which one proposes to hit. An example of such an analogue is furnished by 5-methyl-tryptophan, which does not compete with tryptophan for incorporation into protein, while it does efficiently block tryptophan synthesis by allosteric inhibition (and also by repression) (Trudinger and Cohen, 1956).

Similar considerations evidently apply to the analysis of the mode of action of drugs and antibiotics.

C. Molecular Conversion

As we already noted, the well-known example of the zymogens seemed to suggest that alterations, reversible or not, of the molecular structure of certain enzymes might represent an important type of regulatory mechanism. Surprisingly enough, very few examples of such mechanisms have been discovered. It would be unwise to conclude that "molecular conversions" are not a significant type of mechanisms, especially in view of some of the observations reported here. Tomkin's work on the glutamic-alanine dehydrogenase conversion (see this Symposium, page 331) does more than reveal a possible mechanism of steroid hormone action. His observations show that the same protein may acquire different specific activities, depending upon a reversible alteration of molecular structure. This discovery would seem for the first time to justify the idea, often expressed in the past, that an enzyme might possess, in vivo, several different activities (alternative or not) which might be difficult to recognize in vitro. In Tomkin's case, the conversion involves interaction of the protein with itself. In other cases, it might conceivably depend upon interaction of two different proteins, and might remain undetected for this reason. Such possibilities are also suggested by the work of Yanofsky on the two components of tryptophan synthetase. Whether or not the glutamic-alanine dehydrogenase conversion affords a physiologically valid interpretation of steroid action, it does propose a model of a possibly important type of regulatory mechanism.

To a certain extent, the phosphorylase "conversion" discussed here by Rall and Sutherland (see this Symposium, page 347) pertains to the same general type of mechanism, since the activity of phosphorylase eventually depends upon its interaction with two other specific proteins, which phosphorylate and dephosphorylate respectively the metabolic enzyme. (In passing, it may be of interest to note that certain types of suppressor mutations could be due to interactions of this type.) It will be interesting to see whether the transhydrogenase activation, described by Hagerman, also belongs to the class of molecular conversions. In microorganisms, the formation (induced by aerobic conditions) of L-lactic from

D-lactic dehydrogenase has been reported by Labeyrie, Slonimsky and Naslin (1959). Whether or not this is pure molecular conversion, or involves *de novo* synthesis of part of the enzyme molecule is not established as yet.

We would venture to predict that in the next few years several new examples of molecular conversions will be discovered.

Little has been said during this conference of the mechanisms which control cell division. It should be noted that these mechanisms presumably involve, or govern, certain type of "molecular conversions." This is most clearly indicated by the work of Mazia (1959) following the pioneer investigations of Rapkine (1931). Lwoff and Lwoff (1961) have stressed the fact that in the cycle of the polio virus, cyclic dissociation and association of the coat protein occurs, and they have suggested that similar events, affecting certain proteins, may play an important role in cell division. Systematic inquiries based upon this suggestion would certainly be justified.

D. Specific Control of Protein Synthesis

1. The determinism of protein structure

The discussions at this conference have shown, once more, that the one gene-one enzyme hypothesis is now considered as established beyond reasonable doubt. The early difficulties of the theory were evidently due to insufficient biochemical analysis of the apparent exceptions. In the case of several enzyme-proteins, known to be made up of two or more polypeptide chains, it is now apparent that the structure of each polypeptide chain is governed by an independent gene or cistron. This constitutes a remarkable confirmation of the theory and an important step forward in understanding the mechanisms which govern protein structure. The work of Yanofsky (see this Symposium, page 11) on tryptophan-synthetase has been particularly illuminating in this respect.

Even when the one gene-one enzyme theory is redefined and qualified as the one cistron-one polypeptide chain theory, some complications remain, the interpretations of which are still not elucidated. We refer to intracistronic complementation and to the occurrence of suppressor mutations.

Although the first problem, intracistronic complementation, was not discussed during this conference, it should be briefly mentioned here. It is now generally believed to be often associated with a polymeric state of the normal enzyme protein. Observations made with a number of complementary mutants of glutamic dehydrogenase (Fincham, 1959) and β-galactosidase (Pasteur group) are in keeping with this assumption. The active enzyme, in both cases, is known to be a polymer, while certain mutations, in the case of β-galactosidase, result in the formation of an inactive monomer (Perrin, 1961). Studies of in vitro complementation may be expected to throw much light on the building of tertiary and quaternary structures of proteins. In any case, intracistronic complementation does not seem to offer a serious challenge to the concept that the gene or cistron acts as a *unit* in determining polypeptide structure.

The difficulty of interpreting suppressor mutations appears to be much greater. It has generally been assumed that suppressor mutations acted in some way at the tertiary level of protein synthesis, in contrast to true structural mutations assumed to operate at the primary level. The observations reported by Yanofsky indicate that certain suppressor mutations may actually restore the wild-type peptide structure in a *fraction* of the molecules. The working hypothesis proposed by Yanofsky following earlier suggestions of Benzer (namely that these suppressor mutations modify the specificity of an amino acid-activating-enzyme in such a way that compensatory errors would occur with a certain frequency in the choice of the corresponding amino acid) appears particularly interesting since it involves precise predictions. One of these predictions of course is that in such mutants the properties of one of the 20-odd amino acid activating enzymes should be detectably modified. If so, proof would be virtually obtained that the corresponding sRNA fraction does play the role of an adaptor as assumed by Crick (1958) and others, and a new method of determining amino acid substitutions resulting from structural mutations might become available. Another prediction is that the same suppressor mutation might be found to correct in part the effects of two primary mutations affecting two different enzymes. And lastly one would not expect such suppressor mutations to occur at more than about 20 loci. Thus, confirmation of Yanofsky's hypothesis will be awaited with particular interest.

The two fundamental problems with which we are now faced are the nature of the code and the mechanisms of information transfer from DNA to enzyme-synthesizing centers.

A few years ago, following the beautiful work of Benzer (1957) which demonstrated the linear structure of the genetic material at the ultrafine level and the work of Ingram (1957) on sickle-cell hemoglobin, it seemed that the basic assumption of all coding hypotheses, namely collinearity, would soon be proved. The only proof that has been obtained so far is that optimism is essential to the development of Science; collinearity still remains to be formally demonstrated. However, the reports of Yanofsky, of Streisinger and of Rothman at the conference, and what is known of the work of other laboratories, notably Brenner's, again encourage optimism; one feels confident that the final demonstration will soon be at hand.

The nature of the code itself is another matter. But the new experimental approaches, notably the study of chemical mutagens, are developing so rapidly (cf. Benzer and Freese, 1958; Freese, 1959) that cautious and patient optimism is justified. The study of the effects of reverse mutations occurring at the same site as the primary alteration, may also permit the elimination of certain types of codes. Finally a direct, chemical attack, involving the determination of partial (terminal) sequences in both a protein and the corresponding messenger RNA, may become possible, assuming the mRNA theory to be correct, if and when methods of isolating a specific message will be available.

A new experimental approach to the problem of the universality, or otherwise, of the code has been opened up by the observation of Falkow *et al.* (1961) of genetic transfer between *E. coli* and *Serratia*. Preliminary observations by the Pasteur Institute and M.I.T. groups on β-galactosidase and alkaline phosphatase suggest that the *E. coli* genes are transcribed correctly in *Serratia*. This would seem to indicate that the 20% difference in the $G + C/A + T$ ratio between the two genera is not due to the use of different codes, and would agree with Sueoka's universalist conclusions. Further and more detailed studies of proteins synthesized by such "displaced" genes are evidently required. If the codes in *Serratia* and *Escherichia* and perhaps a few other bacterial genera turn out to be the same, the microbial-chemical-geneticists will be satisfied that it is indeed universal, by virtue of the well-known axiom that anything found to be true of *E. coli* must also be true of Elephants.

However, the remarks of Benzer, and also Yanofsky's interpretation of his suppressor mutations suggest that discrete differences of coding, concerning only one or a few amino acids, might exist between different groups, due to differences in specificity of the activating enzymes. The possibility that the code is universal for certain amino acids, and non-universal for others, seems interesting from an evolutionary point of view.

Assuming the problem of the code to be advancing, albeit slowly, the problem of how the tertiary structures are determined remains very open. But while this question was posed only in general terms until recently, it is now very precisely defined by the beautiful studies of the Cavendish group on the structures of myoglobin and of the α and β chains of hemoglobin. These studies have revealed that the tertiary structure of all three polypeptide chains are closely similar, while the primary structure of myoglobin differs widely from that of both hemoglobin chains, except however for about twelve residues which appear to occupy identical strategic positions in the three proteins (Perutz, 1961). This is a remarkable confirmation of the idea (Crick, 1958) that the tertiary folding is governed by a certain number of key residues, while being largely independent of the nature of residues in other positions. It remains to be seen whether it will ever be possible to formulate any general "folding rules" which would allow one approximately to deduce the tertiary configuration of a protein from knowledge of its primary structure. Yet, this is the goal that one would wish to reach, since this deduction, which we cannot begin to make, seems to be made unfailingly by the protein-synthesizing machinery in the cell.

This brings up another issue which must be mentioned at this point, although it was not discussed during the conference, evidently because it is implicitly considered as settled. A few years ago, the question was often debated whether any further (non-genetic) *structural* information needed to be furnished, or might conceivably be used in some cases, at the stage of tertiary folding in protein synthesis. Such a "finishing touch" has been considered as one of the possible mechanisms which might account for the effect of antigen in antibody synthesis (Pauling, 1940) and of inducer in enzymatic adaptation (Monod and Cohn, 1952). In the latter case, no evidence for, and a great deal of evidence against this possibility has accumulated (cf. Monod, 1956, Jacob and Monod, 1961) and proof has been obtained that inducer action is completely unrelated to the structure of the binding site of the induced enzyme (Perrin *et al.*, 1960). In the meantime, speculations on the origin of antibodies reverted from "instructive" to purely "selective" theories (Burnet, 1959; Lederberg, 1959). While this evolution is justified, in the case of antibodies, by general considerations, direct experimental evidence is yet to be found that would allow "selection" of the correct theory.

2. *The control of gene expression*

As we already pointed out, the purely structural (one gene-one enzyme) theory does not consider the problem of gene expression. The discovery of a new class of genetic elements, the regulator genes, which control the *rate* of synthesis of proteins, the *structure* of which is governed by *other* genes, does not contradict the classical concept, but it does greatly widen the scope and interpretative value of genetic theory. In all the adequately studied cases, it is established that the regulator genes act negatively (i.e. by blocking rather than provoking the synthesis of the proteins which they control) through the intermediacy of a cytoplasmic "aporepressor". Although the chemical nature of the aporepressor is still unknown, we feel that the term "regulator gene", as operationally defined, for instance, in the case of the lactose system of *E. coli,* should not be applied indiscriminately to any gene found to influence, in an unknown way, the formation of an enzyme: it is clear that a *structural* gene might exert such an effect by, e.g. controlling an enzyme which synthesizes an inducer of another system (cf. the observations of Horowitz in this Symposium, page 233).

To avoid confusion, the term "regulator" should be applied only to genes identified by *recessive constitutive mutations* affecting a protein structurally controlled by *another gene.*

In any case, the most urgent problem with respect to regulator genes is to identify their active product. Although it is almost certain that this product cannot be a small molecule, and while it seems likely that it is not a protein, there is no positive evidence to identify it as a nucleic acid. Only when this question is solved shall it be possible to study directly the interaction of inducer or repressor with aporepressor, and to account for the specificity of this interaction.

Concerning this last point, the only statement that can be made at present is a strictly negative one: namely that the specificity of induction or repression is completely independent of the specificity of action of the enzymes involved. Although inducers are in general substrates, or analogues of the substrate, and repressors are products (often distant) of the controlled enzyme, the mechanism of the effect itself imposes no restriction upon the "choice" of the active agent. The specificity therefore must be considered purely as a result of selection, as in the case of allosteric inhibition. This selective freedom may have some important theoretical implications which will be discussed later.

As we have seen (Jacob and Monod, this Symposium, page 193) there are very strong reasons to believe that the site of action of the repressor is genetic; that in fact it is identical with the "operator" locus itself. Besides the arguments derived from the kinetics of enzyme synthesis, to which we shall return, the main reason is the existence, in certain systems, of genetic units of coordinate expression, *i.e.* of "operons" including several structural genes, controlled by a single operator. So far, operons have been recognized only in bacteria, where genes controlling sequential enzymes are frequently, if not generally, tightly clustered (Demerec and Hartmann, 1959). One may wonder whether the concept of operon also applies to organisms where genetic clustering is not usually observed. The fact that pseudoalleles have been discovered in *Drosophila* and maize, wherever genetic methods attained sufficient resolution, suggests that the clustering of cistrons involved in controlling the same biochemical step may in fact be very widespread. It is tempting to speculate that the loci where pseudoallelism is observed control the synthesis of proteins containing two or more different polypeptide chains and that they involve two or more linked cistrons. Thus the operon, in higher organisms, might often correspond to the "gene" as defined by the one gene-one enzyme concept. Moreover, as we have seen, the results obtained with bacteria also permit one to define the operon in a somewhat different manner, namely as the *unit of transcription*. This definition remains valid and useful independently of the number of cistrons covered by a given operon.

Long before regulator genes and operator were recognized in bacteria, the extensive and penetrating work of McClintock (1956) had revealed the existence, in maize, of two classes of genetic "controlling elements" whose specific mutual relationships are closely comparable with those of the regulator and operator: the "Activator" of McClintock appears to work as a *transmitter* of signals, presumably cytoplasmic since they act both in *cis* and in *trans*. By contrast the specific *receiver* of these signals only acts in *cis* upon genes directly linked to it. Although, because of the absence of enzymological data in the maize systems, the comparison cannot be brought down to the biochemical level, the parallel is so striking that it may justify the conclusion that the rate of structural gene expression is controlled, in higher organisms as well as in bacteria and bacterial viruses, by closely similar mechanisms, involving regulator genes, aporepressors, operators and operons.

A last point concerning the operator should be made. As we have seen, the operator locus of the Lac operon in *E. coli*, appears to be part of one extremity of the structural gene controlling galactosidase. In the arginine system (see Vogel; Maas; and Gorini; this Symposium) a single regulator appears to control the expression of several unlinked genes (or clusters) governing the different enzymes of the sequence. The operator segment for each of these genes or clusters presumably has the same structure, and if so one would expect the different enzymes of the system to contain the same sequence in one of their terminal peptides. Apart from the interest of providing a possible test for the preceding assumptions, the evolutionary implications of such a situation are evident.

3. Messenger RNA

The assumption that regulation, in inducible and repressible systems, operates at the genetic level by blocking or releasing the synthesis of the primary genetic product is intimately related to the problem of "messenger-RNA". On the basis of the kinetics of induction and repression, this assumption necessarily implied that the primary product in question is a short-lived intermediate (Jacob and Monod, 1961) and it led to a systematic search for an intermediate endowed with the proper kinetic properties. As we have seen, this search has been remarkably successful.

All or most of the evidence available at present on the so-called "messenger-RNA" fraction has been discussed in detail during the conference and we need not consider it at any length here. It might be useful however to summarize the main conclusions as follows:

a) A RNA fraction endowed with an exceptionally high rate of turnover exists not only in phage-infected cells (Volkin and Astrachan, 1957) but also in normal cells (Gros *et al., see* this Symposium, page 111).

b) The base ratios in this fraction, in contrast to all other RNA fractions approximate the characteristic (group specific) base ratios of DNA (Volkin and Astrachan, 1957; Yčas and Vincent, 1960; Hayes, Hayes and Gros, 1961).

c) "mRNA" appears to form hybrids with homologous but not with heterologous DNA, indicating that the sequences in "mRNA" complement the sequences in DNA (Spiegelman, see this Symposium, page 75).

d) An enzyme system able to synthesize RNA polynucleotides using DNA as primer and reproducing the DNA base ratios in its product exists in *E. coli* from which it has been isolated and purified (Hurwitz *et al., see* this Symposium, page 91).

e) *Escherichia coli* ribosomes appear to be able to synthesize either bacterial protein or viral protein depending on whether the "mRNA" with which they are associated is viral or bacterial; in other words, ribosomes appear to be non-specific with respect to the type of protein which they synthesize. (Brenner *et al., see* this Symposium, page 101).

f) In reconstructed subcellular systems, the presence of DNA appears essential both for the incorporation of amino acid into protein, and for the synthesis of RNA, presumably mRNA, as shown in particular by Tissières' recent results; in the absence of DNA, partially isolated mRNA stimulates incorporation.

The very significant recent findings of Wood, Chamberlain and Berg (1961, in preparation) should be recalled here although they were not discussed at the conference. Using reconstructed systems containing washed ribosomes, they found that amino acid incorporation into protein was almost completely dependent upon the addition of purified polymerase, DNA, and triphosphonucleotides, the absence of any one of these additions resulting in 90 to 95% inhibition of incorporation.

The sum of these observations is impressive and seems to justify the optimistic feeling shared by most of us that the primary product of the genes, the intermediate responsible for the transfer of structural information to protein-forming centers, has been identified, as well as the enzyme system which synthesizes this product by transcribing DNA into RNA. However it must be pointed out that formal proof of the structure-determining function of "mRNA" will be obtained only when the synthesis of a specific protein, known to be controlled by an identified structural gene, is shown to take place in a reconstructed system containing messenger-RNA from genetically competent cells, while all other fractions were prepared from cells known to lack this particular structural gene.

It should also be emphasized that, while the existence of a fraction possessing the properties of "mRNA" was predicted largely on the basis of the assumption that repressive regulation operates at the genetic level, it remains to be proved, also by direct experiments, that inducers and repressors do control the synthesis of the specific messengers corresponding to the proteins which they are known to induce or repress in vivo.

Many other problems are raised by the recent findings on messenger-RNA. One of them is the stoichiometry of the intermediate. The possibility that the stoichiometry is one to one (that is to say that one molecule of messenger is destroyed for each molecule of protein synthesized) is interesting, but it seems to meet with serious difficulties. The possibility that the messenger may be endowed with different stability in different species or groups is at least equally likely, and it may eventually be found to account for the conflicting reports in the literature concerning the effects of enucleation on protein synthesis.

A question which was in the minds of many participants of the meeting was what the role of ribosomes and ribosomal RNA in protein synthesis might be, if indeed all of the specific structural information is provided by mRNA. Among various speculations, for which there is at present no basis and little immediate hope of devising experimental tests, one may mention the possibility that ribosomal RNA can form base pairing bonds with mRNA and thereby stretch it into the correct position for protein synthesis. In addition, the configuration in space of the ribosome-mRNA complex might restrict the freedom of folding of the polypeptide chain and thereby provide certain folding rules.

E. The Glucose Effect

One of the oldest known regulatory effects in enzyme synthesis is generally known today as the "glucose effect" although it is recognized that almost any carbon source may inhibit the synthesis of a wide variety of enzymes, the magnitude of the inhibition depending mostly on the rate of metabolism of the compound. The widespread occurrence and the physiological importance of this effect were illustrated in particular by Magasanik's report (see this Symposium, page 249). Concerning mechanisms however, few conclusions can be drawn at present. The most urgent question in this respect is whether the inhibition by glucose, or other carbon sources, of synthesis of an inducible enzyme is related or not to the mechanism of induction itself. The data summarized by Brown would seem to indicate that, in contrast with previous views, the glucose effect is largely independent of the specific aporepressor-inducer interaction. Brown's findings (Brown and Monod, 1961) would be consistent with a model involving the synthesis, in the presence of glucose, of a more or less non-specific inhibitory compound, indifferent to the presence or absence of the specific aporepressor as well as of the inducer.

The findings of Magasanik and of Neidhardt (see this Symposium, page 249 and 63) on the other hand indicate that the inhibitory agent ultimately responsible for the glucose effect must have some degree of specificity. On the basis of the knowledge acquired concerning the mechanism of specific induction and repression, it would seem that the following questions, concerning the nature of the glucose effect, should be asked and could receive an experimental answer:

a) Is the inhibitory agent specific for certain groups of enzymes? If it is, one would expect to find mutants which have lost the capacity to synthesize this compound and therefore would have lost the glucose effect for certain types of enzymes while retaining it for others.

b) Does the inhibitory agent act at the same level as the specific aporepressor? If so, certain mutations in the operator region might modify quantitatively the glucose effect towards enzymes belonging to the corresponding operon.

c) If the glucose effect does *not* work at the operator level, but rather at the cytoplasmic level (as suggested by some findings of Halvorson, discussion at this Symposium, see page 231)), the quantitative regulatory coordination within an operon, characteristic of specific induction and repression, would not be observed with respect to inhibition by glucose.

III. REGULATION AND DIFFERENTIATION IN HIGHER ORGANISMS

1. General Remarks

The regulatory problems posed by (or to) differentiated organisms are not only of an order of a complexity immeasurably greater than in microorganisms, they are of a different nature. Higher organisms may therefore be expected to possess certain types of cellular regulatory mechanisms which are not found in microorganisms. On the other hand, it seems very unlikely that the main mechanisms recognized in lower forms: allosteric inhibition, induction and repression, should not be used also in differentiated organisms. But it is clear that these mechanisms, by their very nature, can be adapted to widely different situations, and would serve entirely different purposes in *E. coli* and Man, respectively. As we have already pointed out, the specificity of allosteric inhibition, as well as the specificity of induction and repression is inherently "free", in the sense that it results exclusively from the teleonomic construction of the regulatory system. As it turns out, allosteric inhibitors, inducers, and repressors of bacterial systems are, in general, directly related to, or identical with, metabolites of the pathway which they control. This should be considered to reflect the relatively unsophisticated regulatory requirements of free-living unicellular organisms, whose only problems are to preserve their intracellular homeostatic state while adapting rapidly to the chemical challenge of changing environments, and whose success in selection depends on a *single* parameter: the rate of multiplication. Tissue cells of higher organisms are faced with entirely different problems. Intercellular (and not only intracellular) coordination within tissues or between different organs, to insure survival and reproduction of the organism, becomes a major factor in selection, while the environment of individual cells is largely stabilized, eliminating to a large degree the requirements for rapid and extensive adaptability.

2. Nutritional Adaptation

These rather obvious *a priori* considerations may perhaps account in part for the somewhat discouraging results which seem to have been obtained so far in attempts to demonstrate induction by substrate or repression by metabolites of enzyme systems in various tissues. Several reports at the conference did illustrate the fact that the level of liver enzymes may vary greatly, depending on the type of diet to which the animals are submitted. But these reports have also illustrated the difficulties of analyzing the mechanisms involved. As Hiatt (see this Symposium, page 367) and also Feigelson (unpublished), have pointed out, it may be that some of these effects are due to simple stabilization of the enzyme by substrate, rather than to control of their rate of synthesis. Simple stabilization, admittedly, is not a very exciting mechanism. It may well be a physiologically significant one, especially in the liver. The microorganisms have a simple way of getting rid of an enzyme-protein for which there is no more inducer-substrate; they only need to outgrow the protein which has ceased to be synthesized. This simple device is not available to liver cells, and this may justify the selection of the apparently wasteful method of synthesizing enzymes which are stable only in presence of their substrate. It should be added however that many of the systems described here would be difficult to interpret on this basis alone; and one feels confident, in spite of the lack of formal proof, that true induction and/or repression plays an important role in nutritional adaptation of higher organisms.

In any case, it seems clear that nutritional adaptation is not the most important, nor perhaps the most fruitful, field for the investigation of regulatory effects in higher organisms. The development and functioning of these differentiated cellular populations poses three major problems which have hardly begun to be solved at the biochemical and genetic level, namely, differentiation itself, the control of cellular multiplication, and the mechanism of hormone action. Although these three problems are intimately related, we will discuss them separately.

3. Possible Mechanisms of Hormone Action

As we have already seen, there are now several recognized cases of "molecular conversion" where a natural hormone appears to be involved, directly or indirectly. Although it is not clear to what extent these particular effects may account for the physiological action of the hormones in question, the suggestion is that many hormones may act primarily by similar mechanisms. The fact that such mechanisms have not been observed, so far, in bacteria may possibly be significant. It may be recalled that the bacteria, alone among all other forms of life, do not synthesize any steroid. It may also be remarked that an unknown, probably very large, number of microbiologists have at one time or another hopefully added steroids (or adrenalin or insulin) to their bacterial cultures, without ever observing any effect (except catabolic reactions). One is led to wonder whether not only the compounds themselves, but also the type of regulatory mechanism which they control may not be a privilege of differentiated organisms. It would be very unwise however to base such a conclusion on such scanty evidence. And it is to be hoped that, in future years, systematic attempts will be made to verify whether or not certain hormones may not actually act as allosteric inhibitors, inducers, or repressors of certain enzyme systems. The main difficulty of this research will be that no guiding *chemical* principle (based on steric analogy, reactivity, etc.) will help the investigator in the selection of which enzyme systems to test, since again the specificity of induction-repression and of allosteric inhibition is apparently completely independent of the structure and specificity of the controlled enzyme itself. Also, and for the same reasons, it is quite possible that the same hormone may prove to act on different systems, if not by different mechanisms, in different tissues.

4. Differentiation

It may be in the interpretation and analysis of differentiation that the new concepts derived from the study of microorganisms will prove of the greatest value. One point at least already seems to be quite clear: namely that biochemical differentiation (reversible or not) of cells carrying an identical genome, does not constitute a "paradox", as it appeared to do for many years, to both embryologists and geneticists.

This point may require some elaboration. The control mechanisms discovered in microorganisms govern the *expression* of genetic potentialities. Most of the actual systems however are entirely reversible, in the sense that the effects of inhibitors, inducers, or repressors do not survive for any length of time after elimination of the active agent, and the cells soon return to their initial state.

Differentiation, on the other hand, is stable, and persists once it has been induced. Whether differentiation is ever *completely* irreversible (except in non-growing cells), is an exceedingly difficult question, because the experimental operations which might decide this issue generally cannot be performed. In any case, we need not go into this discussion; let us consider that differentiation may be more or less stable, even attaining irreversibility in some cases. It might then be argued that since the microbial systems are completely reversible, similar mechanisms could not account for stable differentiation. But it should be clear that the microbial systems must have been geared precisely for reversibility, since selection, in microorganisms, will necessarily favor the most rapid response to any change of environment. Moreover, it is obvious from the analysis of these mechanisms that their known elements could be connected into a wide variety of "circuits", endowed with any desired degree of stability. In order to illustrate some of these possibilities, let us study a certain number of theoretical model systems in which we shall use only the controlling elements known to exist in bacteria, interconnected however in an arbitrary manner.

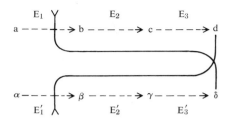

Fig. 1. *Model I. The reactions along the two pathways $a \to b \to c \to d$, and $\alpha \to \beta \to \gamma \to \delta$, are catalyzed by enzymes E'_1, E_2, E_3 and E'_1, E'_2, E'_3. Enzyme E_1 is inhibited by δ, the product of the other pathway. Conversely, enzyme E'_1 is inhibited by metabolite d, produced by the first pathway.*

Consider for instance the following model, which uses the properties of the allosteric inhibition effect, assuming two independent metabolic pathways, giving rise to metabolites a, b, c, d, and α, β, γ, δ (Fig. 1). Assume that the enzymes catalyzing the first reaction in each pathway are inhibited by the final product of the *other* pathway. By such "crossfeedback" a system of alternative stable states is created where one of the two pathways, provided it once had a head-start or a temporary metabolic advantage, will permanently inhibit the other. Switching of one pathway to the other could be accomplished by a variety of methods, for instance by inhibiting temporarily any one of the enzymes of the active pathway. It should be noted that a model formally identical with this one was proposed by Delbrück (1949) (long before feedback inhibition was discovered) to account for certain alternative steady-states found in ciliates.

The following model corresponds to a classical induction system, with the only specific assumption that the active inducer is not the substrate, but the *product* of the controlled enzyme. (Fig. 2). Such a system is autocatalytic and self-sustaining. Although it is not self-reproducing in the genetic sense, it should mimic certain properties of genetic elements. In the absence of any exogenous inducing agent, the enzyme will not be synthesized unless already present, when it will maintain itself indefinitely. When the system is locked, temporary contact with an inducer will unlock it permanently. Actually, certain inducible permease systems in *E. coli* may be described in this way, and behave accordingly, as shown by Novick and Weiner (1959), and by Cohn and Horibata (1959). A similar

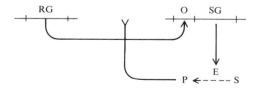

Fig. 2. *Model II. Synthesis of enzyme E, genetically determined by the structural gene SG, is blocked by the repressor synthesized by the regulator gene RG. The product P of the reaction catalyzed by enzyme E acts as an inducer of the system by inactivating the repressor.*

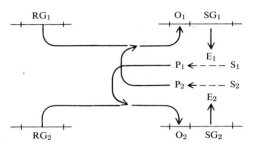

Fig. 3. *Model III. Synthesis of enzyme E_1, genetically determined by the structural gene SG_1, is regulated by the regulator gene RG_1. Synthesis of enzyme E_2, genetically determined by the structural gene SG_2, is regulated by the regulator gene RG_2. The product P_1 of the reaction catalyzed by enzyme E_1 acts as corepressor in the regulation system of enzyme E_2. The product P_2 of the reaction catalyzed by enzyme E_2 acts as corepressor in the regulation system of enzyme E_1.*

mechanism appears to account for the so-called "slow adaptation" of yeast to galactose, without having recourse to some kind of "plasmagene" as previously believed by Spiegelman (1951).

Two different inducible or repressible systems may be interconnected by assuming that each one produces the metabolic repressor or the inducer of the other. In the first case, as illustrated below (Fig. 3) the enzymes would be mutually exclusive. The presence of one would permanently block the synthesis of the other. Switching from one state to the other could be accomplished by eliminating temporarily the substrate of the live system. In the second case, which may be represented as shown in Fig. 4, the two enzymes would be mutually dependent; one could not be synthesized in the absence of the other, although of course they might function in apparently unrelated pathways. Temporary inhibition of one of the enzymes, or elimination of its substrate, would eventually result in the permanent suppression of both.

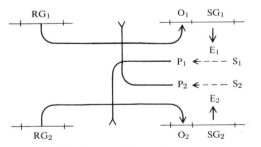

Fig. 4. *Model IV. Synthesis of enzyme E_1, genetically determined by the structural gene SG_1, is blocked by the repressor synthesized by the regulator gene RG_1. Synthesis of another enzyme E_2, controlled by structural gene SG_2, is blocked by another repressor synthesized by regulator gene RG_2. The product P_1 of the reaction catalyzed by enzyme E_1 acts as an inducer for the synthesis of enzyme E_2 and the product P_2 of the reactions catalyzed by enzyme E_2 acts as an inducer for the synthesis of enzyme E_1.*

In the preceding models, the systems were interconnected by assuming that the metabolic product of one is an inducer or a repressor of the other. Another type of interconnection, independent of metabolic activity, would be obtained by assuming a regulator gene controlled by an operator, sensitive to another regulator. For instance, in the system shown below (Fig. 5) a regulator gene controls the synthesis of enzymes within an operon which includes another regulator gene acting upon the operator to which the first one is attached. Such a system would be completely independent of the actual metabolic activity of the enzymes, and could be switched from the inactive to the active state by transient contact with a specific inducer, produced for instance only by another tissue. Once activated, the system could not be switched back except by addition of the apo-repressor made by the first regulator gene. The change of state would therefore be virtually irreversible. It is easy to see that, conversely, starting from the active state, transient contact with an inducer acting on the product of RG_2 would switch the system, permanently, to the inactive state.

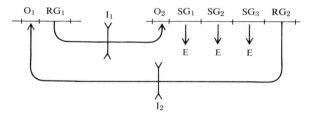

Fig. 5. Model V. *The regulator gene RG_1 controls the activity of an operon containing three structural genes (SG_1, SG_2, SG_3) and another regulator gene RG_2. The regulator gene RG_1 itself belongs to another operon sensitive to the repressor synthesized by RG_2. The action of RG_1 can be antagonized by an inducer I_1, which activates SG_1, SG_2, SG_3 and RG_2 (and therefore inactivates RG_1). The action of RG_2 can be antagonized by an inducer I_2 which activates RG_1 (and therefore inactivates the systems SG_1, SG_2, SG_3 and RG_2).*

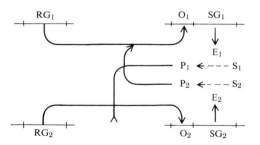

Fig. 6. Model VI. *Synthesis of enzyme E_1, genetically determined by the structural gene SG_1, is blocked by the repressor synthesized by the regulator gene RG_1. Synthesis of another enzyme E_2, controlled by structural gene SG_2, is blocked by another repressor synthesized by regulator gene RG_2. The product P_1 of the reaction catalyzed by enzyme E_1 acts as an inducer for the synthesis of enzyme E_2 while the product P_2 of the reaction catalyzed by enzyme E_2 acts as a corepressor for the synthesis of enzyme E_1.*

Finally the following type of circuit might be interesting to consider in relation to cyclic phenomena. In this circuit, the product of one enzyme is an inducer of the other system while the product of the second enzyme is a corepressor (Fig. 6). A study of the properties of this circuit will show that, provided adequate time constants are chosen for the decay of each enzyme and of its product, the system will oscillate from one state to the other.

These examples should suffice to show that, by the use of the principles which they illustrate, any number of systems may be interconnected into regulatory circuits endowed with virtually any desired property. The essential point about the imaginary circuits which we examined, is that their elements are not imaginary. The particular properties of each circuit are obtained only by assuming the proper type of specific interconnection. Such assumptions are freely permitted since, as we have already seen, the specificity of induction-repression and of allosteric inhibition is not restricted by any chemical principle of analogy, and apparently is *exclusively* the result of selection for the most efficient regulation.

The models involving only metabolic steady-states maintained by allosteric effects are insufficient to account for differentiation, which must involve directed alterations in the capacity of individual cells to *synthesize* specific proteins. Such models would seem to be most adequate to account for the almost instantaneous, and thereafter more or less permanent, "memorization" by cells of a chemical event. The problem of memory itself might usefully be considered from this point of view.

It has long been recognized, by embryologists and biochemists alike, that "enzymatic adaptation" might offer an experimental approach toward the interpretation of differentiation. The realization that induction and repression are governed by specialized regulatory genes, that both eventually operate by controlling negatively the activity of structural genes, and that the specificity of inducers or repressors is entirely *suigeneris*, allows, as we have just seen, the construction of models capable, in principle, of accounting for virtually any type of differenti tion. The fact that these mechanisms are not only genetically controlled, but operate directly at the genetic level, and may be in some cases quite independent of any metabolic event in the cell itself, is evidently of special value, since the transitions of state in such systems should very closely mimic true transmissible alterations of the genetic material itself. That differentiation involves induced, specific, and permanent alterations of the genetic information of somatic cells has often been proposed as the only possible interpretation of the "paradox". It should be clear that this type of hypothesis, which meets with almost insuperable difficulties, is in fact completely unnecessary (except perhaps in certain exceptional cases, such as that of the reticulocytes and red cells), since as we have seen the transcription of a gene, not only in a cell, but in a whole cell lineage, may be permanently repressed, or derepressed, depending on an initial, transient event, which would not involve any alteration of the information carried by the gene. And it might be noted that this type of interpretation would not, in any way, be incompatible with the beautiful experiments of Briggs and King (1955) which showed that the nuclei of certain embryonic tissues, in the frog, had lost certain potentialities of expression possessed by the original nucleus of the egg.

The microbial systems actually offer some examples of irreversible effects resulting from repression or derepression. For instance, both lysogenization by an infecting temperate phage, and induction of a lysogenic bacterium, are irreversible consequences of transient conditions favoring, in the first instance, the establishment of a permanent state of self-repression, and in the second a release of the repressed condition. In the repressed (prophage) state which is maintained indefinitely in the absence of inducing agents, the viral genes are inactive in transcription; they are fully active in the vegetative state. Yet the transition from one to the other does not involve any alteration of the information contained in the genetic material of the phage.

The lysogenic systems may also be of some use in thinking about the problem of the control of cellular multiplication. In the prophage (i.e., repressed) state, the phage DNA replicates synchronously with the host cell DNA. In the derepressed state, it replicates about 20 times as fast. The presence of the repressor cannot, by itself, account for this difference. But it is a fact that the decision between synchronous or "wild" replication depends initially upon the regulator-operator interaction. It is most probable that in tissue cells the regulation of multiplication is very complex, since it must simultaneously control several systems which have to be kept in pace. And it may be of some interest to note that even relatively simple regulatory systems may go astray in several different ways. We know for instance that the constitutive state may be obtained by mutation of either the regulator or the operator. In a system such as the one shown in Fig. 6, mutations of either one of the two operators, or of one of the regulator genes, would abolish the repressive control, resulting either in a constitutive or in a "super-repressed" phenotype. In addition even *temporary* inactivation of one of the loci (for instance by reversible lesions such as are known to be produced by UV light) or temporary blocking of one of the repressors by a complexing agent, would lead precisely to the same permanent phenotypes, which might or might not be reversible by an inducer, depending upon the specific properties of the system. Only by a very thorough genetic and biochemical analysis of such a system could one decide whether the transition was brought about by true mutation, or by temporary inactivation.

These observations may have some bearings on the problem of the initial event leading to malignancy. Malignant cells have lost sensitivity to the conditions which control multiplication in normal tissues. That the disorder is genetic cannot be doubted. That, following an initial event, mutations within the cellular population are progressively selected, leading towards greater independence, i.e., heightened malignancy, is now quite clear, due in particular to the work of Klein and Klein (1958). But while the initial event, responsible for setting up the new selective relationships, may of course be a genetic mutation, it might also be brought by the transient action of an agent capable of complexing or inactivating *temporarily* a genetic locus, or a repressor, involved in the control of multiplication.

It is clear that a wide variety of agents, from viruses to carcinogenes, might be responsible for such an initial event.

As a conclusion to this discussion of theoretical models, one would like to turn to experimental examples, and see whether they might, or might not, fit with the interpretations. Unfortunately, in the face of formidable technical difficulties, the study of differentiation either from the genetic or from the bio-chemical point of view has not attained a state which would allow any detailed comparison of theory with experiment. This is our excuse for using microbial systems as models for the interpretation of differentiation. Eventually, however, differentiation will have to be studied in differentiated cells. The remarkable advances achieved in the methodology of cell cultures encourage optimism. The greatest obstacle is the impossibility of performing genetic analysis, without which there is no hope of ever dissecting out the mechanisms of differentiation. But it should be noted that actual genetic mapping may not necessarily be required. Adequate techniques of nuclear transfer, combined with systematic studies of possible inducing or repressing agents, and with the isolation of regulatory mutants, may conceivably open the way to the experimental analysis of differenti-ation at the genetic-biochemical level.

REFERENCES

Benzer, S. 1957. The elementary units of heredity. pp. 70–93. *"The Chemical Basis of Heredity"*. ed. W. D. McElroy and B. Glass, Baltimore: Johns Hopkins Press.

Benzer, S., and E. Freese. 1958. Induction of specific mutations with 5-bromouracil. Proc. Nat. Acad. Sci., *44:* 112–119.

Briggs, R. W., and T. J. King. 1955. Specificity of nuclear functions in embryonic development. pp. 207–228. *Biological Specificity and Growth,* ed. E. G. Butler. Princeton: Princeton University Press.

Brown, D. D., and J. Monod. 1961. Carbon source repression of β-galactosidase in *E. coli.* Federation Proc., *20:* 222.

Burnet, F. M. 1959. The clonal selection theory of acquired immunity. Cambridge: Cambridge University Press.

Cohn, M., and K. Horibata. 1959. Analysis of the differentiation and of the heterogeneity within a population of *Escherichia coli* undergoing induced β-galactosidase synthesis. J. Bact., *78:* 613–623.

Crick, F. H. C. 1958. On protein synthesis. "Biological Replication of Macromolecules". 12th Symp. Soc. Exp. Biol., 138–163.

Delbrück, M. 1949. In "Unitès biologiques douées de continuité génétique", Edit. du CNRS, Paris, 33–34.

Demerec, M., and P. E. Hartman. 1959. Complex loci in microorganisms. Ann. Rev. Microb., *13:* 377–406.

Falkow, S., and L. Baron. 1961. An episomic element in a strain of *Salmonella typhosa.* Bact. Proc. (G 98), 96.

Fincham, J. R. S. 1959. The role of chromosomal loci in enzyme formation. Proc. Xth Int. Cong. Genetics, *1:* 355–363.

Freese, E. 1959. On the molecular explanation of spontaneous and induced mutation. *Structure and Function of genetic elements,* Brookhaven Symposia, *12:* 63–75.

Hayes, D., F. Hayes, and F. Gros. 1961. In preparation.

Ingram, V. M. 1957. Gene mutation in human haemoglobin: the chemical difference between normal and sickle-cell haemoglobin Nature, *180:* 326–328.

Jacob, F., and J. Monod. 1961. Genetic regulatory mechanisms in the synthesis of proteins. J. Mol. Biol., *3:* 318–356.

Klein, G., and E. Klein. 1958. Histocompatibility changes in tumors. J. Cell. Comp. Physiol., *52:* 125–168.

Koshland, D. E., Jr. 1959. Enzyme flexibility and enzyme action. J. Cell. Comp. Physiol., *54:* 245–258.

Labeyrie, F., P. P. Slonimsky, and N. Naslin. 1959. Sur la différence de stéréospécificité entre la déshydrogénase lactique extraite de la levure anaérobie et celle extraite de la levure aérobie. Biochim. Biophys. Acta, *34:* 262–265.

Lederberg, J. 1959. Antibody formation by single cells. Science, *130:* 1427.

Lwoff, A., and M. Lwoff. 1961. In preparation.

Mazia, D. 1959. Cell Division. Harvey Lectures, 1957–1958, *53:* 130–170.

McClintock, B. 1956. Controlling elements and the gene. Cold Spring Harbor Symp. on Quant. Biol., *21:* 197–216.

Monod, J. 1956. Remarks on the mechanism of enzyme induction. *"Eznymes: Units of biological Structure and Function",* Henry Ford Hospital. Intern. Symp. pp. 7–28. New York: Academic Press.

Monod, J., and M. Cohn. 1952. La biosynthèse induite des enzymes (adaptation enzymatique). Adv. Enzymol., *13:* 67–119.

Novick, A., and L. Szilard. 1954. Experiments with the chemostat on the rates of amino acid synthesis in bacteria. p. 21. *"Dynamics of Growth Processes".* Princeton University Press.

Novick, A., and M. Weiner. 1959. The kinetics of β-galactosidase induction. Symp. on Molecular Biology. ed. R. E. Zirkle, University of Chicago Press, 78–90.

Pardee, A. B. Personal communication.

Pauling, L. 1940. A theory of the structure and process of formation of antibodies. J. Am. Chem. Soc., *62:* 2643–2657.

Perrin, D. 1961. In preparation.

Perin, D., F. Jacob, and J. Monod. 1960. Biosynthèse induite d'une protéine génétiquement modifiée, ne présentant pas d'affinité pour l'inducteur. C. R. Acad. Sci., *251:* 155–157.

Perutz, M. 1961. 50th Anniversary Symposium of the Biochemical Society, London. In press.

Rapkine, L. 1931. Sur les processus chimiques au cours de la division cellulaire. Ann. Physiol. Physicochim. Biol., *7:* 382–418.

Roberts, R. B., P. H. Abelson, D. B. Cowie, E. T. Bolton, and R. J. Britten. 1955. Studies of biosynthesis in *Escherichia coli*. Carnegie Institution of Washington Publ., 607.

Spiegelman, S. 1951. The particulate transmission of enzyme-forming capacity in yeast. Cold Spring Harbor Symp. on Quant. Biol., *16:* 87–98.

Trudinger, P. A., and G. N. Cohen. 1956. The effect of 4-methyltryptophan on growth and enzyme system of *Escherichia coli*. Biochem. J., *62:* 488–491.

Volkin, E., and L. Astrachan. 1957. RNA metabolism in T2-infected *Escherichia coli*. pp. 686–694. *"The Chemical Basis of Heredity"*, ed. W. D. McElroy and B. Glass, Baltimore: Johns Hopkins Press.

Wood, W. B., M. Chamberlain, and P. Berg. In Preparation.

Yčas, M., and W. S. Vincent. 1960. A ribonucleic acid fraction from yeast related in composition of desoxyribonucleic acid. Proc. Nat. Acad. Sci., *46:* 804–810.

Section V
Ecology, Species, and Evolution

Introduction

Underlying all discussions of evolution are two major biological concepts:
(1) the intimate ecological relationships which exist between one organism and
another or between organisms and the physical environment; and (2) the nature
of species—the determination of the anatomical, physiological, or behavioral
boundaries between one species and another. The first three papers in this
section speak to one aspect of the first question: the factors controlling
population size. In a general sense these papers show the forces which keep the
size of the natural populations balanced over long periods of time. Since the
size of our present human population is reaching serious proportions, these
papers have more than a theoretical significance today. They provide some
insight into the necessity of controlling the growth of our own population, and
portray—as in, for example, the paper by Leopold—the serious consequences of
over-population.

The fourth paper deals with the question of species as a biological unit. In a
thorough and analytical review, Ernst Mayr explores the difficulties of providing
a simple definition of species. Yet an understanding of the biological reality of
species, Mayr contends, is essential to an understanding of how groups of
animals ₍nd plants live together in communities and how new species evolve
through variation and natural selection.

The last three readings are concerned with the mechanism of natural
selection itself. The first is a joint publication by Alfred Russell Wallace and
Charles Darwin, who by 1858 had independently arrived at the idea of natural
selection. The two papers presented here were read before a meeting of the
Linnaean Society of London on July 1, 1858, and were published in its journal
in 1859. In these accounts, Darwin and Wallace outline the mechanism of
natural selection and show how it could account for the origin of adaptations,
and thereby ultimately the origin of new species. Darwin, who had been
working on the problem considerably longer than Wallace, published *The*

Origin of the Species in 1859, and Wallace eventually became a leading spokesman for the Darwinian theory.

The last two papers, by H. B. Kettlewell and A. C. Allison present modern experimental evidence for two cases of evolution: the former in moths and the latter in man. The Kettlewell paper derives its significance especially from providing clear observational and statistical proof that phenotypical characters have distinct survival values in nature. In addition, this paper explores the resulting change in frequency of certain phenotypes of moth under changing environmental conditions (i.e., the gradual darkening of the vegetative cover in industrial areas over the past century). This change in phenotypic frequency is an example of evolution. The final paper, by Allison, illustrates clearly how a given phenotypic character (in this case sickle-cell anemia) can have differential survival value in different environments. Allison's work also shows the important relationship between mutation, change in protein structure, and survival of an organism.

Population: The First Essay

by THOMAS R. MALTHUS

It has been said that the great question is now at issue, whether man shall henceforth start forwards with accelerated velocity towards illimitable, and hitherto unconceived, improvement, or be condemned to a perpetual oscillation between happiness and misery, and after every effort remain still at an immeasurable distance from the wished-for goal. . . .

It is an acknowledged truth in philosophy that a just theory will always be confirmed by experiment. Yet so much friction and so many minute circumstances occur in practice, which it is next to impossible for the most enlarged and penetrating mind to foresee, that on few subjects can any theory be pronounced just that has not stood the test of experience. But an untried theory cannot fairly be advanced as probable, much less as just, till all the arguments against it have been maturely weighed and clearly and consistently refuted.

I have read some of the speculations on the perfectibility of man and of society with great pleasure. I have been warmed and delighted with the enchanting picture which they hold forth. I ardently wish for such happy improvements. But I see great, and, to my understanding, unconquerable difficulties in the way to them. These difficulties it is my present purpose to state, declaring, at the same time, that so far from exulting in them, as a cause of triumph over the friends of innovation, nothing would give me greater pleasure than to see them completely removed. . . .

In entering upon the argument I must premise that I put out of the question, at present, all mere conjectures, that is, all suppositions, the probable realization of which cannot be inferred upon any just philosophical grounds. A writer may tell me that he thinks man will ultimately become an ostrich. I cannot properly contradict him. But before he can expect to bring any reasonable person over to his opinion, he ought to shew that the necks of mankind have been gradually elongating, that the lips have grown harder and more prominent, that the legs and feet are daily altering their shape, and that the hair is beginning to change into stubs of feathers. And till the probability of so wonderful a conversion can be shewn, it is surely lost time and lost eloquence to expatiate on the happiness

---

Abridged from Thomas R. Malthus, "Population: The First Essay," in *An Essay on Population* (London: Johnson, 1798), Chapter 1.

of man in such a state; to describe his powers, both of running and flying, to paint him in a condition where all narrow luxuries would be condemned, where he would be employed only in collecting the necessaries of life, and where, consequently, each man's share of labour would be light, and his portion of leisure ample.

I think I may fairly make two postulata.

First, That food is necessary to the existence of man.

Secondly, That the passion between the sexes is necessary and will remain nearly in its present state.

These two laws, ever since we have had any knowledge of mankind, appear to have been fixed laws of our nature, and, as we have not hitherto seen any alteration in them, we have no right to conclude that they will ever cease to be what they now are, without an immediate act of power in that Being who first arranged the system of the universe, and for the advantage of his creatures, still executes, according to fixed laws, all its various operations.

I do not know that any writer has supposed that on this earth man will ultimately be able to live without food. But Mr. Godwin has conjectured that the passion between the sexes may in time be extinguished. As, however, he calls this part of his work a deviation into the land of conjecture, I will not dwell longer upon it at present than to say that the best arguments for the perfectibility of man are drawn from a contemplation of the great progress that he has already made from the savage state and the difficulty of saying where he is to stop. But towards the extinction of the passion between the sexes, no progress whatever has hitherto been made. It appears to exist in as much force at present as it did two thousand or four thousand years ago. There are individual exceptions now as there always have been. But, as these exceptions do not appear to increase in number, it would surely be a very unphilosophical mode of arguing to infer merely from the existence of an exception that the exception would, in time, become the rule, and the rule the exception.

Assuming, then, my postulata as granted, I say that the power of population is indefinitely greater than the power in the earth to produce subsistence for man.

Population, when unchecked, increases in a geometrical ratio. Subsistence increases only in an arithmetical ratio. A slight acquaintance with numbers will shew the immensity of the first power in comparison of the second.

By that law of our nature which makes food necessary to the life of man, the effects of these two unequal powers must be kept equal.

This implies a strong and constantly operating check on population from the difficulty of subsistence. This difficulty must fall somewhere and must necessarily be severely felt by a large portion of mankind.

Through the animal and vegetable kingdoms, nature has scattered the seeds of life abroad with the most profuse and liberal hand. She has been comparatively sparing in the room and the nourishment necessary to rear them. The germs of existence contained in this spot of earth, while ample food and ample room to expand in, would fill millions of worlds in the course of a few thousand years.

Necessity, that imperious all-pervading law of nature, restrains them within the prescribed bounds. The race of plants and the race of animals shrink under this great restrictive law. And the race of man cannot, by any efforts of reason, escape from it. Among plants and animals its effects are waste of seed, sickness, and premature death; among mankind, misery and vice. The former, misery, is an absolutely necessary consequence of it. Vice is a highly probable consequence, and we therefore see it abundantly prevail, but it ought not, perhaps, to be called an absolutely necessary consequence. The ordeal of virtue is to resist all temptation to evil.

This natural inequality of the two powers of population and of production in the earth and that great law of our nature which must constantly keep their effects equal form the great difficulty that to me appears insurmountable in the way to the perfectibility of society. All other arguments are of slight and subordinate consideration in comparison of this. I see no way by which man can escape from the weight of this law which pervades all animated nature. No fancied equality, no agrarian regulations in their utmost extent could remove the pressure of it even for a single century. And it appears, therefore, to be decisive against the possible existence of a society, all the members of which should live in ease, happiness, and comparative leisure; and feel no anxiety about providing the means of subsistence for themselves and families. . . .

Community Structure, Population Control, and Competition

by NELSON G. HAIRSTON, FREDERICK E. SMITH, and LAWRENCE B. SLOBODKIN

The purpose of this note is to demonstrate a pattern of population control in many communities which derives easily from a series of general, widely accepted observations. The logic used is not easily refuted. Furthermore, the pattern reconciles conflicting interpretations by showing that the populations in different trophic levels are expected to differ in their methods of control.

Our first observation is that the accumulation of fossil fuels occurs at a rate that is negligible when compared with the rate of energy fixation through photosynthesis in the biosphere. Apparent exceptions to this observation, such as bogs and ponds, are successional stages in which the failure of decomposition hastens

Abridged from Nelson G. Hairston, Frederick E. Smith, and Lawrence B. Slobodkin, "Community Structure, Population Control, and Competition," *The American Naturalist* **94** (1960), 421–425. Reprinted by permission.

the termination of the stage. The rate of accumulation when compared with that of photosynthesis has also been shown to be negligible over geologic time.

If virtually all of the energy fixed in photosynthesis does indeed flow through the biosphere, it must follow that all organisms taken together are limited by the amount of energy fixed. In particular, the decomposers as a group must be food-limited, since by definition they comprise the trophic level which degrades organic debris. There is no a priori reason why predators, behavior, physiological changes induced by high densities, etc. could not limit decomposer populations. In fact, some decomposer populations may be limited in such ways. If so, however, others must consume the "left-over" food, so that the group as a whole remains food-limited; otherwise fossil fuel would accumulate rapidly.

Any population which is not resource-limited must, of course, be limited to a level *below* that set by its resources.

Our next three observations are interrelated. They apply primarily to terrestrial communities. The first of these is that cases of obvious depletion of green plants by herbivores are exceptions to the general picture, in which the plants are abundant and largely intact. Moreover, cases of obvious mass destruction by meteorological catastrophes are exceptional in most areas. Taken together, these two observations mean that producers are neither herbivore-limited nor catastrophe-limited, and must therefore be limited by their own exhaustion of a resource. In many areas, the limiting resource is obviously light, but in arid regions water may be the critical factor, and there are spectacular cases of limitation through the exhaustion of a critical mineral. The final observation in this group is that there are temporary exceptions to the general lack of depletion of green plants by herbivores. This occurs when herbivores are protected either by man or natural events, and it indicates that the herbivores are able to deplete the vegetation whenever they become numerous enough, as in the cases of the Kaibab deer herd, rodent plagues, and many insect outbreaks. It therefore follows that the usual condition is for populations of herbivores *not* to be limited by their food supply.

The vagaries of weather have been suggested as an adequate method of control for herbivore populations. The best factual clues related to this argument are to be found in the analysis of the exceptional cases where terrestrial herbivores have become numerous enough to deplete the vegetation. This often occurs with introduced rather than native species. It is most difficult to suppose that a species had been unable to adapt so as to escape control by the weather to which it was exposed, and at the same time by sheer chance to be able to escape this control from weather to which it had not been previously exposed. This assumption is especially difficult when mutual invasions by different herbivores between two countries may in both cases result in pests.

The remaining general method of herbivore control is predation (in its broadest sense, including parasitism, etc.). It is important to note that this hypothesis is not denied by the presence of introduced pests, since it is necessary only to suppose that either their natural predators have been left behind, or that while the herbivore is able to exist in the new climate, its enemies are not. There are, furthermore, numerous examples of the direct effect of predator removal. The history of the Kaibab deer is the best-known example, although deer across the northern portions of the country are in repeated danger of winter starvation as a result of protection and predator removal.

Thus, although rigorous proof that herbivores are generally controlled by predation is lacking, supporting evidence is available, and the alternate hypothesis of control by weather leads to false or untenable implications.

The foregoing conclusion has an important implication in the mechanism of control of the predator populations. The predators and parasites, in controlling the populations of herbivores, must thereby limit their own resources, and as a group they must be food-limited. Although the populations of some carnivores are obviously limited by territoriality, this kind of internal check cannot operate for all carnivores taken together. If it did, the herbivores would normally expand to the point of depletion of the vegetation, as they do in the absence of their normal predators and parasites.

There thus exists either direct proof or a great preponderance of factual evidence that in terrestrial communities decomposers, producers, and predators, as whole trophic levels, are resource-limited in the classical density-dependent fashion. Each of these three can and does expand toward the limit of the appropriate resource. We may now examine the reasons why this is a frequent situation in nature.

Whatever the resource for which a set of terrestrial plant species compete, the competition ultimately expresses itself as competition for space. A community in which this space is frequently emptied through depletion by herbivores would run the continual risk of replacement by another assemblage of species in which the herbivores are held down in numbers by predation below the level at which they damage the vegetation. That space once held by a group of terrestrial plant species is not readily given up is shown by the cases where relict stands exist under climates no longer suitable for their return following deliberate or accidental destruction.

A second general conclusion follows from the resource limitation of the species of three trophic levels. This conclusion is that if more than one species exists in one of these levels, they may avoid competition only if each species is limited by factors completely unutilized by any of the other species. It is a fact, of course, that many species occupy each level in most communities. It is also a fact that they are not sufficiently segregated in their needs to escape competition. Although isolated cases of nonoverlap have been described, this has never been observed for an entire assemblage. Therefore, interspecific competition for resources exists among producers, among carnivores, and among decomposers.

It is satisfying to note the number of observations that fall into line with the foregoing deductions. Interspecific competition is a powerful selective force, and we should expect to find evidence of its operation. Moreover, the evidence should be most conclusive in trophic levels where it is necessarily present. Among decomposers we find the most obvious specific mechanisms for reducing populations of competitors. The abundance of antibiotic substances attests to the frequency with which these mechanisms have been developed in the trophic level in which interspecific competition is inevitable. The producer species are the next most likely to reveal evidence of competition, and here we find such phenomena as crowding, shading, and vegetational zonation.

Among the carnivores, however, obvious adaptations for interspecific competition are less common. Active competition in the form of mutual habitat-exclusion has been noted in the cases of flatworms and salamanders. The commonest situation takes the form of niche diversification as the result of interspecific competition. This has been noted in birds, salamanders, and other groups of carnivores. Quite likely, host specificity in parasites and parasitoid insects is at least partly due to the influence of interspecific competition.

Of equal significance is the frequent occurrence among herbivores of apparent exceptions to the influence of density-dependent factors. The grasshoppers described by Birch and the thrips described by Davidson and Andrewartha are well-known examples. Moreover, it is among herbivores that we find cited examples of coexistence without evidence of competition for resources, such as the leafhoppers reported by Ross and the psocids described by Broadhead. It should be pointed out that in these latter cases coexistence applies primarily to an identity of food and place, and other aspects of the niches of these organisms are not known to be identical.

Difficulties and Importance of the Biological Species Concept

by ERNST MAYR

To bring into focus the picture that emerges from this symposium one must consider very diverse material on which the seven contributors have based their discussions—living organisms and fossils, animals and plants, freshwater and terrestrial organisms, vertebrates and invertebrates.[1] It would not have been surprising if the seven speakers had represented seven entirely different viewpoints. This did not happen. Indeed, the general agreement among the speakers was quite far-reaching; for instance, all speakers with one exception have emphatically endorsed the biological species concept. Yet it is evident that we have

Ernst Mayr, "Difficulties and Importance of the Biological Species Concept," in *The Species Concept* (Washington, D.C.: American Association for the Advancement of Science, 1957), pp. 371–388. Reprinted by permission.

[1] The revised version of T. M. Sonneborn's contribution was not available when this discussion was prepared.

not yet reached a true synthesis. The approach of every worker in this field is still largely colored by his intimate knowledge of the material with which he himself works. Let me illustrate this with a few examples. When an ornithologist speaks of "species" he has a phenomenon in mind in which hybridization or lack of sexuality are of no consequence. He has great difficulty in determining whether or not species in birds and species in plants are the same kind of phenomenon. Or let us take another case. The population geneticist who has emerged in the last thirty years from the typological thinking of mutationism is likely to consider everything as new that he himself is learning about species. He is unaware of the fact that thinking in terms of populations, and indeed the whole biological species concept, came from systematics into genetics rather than the reverse (Mayr, 1955). Population genetics has, often quite independently, rediscovered much that has been considered axiomatic in population systematics for seventy to eighty years.

Our thinking on these questions is one-sided not only because it is so strongly affected by our working material, but also because it is based on a limited number of selected examples. An author who works with a hybrid complex will be impressed by the importance of hybridization, another one who works with insular forms by the importance of geographic isolation. We now have reached the point where we are badly in need of comparative systematics and of a strictly quantitative approach. Analyses such as were done by Verne Grant (this symposium) should be done for as many groups of animals and plants as possible. Obviously, this method can be applied only where the group has reached a considerable degree of taxonomic maturity, but there are now many such groups in the vertebrates, insects, and plants. The need for such comparative systematics emphasizes the importance of sound orthodox taxonomic monographs.

DIFFICULTIES IN THE APPLICATION OF SPECIES CONCEPTS

In the introduction I attempted to describe the three basic philosophical species concepts which play a role in systematics. Much of the discussion of this symposium dealt with the problem of the utilization of such concepts in the taxonomic practice. It may be useful at this point to say a word or two on the basic method of the application of concepts. In particular it must be emphasized that a concept is not necessarily invalidated if it cannot be applied in an individual case. The concept tree is unquestionably valid, yet one may have doubts whether or not to include in this concept such plants as a spreading juniper, a dwarf willow, a giant cactus, and a strangler fig. Some of our most universally accepted concepts encounter the same difficulties as the species concept, namely, borderline cases or insufficient information. Child and adult are two concepts which are not invalidated by the fact that the adolescent is a borderline stage. Father is a completely valid concept, but its application sometimes encounters difficulties as is evident in paternity suits.

The student who attempts to apply the species concept to concrete situations in nature faces, as all the speakers have emphasized, numerous difficulties. At first sight there appears to be a bewildering diversity of perplexities, but these can be classified into some major groups as was shown by Grant (this symposium), and a study of the various classes of difficulties helps considerably in an understanding of the species problem. Basically all obstacles in the application of a biological species concept are due either to a lack of pertinent information on some essential property of the investigated material or to its evolutionary intermediacy.

LACK OF INFORMATION

Different kinds of information are needed to permit the correct assignment of individuals to species. Most commonly the question arises whether certain morphologically rather distinct individuals belong to the same species or not. The long list of synonyms, characteristic for some groups of animals and plants, are a concrete expression of this difficulty (Mayr, Linsley, and Usinger, 1953). This difficulty is particularly acute in three branches of animal taxonomy. In many families of insects, particularly hymenoptera, males and females are so different that separate classifications for males and females have to be adopted until the proper associations have been made. Even more different are the larval stages in many groups of insects and aquatic organisms. The same is true for parasites for which it is likewise sometimes necessary to have two sets of names, one for larval and one for adult stages, until association can be demonstrated through elucidation of the life cycle. The difficulties caused by sexual dimorphism, age differences, or nongenetic habitat differences which the neontologist faces in his work must be emphasized because some taxonomists seem to believe that paleontologists are the only ones who have to cope with the difficulty of having to draw inferences from morphological types. That this difficulty is particularly acute in paleontology no one will deny. The worker who finds two or more essentially similar, yet somewhat different, morphological types in a single sample of fossils is forced to make a somewhat arbitrary decision whether to consider them as variants within a single interbreeding population or rather as several similar species. There is no automatic solution. The splitting of every bimodal curve into two morphological species would lead to the separation of males and females or of age classes into separate species and to other equally unbiological conclusions. Sylvester-Bradley (1956) and Imbrie (this symposium) have pointed to the fallacy of this approach. "The paleontologist who classes members of a single interbreeding community in more than one species is liable to confuse even himself when he refers to hybridism. The distinction, in fact, between morphological species and bio-species can only be overlooked at the peril of utter confusion." Paleontologists cannot afford to forget that fossils are nothing but the remains of formerly living organisms and that these organisms when still alive occurred in the form of genetically defined populations exactly as the species still living today. It is these populations which the paleontologist attempts to classify with the help of fossil remains, and morphological criteria are used merely as a means to an end.

Paleontologists classify their material on the basis of inferences. The better they understand the nature of biological populations, the relations of genotype and phenotype, and the results of developmental physiology, the more skillfully they can interpret the available morphological evidence. There is no justification for abandoning the biological approach merely because it is sometimes difficult to decide whether or not several morphological types in a population are conspecific.

A second type of difficulty is introduced when there is insufficient information on the reproductive isolation of populations that are not in contact with each other. Some paleontologists have insisted that the classification of samples of discontinuous vertical sequences introduces a new element in the evaluation of populations, not appreciated by the neontologist. This is not altogether true. The taxonomic, genetic, and ecological problems of the multidimensional species are quite the same whether one deals with a series of populations in a chronological series, as does the paleontologist, or with geographically isolated populations, as does the neontologist. This has been recognized correctly by the paleontologist Gwynn Thomas (1956): "The essential similarity of temporal and spatial variation in fossils also makes the paleontological species concept for practical purposes almost identical with the neontological in fragmentary lineage segments." In either case we are dealing with isolated samples, and in either case we have to base a somewhat arbitrary decision as to species status on a good deal of indirect evidence. Again the difficulty is not with the yardstick but with its application.

There is a third group of cases where we lack information on the reproductive isolation of individuals, namely, all forms of asexuality. However, in this case more is involved than mere lack of information because here we are not dealing with populations. This then is a much more formidable and more fundamental obstacle to the application of the species concept, and the discussion of this difficulty shall therefore be postponed to a later section. (See below.)

EVOLUTIONARY INTERMEDIACY

A species definition postulates at least a discontinuity and, under the most favorable conditions, a triad of characteristics: reproductive isolation, ecological difference, and morphological distinguishability. However, evolution is a gradual process and so is the multiplication of species. As a consequence, there are many instances where a population is on the borderline and has acquired some but not yet all the attributes of a distinct species. The gradual nature of the speciation process raises the following difficulties for the student of multidimensional species.

Evolutionary continuity. Species that are widespread in space or time may have terminal populations which satisfy the criteria of distinct species, yet are connected by an unbroken chain of populations. Dr. Moore has described such a situation for contemporary populations of *Rana pipiens*; they are indeed not rare in polytypic species. Theoretically this should be the standard condition in paleontology, yet one has difficulty finding such cases in the literature because breaks in the fossil record are sufficiently frequent to prevent the piecing together of unbroken lineages. One of the best substantiated ones is that of *Micraster* discussed by Imbrie (this symposium). On the other hand, there are conspicuous gaps in most of the celebrated cases of so-called unbroken lineages such as for instance Brinkmann's Kosmoceras. In some cases of real continuity between morphological species the differences are so slight that most contemporary neontologists would not hesitate to consider these forms merely subspecies of a single polytypic species. Even though the number of cases that cause real difficulties is very small, the fact remains that an objective delimitation of species in a multi-dimensional system is an impossibility.

Acquisition of reproductive isolation without equivalent morphological change. The reconstruction of the genotype which is responsible for the reproductive isolation between two species takes place sometimes without visible effect on the phenotype. The resulting "sibling species" qualify as biological species, but not as morphological species. Sonneborn has shown that the varieties of *Paramecium* belong in this class. In plants most sibling species appear to be autopolyploids. Where such sibling species clearly differ in their ecology, nothing is gained by ignoring them merely because the morphological difference is slight. On the other hand, where morphological and ecological differences are not discernible, as seems to be the case in some instances of autopolyploidy in plants or where the differences can be established only by breeding in the laboratory such as the varieties of *Paramecium*, it would seem impractical to separate these forms as species in routine taxonomic work.

Strong morphological differences without reproductive isolation. A number of genera of animals and plants are known where even strikingly different populations interbreed freely wherever they come in contact. Grant (this symposium) has discussed this situation in detail and has given numerous illustrations. The attitude of calling every morphologically distinct population a species, which was widespread among classical taxonomists, is definitely losing ground. Yet to combine all morphological species that freely hybridize in zones of contact also leads to absurdity. Full agreement as to where to compromise between these two extremes has not yet been reached. Such situations occur also in the animal kingdom as, for instance, in the snail genus *Cerion* (Mayr and Rosen, 1956). When the morphological differences between such populations far exceed those normally found between good species in related genera, the taxonomist is reluctant to unite them into a single species. These cases are in a way the exact opposite to sibling species. The acquisition of reproductive isolating mechanisms is lagging far behind the general genetic divergence of these populations as indicated by their morphological divergence.

Deficiencies in the isolating mechanisms. One, if not the most important, attribute of a species is its possession of isolating mechanisms. These isolating mechanisms are usually composite and mutually reinforcing, but often they maintain only partial isolation between populations. This becomes evident when a temporary isolation between geographical isolates breaks down, resulting in allopatric, or if the isolation was primarily ecological, in sympatric hybridization. Numerous cases are known where natural populations acted toward each other like good species in areas of contact as long as their habitats were undisturbed. Yet when the characteristics of these habitats were suddenly changed in a drastic manner, usually by the interference of man, the reproductive isolation broke down. Before this breakdown everyone would have agreed that these populations were species, but after the breakdown and after the loss of reproductive isolation, they agreed better with the specifications of conspecific populations.

The frequency of hybridization, that is, the susceptibility to a secondary breakdown of partial reproductive isolation, is very different in different groups of animals and plants. In most higher animals hybridization is sufficiently rare (or else the hybrids sterile) not to cause any serious difficulties in species delimitation. In cases like the snail genus *Cerion*, discussed above, it is a major source of difficulty. Grant has discussed in detail (in this symposium) the effect of this phenomenon on the species problem in plants and has supplied quantitative data indicating its relative importance in different genera. It is obvious that the delimitation of species becomes a serious problem in genera where species hybridize freely with each other and where introgression is a major factor.

The role of isolating mechanisms for the species problem is brought into sharp focus by a consideration of hybridization. Moore has paid special attention to this side of the species problem in his discussion of the origin of isolating mechanisms (this symposium). He concludes that they originate as a consequence of the genetic differences which accumulate among isolated populations during adaptation to local conditions. This thesis seems well substantiated and corresponds indeed to my own analysis of the situation. Yet part of his evidence may have to be interpreted in a different manner, namely, the significance of the climatic races of *Rana pipiens*. Moore has shown that the various geographic races of this species are adapted in their embryonic development to prevailing local water temperatures. When individuals of a cold-adapted race are crossed with ones of a warm-adapted race, a more or less inviable hybrid will result. Moore concludes from this "that the northern and southern forms have developed isolating mechanisms, in reference to each other, to such a degree that they could coexist and remain distinct." I am not convinced that this conclusion is warranted. It is quite possible, if not probable, that much of this local adaptation is purely ecotypic and essentially reversible. If a warm climate race would reinvade a cool climate, its developmental rates and temperature tolerance would have to be modified by selection to permit survival in the cooler waters. If it should subsequently come into contact with a local cool water race, it might hybridize with it and produce harmonious viable zygotes. That this is not pure speculation is indicated by the *Rana pipiens* population in the mountains of Costa Rica, which in the cool waters has acquired the developmental properties of Vermont frogs and when crossed with them produces normal viable zygotes. Differences that are purely ecotypic local adaptations are not necessarily good isolating mechanisms because they tend to disappear as soon as the environmental differences disappear. This does not preclude the possibility of other incipient isolating mechanisms in previously isolated populations.

Different levels of speciation in different local populations of the same polytypic species. The amount of genetic divergence may differ in various isolated populations of a polytypic species. This inequality in the level of speciation takes different forms. Particularly spectacular are the cases of circular overlap, an increasing number of which are cited in the literature. Other cases are sympatric species, which are completely distinct at certain localities but hybridize freely at others. Lorkovicz (1953) has suggested broadening the term semispecies (Mayr, 1940) to include all isolated populations which on the basis of some criteria have reached species level, but not on the basis of others. Grant (this symposium) has made a similar suggestion to broaden the application of the term semispecies. All these difficulties demonstrate the fact that the clear-cut alternatives of the nondimensional situation are absent in a multidimensional system.

The species indicates a discontinuity above the level of the individual, but a new difficulty is introduced by the fact that there may be several such discontinuities, not all of them being species. If we designate as isolate any more or less isolated population or population segment, we can distinguish in sexually reproducing organisms between geographical, ecological, and reproductive isolates of which only the latter are species. Among asexually reproducing organisms every clone and, in fact, every individual is an isolate. Here, obviously, the species and the isolate can even less be synonymized with each other than in sexually reproducing organisms.

ASEXUALITY AND THE SPECIES PROBLEM

The essence of the biological species concept is discontinuity due to reproductive isolation. Without sexuality this concept cannot be applied. Asexuality then is the most formidable and most fundamental obstacle of a biological species concept. In truly asexual organisms there are no "populations" in the sense in which this term exists in sexual species nor can "reproductive isolation" be tested. Students of the species problem have neglected asexual situations for a number of reasons. The geneticist is interested only in sexual species because it is the recombining of genetic factors through the sexual process which permits formal genetics. The only event of genetic interest that happens in asexually reproducing organisms is an occasional mutation the effects of which will be invisible unless it is dominant or the organism is haploid. Absence of sexuality in existing organisms is almost certainly a secondary, derived phenomenon (Dougherty, 1955) and consequently does not require the setting up of a primarily different species category. Finally, widespread though it is in certain groups of organisms, asexuality is an exception rather than the rule, and species can be defined and delimited in most groups of organisms without any reference to loss of sexuality.

What can one do if one wants to apply the species concept to asexual organisms in view of the breakdown of the usual criteria? A number of different solutions have been proposed. The first is to find a species definition which would be equally suitable for sexual and asexual organisms. Du Rietz (1930) thought that the following definition was satisfactory: "The smallest natural populations permanently separated from each other by a distinct discontinuity in the series of biotypes are called species." This forgets that asexual organisms do not form "natural populations" and that in asexual organisms every individual and every clone is such a distinct biotype. The clear realization of this difficulty has led some authors to go one step farther and abandon the biological concept altogether, because of its inapplicability to asexual situations. Frankly, it appears to me that there is nothing to recommend this solution. In exchange for the biological species with all its advantages, it reintroduces the morphological species with all its weaknesses pointed out by most of the speakers at this symposium.

A second solution is to restrict the term species to sexually reproducing organisms and use it only in the sense of biological species. This proposal comes closer to a satisfactory solution, but it still leaves open the question how to classify morphologically differing individuals in asexual organisms. It has been suggested to use for them a neutral term, such as the term binom, mentioned by Grant (this symposium). The suggestion overlooks the fact that the word species has not only the biological meaning of a reproductively isolated population but also the purely formal meaning "kind of," simply a classifying unit. The term "agamo-species" has been used to designate "totally asexual populations" but, as stated above, an "asexual population" is a biological impossibility.

The most satisfactory solution in taxonomic practice has been a frankly dualistic one. It consists in defining the term species biologically in sexual organisms and morphologically in asexual ones. There is more justification in this procedure than a mere pragmatic one. The growing elucidation of the relations between genotype and phenotype also justify this approach. Reproductive isolation is effected by physiological properties which have a genetic basis. Morphological characters are the product of the same gene complex. Once this is clearly understood, a new role can be assigned to morphological differences associated with reproductive isolation, namely that of indicators of specific distinctness. This permits the assumption that the amount of genetic difference which, in a given taxonomic group, results in reproductive isolation will be correlated with a certain amount of morphological difference. If this is true, it is permissible to conclude from the degree of morphological difference on the probable degree of reproductive isolation. To base this inference on genetic reasoning is new; the method itself, however, of determining empirically with the help of morphological criteria whether or not a population has reached species status goes back to classical taxonomy. This inference method is by no means a return to a morphological species concept since reproductive isolation always remains the primary criterion and degree of morphological difference only a secondary indicator, which will be set aside whenever it comes in conflict with the biological evidence.

It is possible to use the same kind of inference to classify asexual organisms into species. Those asexual individuals are included in a single species that display no more morphological difference from each other than do conspecific individuals in related sexual species. Criteria must be adjusted to individual situations since there is great diversity in the forms of asexuality. Where sexuality is abandoned only temporarily, as in the cases of seasonal parthenogenesis in *Daphnia* and aphids, there is no problem. It is customary and biologically sound to consider such temporary clones as portions of the total gene pool of a species. Nor is there any major difficulty where sexuality is lost in a single species of a genus or in a number of lines which can be clearly traced back to a common ancestor and where the morphological differences are still slight enough to justify combining these "microspecies" into a single collective species (Mayr, 1951). By far more difficult is the situation in many microorganisms where sexual reproduction or its genetic equivalents are totally absent in large groups or at best highly sporadic. To include all descendants of a common ancestor in a single collective species is also impossible in groups like the bdelloid rotifers which, apparently without sexual reproduction, have grown to an order with four families, some twenty genera, and several hundred "species" all reproducing parthenogenetically and possibly all descendants from a single ancestor. If such a group were a complete morphological continuum, any attempt to break it up into species would be doomed to failure. Curiously enough there seem to be a number of discontinuities which make taxonomic subdivision possible. The most reasonable explanation of this phenomenon is that the existing types are the survivors among a great number of produced forms, that the surviving types are clustered around a limited number of adaptive peaks, and that ecological factors have given the former continuum a taxonomic structure. Each adaptive peak is occupied by a different "kind" of organism, and it is legitimate to call each of these clusters of biotypes a species.

The large list of difficulties which the application of the species concept faces may seem to confirm the opinion of those who consider the species as something purely subjective and arbitrary. To counterbalance this impression it must be emphasized *(a)* that none of these difficulties of application invalidates the three basic concepts of the species; *(b)* that these difficulties are infrequent in most groups of animals and higher plants and that the frequency and significance of their occurrence can be determined rather accurately; *(c)* that such difficulties are usually of minor importance in nondimensional situations which are those most frequently encountered by the taxonomist; and *(d)* that in spite of these difficulties it is usually possible to classify doubtful entities into taxonomic species which satisfy at least one or the other species concept. To use the words of G. G. Simpson (1943): "A taxonomic species is an inference as to the most probable characters and limits of the morphological species from which a given series of specimens is drawn."

THE PRACTICAL IMPORTANCE OF SPECIES

Those who maintain that species are something purely subjective, vague, and arbitrary sometimes ask: "What is gained by recognizing species?" The answer is that the attempt to determine species status has led in many cases not only to a more precise formulation of a biological problem but very often also to its solution. As an illustration I will call attention to only three areas of biological research where this is true.

The clarification of simplification of classification. The need for classifying the morphological diversity of nature into biological species forces an unequivocal decision how to handle morphological variants. Accepting the biological species concept no longer permits either describing all variants as morphological species or listing the more pronounced ones as species and the less distinct ones as varieties. Now only those variants are given species rank which satisfy the criterion of the biological species concept, namely, reproductive isolation. The result is a simplification of classification which is not only of practical help to the working taxonomist but also actually aids the understanding of distribution, ecology, and phylogeny. In ornithology it has permitted a reduction in the number of species from nearly 20,000 to 8,600, and a similar simplification is apparent throughout zoology. There are still some authors who resent having to make such decisions, some of which by necessity will be incorrect, and who prefer to classify all organisms into meaningless but comparable morphological species. It is quite evident that these workers fight a losing battle because biologically trained taxonomists are unhappy to be degraded into pebble sorters. They would much rather make an occasional mistake than be burdened forever with a multitude of purely morphologically defined pigeon holes.

Fossil species. The need to evaluate fossil specimens in terms of biological species has led and is leading to a new outlook in paleontological classification (Sylvester-Bradley, 1956). It forces the paleontologist to make clear decisions: Different specimens found in the same exposure (the same sample) must be either different species or intrapopulation variants, "for two geographical subspecies cannot come from the same locality, and two chronological subspecies cannot come from the same horizon" (Sylvester-Bradley, *op. cit.*). The recognition of subspecies and polytypic species in paleontology leads to the same simplification and greater precision as it has in neontology. In all this work the evidence is largely morphological, but the interpretation is based on biological concepts. An occasional error of interpretation in the synthesis of polytypic species in paleontology is vastly to be preferred to the chaotic accumulation of morphologically defined entities without biological meaning.

Biological races. The shift of emphasis from morphological difference to reproductive isolation has necessitated a reanalysis of the whole complex of phenomena loosely referred to as "biological races." These are of great practical importance since most of these so-called biological races were found during the study of disease vectors or of injurious animals. Here again the need for a clear decision, species or not, has led to clarification and simplification. The study of sibling species which has been the major outcome of this analysis has been, in many cases, of great practical importance in applied biology.

The species is, however, of more than purely practical importance. It has a very distinct biological significance which has been described above (Introduction). Finally, a new field of research is growing around the species.

THE SCIENCE OF THE SPECIES

It has become apparent within recent years that a new branch of biology is developing, the science of species. It is devoted to the many-sided aspects of the species and to the understanding of the level of integration which is denoted by the term species. This branch of biology is as legitimate as is cytology, devoted to the level of the cell, or histology, dealing with the level of the tissue. The species is an important unit in evolution, in ecology, in the behavioral sciences, and in applied biology.

The study of the biological properties of species has within recent decades led to the development of several new fields in biology, each being a borderline field between the science of species on the one hand and some other branch of biology, e.g., genetics, ecology, animal psychology on the other. It would lead too far to paint a detailed picture of this recent development, and I will content myself to outline it with a few bold strokes. These new fields are:

The study of speciation. Darwin, as we saw, had fallen down in his attempt to explain the multiplication of species because he was not fully aware of the multiple aspects of species. Nor did he realize that multiplication of species, an origin of discontinuities, is not the same as simple evolutionary change. The study of the mechanisms and modes of speciation has become an interesting borderline field between systematics, genetics, and evolution.

The study of isolating mechanisms. The appreciation of the fact that in addition to sterility there are many other factors which safeguard the genetic integrity of species has led to the development of a new field of study. As far as animals are concerned, contact was established with the field of animal psychology because the ethological isolating mechanisms are among the most conspicuous manifestations of animal behavior. The study of courtship behavior has importantly contributed to the concepts of Lorenz and Tinbergen and has led to a reinterpretation of many facts which Darwin had grouped together under the heading "Sexual Selection."

The study of intraspecific and interspecific competition. The realization that there is a subtle difference between the competition that goes on among conspecific individuals and that among individuals belonging to different species has had a very stimulating effect in the field of ecology. That interspecific competition is an important centrifugal factor in evolution has been demonstrated by various recent authors. Attempts to determine and to measure such competition more precisely have led to a much more detailed study of the ecology and the population structure of species than was attempted by the ecologists of preceding decades.

Study of the genetic structure of species. The realization that local populations belong to a broader system, the species, and that the total genetic content of these intercommunicating populations are the gene pool of the species has had a profound effect on population genetics. It has led to new questions and has facilitated the understanding of certain intrapopulation phenomena. Studies of the balance of the gene complex, of the balance between local adaptation and compatibility with gene dispersal and of hybridization between species have led to a broadening of genetics which transcends considerably the genetics of the early Mendelian period.

The study of physiological species differences. In physiology a development is taking place which parallels that in genetics. It involves the realization that the ecotypic physiological differences of local populations are of a different order of magnitude from that existing between good species. Each species is a separate physiological system, and these physiological differences are of different kinds as pointed out by Prosser (in this symposium). With physiological characteristics of populations, special care must be exercised to distinguish between genetically controlled characters and others. Prosser has shown that nongenetic acclimatizations are particularly frequent in marine animals with pelagic larval stages. Such organisms must be capable of coping with the water conditions in the area where they settle. It would be a mistake, however, to conclude from this special case that all infraspecific population differences of physiological characters are nongenetic. There is not only the excellent work of the Stanford group (Clausen, Hiesey, and Keck) and their associates, which clearly establishes the genetic nature of physiological differences between local races of plants, and similar results have been obtained elsewhere, but also a large body of fact demonstrating geographic variation of physiological characters in terrestrial animals. The ultimate differences between species are in part built up from such population differences. However, a distinction must be made between purely ecotypic local adaptation to purely local conditions and a more general physiological divergence which is almost always found in isolated populations (Mayr, 1956). Physiological differentiation sometimes proceeds more rapidly than morphological change, and this is the explanation for the occurrence of sibling species in many groups.

The study of physiological adaptations and limitations is still very much at the beginning. This seems to be one of the most promising branches of comparative physiology. A study of the physiological differences between species, particularly aquatic species, with respect to rates of development, temperature adaptation, and temperature tolerance has already yielded most interesting findings.

These are only a few indications of newly developing branches of biology specifically dealing with the species level. They refer to the development I had in mind when I said that we were witnessing at the present time the growth of a "science of species."

CONCLUSION

The discussions of this symposium show clearly that species are still a stimulating subject and that the species problem still offers a challenge. There are many difficulties in applying the species concept to the vast variety of discontinuities found in organic nature. Yet many biological phenomena would make no sense if individuals were not organized into populations, and these populations into species. Species are an important biological phenomenon, important to every biologist because every biologist works with species.

REFERENCES

Arkell, W. J. 1956. The species concept in paleontology. *Systematics Assoc. Publ. No. 2,* pp. 97–99.

Bachmann, H. 1905. Der Speziesbegriff. *Verhandl. schweiz. naturforsch. Ges.,* **87**, 161–208.

Baer, K. E. von. 1828. *Entwickelungs-Geschichte der Thiere.* Königsberg.

Besnard, A. F. 1864. Altes und Neues zur Lehre über die organische Art (Spezies). *Abhandl. zool. mineral. Ver. Regensburg,* **9**, 1–72.

Bessey, C. E. 1908. The taxonomic aspect of the species question. *Am. Naturalist,* **42**, 218–24.

Brauer, F. 1885. Systematisch-zoologische Studien. *Sitzber. Akad. Wiss. Wien,* **91** (Abt. 1), 237–413.

Britton, N. L. 1908. The taxonomic aspect of the species question. *Am. Naturalist,* **42**, 225–42.

Burma, B. H. 1949a. The species concept: A semantic review. *Evolution,* **3**, 369–70.

Burma, B. H. 1949b. The species concept: Postscriptum. *Evolution,* **3**, 372–73.

Burma, B. H. 1954. Reality, existence, and classification: A discussion of the species problem. *Madroño,* **7**, 193–209.

Cain, A. J. 1953. Geography, ecology and coexistence in relation to the biological definition of the species. *Evolution,* **7**, 76–83.

Camp, W. H., and C. L. Gillis. 1943. The structure and origin of species. *Brittonia,* **4**, 323–85.

Darwin, C. 1859. *On the Origin of the Species by Means of Natural Selection.* London.

Dobzhansky, T. 1935. A critique of the species concept in biology. *Phil. Sci.,* **2**, 344–55.

Dobzhansky, T. 1950. Mendelian populations and their evolution. *Am. Naturalist,* **84**, 401–18.

Doederlein, L. 1902. Über die Beziehungen nahe verwandter "Thierformen" zu einander. *Z. Morphol. Anthropol.,* **26**, 23–51.

Dougherty, E. C. 1955. Comparative evolution and the origin of sexuality. *Systematic Zool.,* **4**, 145–69.

Du Rietz, G. E. 1930. The fundamental units of botanical taxonomy. *Svensk. Bot. Tidsskr.,* **24**, 333–428.

Eimer, G. H. T. 1889. *Artbildung und Verwandtschaft bei Schmetterlingen.* Jena, Vol. II, p. 16.

Geoffroy Saint Hilaire, I. 1859. Histoire naturelle génerale des règnes organiques, **2**, 437, Paris.

Ginsburg, I. 1938. Arithmetical definition of the species, subspecies and race concept, with a proposal for a modified nomenclature, *Zoologica,* **23**, 253–86.

Gloger, C. L. 1833. *Das Abändern der Vögel durch Einfluss des Klimas.* Breslau.

Gloger, C. L. 1856. Ueber den Begriff von "Art" ("Species") und was in dieselbe hinein gehört. *J. Ornithol.,* **4**, 260–70.

Godron, D. A. 1853. *De l'espèce et des races dan les êtres organisés et specialment de l'unité de l'espèce humaine.* Paris, 2 vols.

Green, E. L. 1912. Linnaeus as an evolutionist. In *Carolus Linnaeus,* pp. 73–91. C. Sower & Co., Philadelphia, Pa.

Gregg, J. R. 1950. Taxonomy, language and reality. *Am. Naturalist,* **84**, 419–35.

Huxley, J. 1942. *Evolution, the Modern Synthesis.* Allen and Unwin, London.

Illiger, J. C. W. 1800. *Versuch einer systematischen vollständigen Terminologie für das Thierreich und Pflanzenreich.* Helmstedt.

Jordan, K. 1896. On mechanical selection and other problems. *Novit. Zool.,* **3**, 426–525.

Jordan, K. 1905. Der Gegensatz zwischen geographischer und nichtgeographischer Variation. *Z. wiss. Zool.,* **83**, 151–210.

Kuhn, E. 1948. Der Artbegriff in der Paläontologie. *Eclogae Geolog. Helv.,* **41**, 389–421.

Lorkovicz, Z. 1953. Spezifische, semispezifische und rassische Differenzierung bei *Erebia tyndarus* Esp. *Rad Acad. Yougoslave,* **294**, 315–58.

Mayr, E. 1940. Speciation phenomena in birds. *Am. Naturalist,* **74**, 249–78.

Mayr, E. 1942. *Systematics and the Origin of Species.* Columbia University Press, New York, N.Y.

Mayr, E. 1949. The species concept: Semantics versus semantics. *Evolution,* **3**, 371–72.

Mayr, E. 1951. Concepts of classification and nomenclature in higher organisms and micro-organisms. *Ann. N.Y. Acad. Sci.,* **56**, 391–97.

Mayr, E. 1955. Karl Jordan's contribution to current concepts in systematics and evolution. *Trans. Roy. Entomol. Soc. London,* pp. 45–66.

Mayr, E. 1956. Geographical character gradients and climatic adaptation. *Evolution,* **10**, 105–8.

Mayr, E., and C. Rosen. 1956. Geographic variation and hybridization in populations of Bahama snails *(Cerion).* *Am. Museum Novit.,* **1806**, 1–48.

Mayr, E., E. G. Linsley, and R. L. Usinger. 1953. *Methods and Principles of Systematic Zoology.* McGraw-Hill Book Co., New York, N.Y.

Meglitsch, P. A. 1954. On the nature of the species. *Systematic Zool.,* **3**, 49–65.

Niggli, P. 1949. *Probleme der Naturwissenschaften* (Der Begriff der Art in der Mineralogie). Basel.

Plate, L. 1914. Prinzipien der Systematik mit besonderer Berücksichtigung des Systems der Tiere. In *Die Kultur der Gegenwart,* III (iv, 4), pp. 92–164.

Poulton, E. B. 1903. What is a species? *Proc. Entomol. Soc. London* for 1903, pp. lxxvii–cxvi.

Quatrefages, A. de. 1892. Darwin et les précurseurs français. Paris.

Ramsbottom, J. 1938. Linnaeus and the species concept. *Proc. Linnean Soc. London.* (150 session), pp. 192–219.

Ray, J. 1686. *Historia Plantarum,* p. 40.

Rensch, B. 1929. *Das Prinzip geographischer Rassenkreise und das Problem der Artbildung.* Bornträger Verl., Berlin.

Schopenhauer, A. 1851. *Parerga und Paralipomena: kleine philosophische Schriften.* Vol. 2, pp. 121–22. Berlin.

Simpson, G. G. 1943. Criteria for genera, species, and subspecies in zoology and paleozoology. *Ann. N.Y. Acad. Sci.,* **44**, 145–78.

Simpson, G. G. 1951. The species concept. *Evolution,* **5**, 285–98.

Sirks, M. J. 1952. Variability in the concept of species. *Acta Biotheoretica,* **10**, 11–22.

Spring, A. F. 1838. *Ueber die naturhistorischen Begriffe von Gattung, Art und Abart und über die Ursachen der Abartungen in den organischen Reichen.* Leipzig.

Spurway, H. 1955. The sub-human capacities for species recognition and their correlation with reproductive isolation. *Acta XI Congr. Intern. Orn.,* Basel, 1954, pp. 340–49.

Stresemann, E. 1919. Über die europäischen Baumläufer. *Verhandl. Orn. Ges. Bayern,* **14**, 39–74.

Sylvester-Bradley, P. C. 1956. The species concept in paleontology. Introduction. *Systematics Assoc. Publ. No. 2.*

Thomas, G. 1956. The species concept in paleontology. *Systematics Assoc. Publ. No. 2,* pp. 17–31.

Uhlmann, E. 1923. Entwicklungsgedanke und Artbegriff in ihrer geschichtlichen Entstehung und sachlichen Beziehung. *Jena. Z. Naturw.,* **59**, 1–114.

Valentine, D. H. 1949. The units of experimental taxonomy. *Acta Biotheoretica,* **9**, 75–88.

Voigt, F. S. 1817. *Grundzüge einer Naturgeschichte als Geschichte der Entstehung und weiterer Ausbilding der Naturkörper.* Frankfurt a.M.

Wallace, A. R. 1889. *Darwinism: An Exposition of the Theory of Natural Selection, with Some of Its Applications.* London.

Yapp, W. B. 1951. Definitions in biology. *Nature,* **167**, 160.

Deer Irruptions

by ALDO LEOPOLD

From the fifteenth century until 1910, the deer problem of North America was a matter of too few, rather than of too many.

About 1910 the Kaibab deer herd in Arizona, long stabilized at a level of about 4000 head, began to pyramid its numbers. By 1918 the range showed over-browsing. Between 1918 and 1924, seven successive investigators warned of impending disaster, but nothing was done.

In 1924, at a probable level of 100,000 head, came the first of two catastrophic famines which reduced the herd 60 per cent in two winters. By 1939 the herd had dropped to a tenth of its peak size, and the range had lost much of its pre-irruption carrying capacity.

This was the first of a series of irruptions which have since threatened the future productivity of deer ranges from Oregon to North Carolina, California to Pennsylvania, Texas to Michigan. Wisconsin is one of the more recent irruptive states. . . .

(B) *Kaibab plateau.* Unlike the George Reserve irruption, which was terminated by removing deer, the Kaibab irruption terminated itself by starvation. Some deer were in fact removed, but only after starvation had begun. The period of six years between the first warning (1918) and the final catastrophe (1924) was consumed in debate and litigation.

The effect of prolonged overstocking on the winter food plants was very severe. In 1931, after four-fifths of the herd had starved and only 20,000 deer were left, one investigator says "the range had been so severely damaged that 20,000 was an excessive population. The herd continued to decrease slowly until an estimated 10,000 were present in 1939."

Another investigator estimates the loss in carrying capacity as high as 90 per cent in some areas.

In short, the Kaibab, by reason of the irruption, lost a large part of its deer food without any gain in deer. . . .

These histories exhibit certain common characters of deer herds, of deer food plants, and of human attitudes toward deer, which seem worth recording as background for the Wisconsin problem.

COMMON CHARACTERS

They also exhibit a common sequence of stages which may help to interpret current events, to anticipate research needs, and to guide administrative policy.

Aldo Leopold, "Deer Irruptions," *Wisconsin Conservation Bulletin,* Publication 321 (1943), 1–11. Reprinted by permission.

Winter food. Deer irruptions are a problem in winter food. The summer range usually exceeds the winter range in carrying capacity.

Except in agricultural regions where deer have access to corn, alfalfa, or winter grains, deer subsist in winter mainly on twigs, buds, and catkins of woody plants, i.e. "browse." The browse species differ in palatability. Many investigators have shown that palatable browse is nutritious browse, while unpalatable browse cannot sustain deer in winter.

As a herd increases, the pressure on palatable browse plants weakens them and ultimately kills them. It also prevents their reproduction, or the emergence of their reproduction above snow level. Artificial plantings to reestablish browse are eaten up before they have a chance to grow.

The unpalatable species are thus given a competitive advantage over palatable ones, and replace them. . . .

Winter deer behavior. Most animals, when crowded and hungry, disperse by their own social pressure. Deer herds, at least in winter, seem devoid of such pressure. State after state reports instances of deer stubbornly refusing to leave (or even to be driven from) a depleted winter range. Paraphrased in human terms, "deer would starve rather than move."

This trait results in *spotty* damage to the winter range. The Kaibab, Pennsylvania, New York, and Michigan, all report this spotty character, and it is now visible in Wisconsin. It confuses laymen, who see spots of undamaged winter browse and conclude that no crisis exists.

Perhaps wolves and cougars originally performed for deer the function of dispersal from congested spots which most species perform for themselves.

Limitations of artificial feeding. The first human reaction to deer starvation is always an impulse to feed the herd, rather than to reduce it. Winter feeding of game birds and songbirds carries no known penalties, why not feed the deer?

The main difference lies in the effect of artificial feeding on the supply of natural foods. . . .

Deer, on the other hand, subsist on palatable browse which is limited in quantity. Over-consumption progressively reduces next year's growth by attrition, nonreproduction, and replacement. Hence artificial deer food is not a net addition to natural food, and may become a net subtraction. For this reason, the most experienced states have come to doubt the wisdom of artificial feeding, except temporarily, or in emergency. . . .

PREDISPOSING EVENTS

Predators. We have found no record of a deer irruption in North America antedating the removal of deer predators. Those parts of the continent which still retain the native predators have reported no irruptions. This circumstantial evidence supports the surmise that removal of predators predisposes a deer herd to irruptive behavior.

In weighing this question, one must distinguish between the substantial removal of predators and the extirpation of the last individual. . . .

In most parts of the west, the substantial extirpation of deer predators took place within a decade after 1910, when the present system of paid hunters came into full-scale operation. Thus on the Kaibab, wolves were a factor in 1910 but gone by 1926. Cougars were abundant up to about 1915; they are still present but are now kept reduced to a very low level. The Kaibab deer irrupted almost immediately after the extirpation of wolves and the substantial removal of cougars. . . .

Coyotes do not seem to be effective predators in the sense of controlling irruptions, for the Kaibab herd irrupted in the presence of numerous coyotes. . . .

It appears, then, that cougars and wolves are the most effective deer predators. The evidence available supports the surmise that their removal does not cause irruptions, but paves the way for irruptive behavior, either at once or at some future time.

Cuttings. It is common knowledge that in human regions, where the original forests were so dense as to shade out browse, deer "followed the slashings", i.e. did not become abundant until after large areas had been converted to brush. Thus there were few or no deer around Lake Superior before the lumbering era, and deer have spread north into Canada coincident with cuttings. . . .

Buck laws. Laws protecting antlerless deer predispose a herd to irruptive behavior to the extent that they are enforced, for the killing of males in a polygamous species has, within ordinary limits, no effect on reproductive rate. . . .

Fire. There is general agreement that a little fire improves deer range, but that wholesale burning destroys it. When deer happen to irrupt a decade or two after the first effective fire control, damage to deer and range is exaggerated by the closure of tree crowns, for this shades out much browse at a time of maximum need for browse. The present deer crisis in Wisconsin is exaggerated by the present closure of tree crowns which grew up following the fire-control system established about 1930.

In parts of the west, there was widespread reproduction of forest trees following early overgrazing and later fire control. These new forests have now closed their crowns, and thus shaded out much browse. . . .

On the Tendency of Species to form Varieties; and on the Perpetuation of Varieties and Species by a Natural Means of Selection

by CHARLES R. DARWIN and ALFRED R. WALLACE

Read July 1st, 1858
London, June 30th, 1858

My Dear Sir:

The accompanying papers, which we have the honor of communicating to the Linnaean Society, and which all relate to the same subject, viz., the Laws which affect the production of Varieties, Races, and Species, contain the results of the investigations of two indefatigable naturalists, Mr. Charles Darwin and Mr. Alfred Wallace.

These gentlemen having, independently and unknown to one another, conceived the same very ingenious theory to account for the appearance and perpetuation of varieties and of specific forms on our planet, may both fairly claim the merit of being original thinkers in this important line of inquiry; but neither of them having published his views, though Mr. Darwin has for many years past been repeatedly urged by us to do so, and both authors having now unreservedly placed their papers in our hands, we think it would best promote the interests of science that a selection from them should be laid before the Linnaean Society.

Taken in the order of their dates, they consist of:—

1   Extracts from a MS. work on Species, by Mr. Darwin, which was sketched in 1839, and copied in 1844, when the copy was read by Dr. Hooker, and its contents afterwards communicated to Sir Charles Lyell. The first part is devoted to "The Variation of Organic Beings under Domestication and in their Natural State"; and the second chapter of that Part, from which we propose to read to the Society the extracts referred to, is headed, "On the Variation of Organic Beings in a state of Nature; on the Natural Means of Selection; on the Comparison of Domestic Races and true Species."

2   An abstract of a private letter addressed to Professor Asa Gray, of Boston, U.S., in October 1857, by Mr. Darwin, in which he repeats his views, and which shows that these remained unaltered from 1839 to 1857.

3   An Essay by Mr. Wallace, entitled "On the Tendency of Varieties to depart indefinitely from the Original Type." This was written at Ternate in February

Charles R. Darwin and Alfred R. Wallace, "On the Tendency of Species To Form Varieties; and on the Perpetuation of Varieties and Species by a Natural Means of Selection," *Journal of the Linnean Society of London* 3 (1859), 45 ff. Reprinted by permission.

1858, for the perusal of his friend and correspondent Mr. Darwin, and sent to him with the expressed wish that it should be forwarded to Sir Charles Lyell, if Mr. Darwin thought it sufficiently novel and interesting. So highly did Mr. Darwin appreciate the value of the views therein set forth, that he proposed in a letter to Sir Charles Lyell, to obtain Mr. Wallace's consent to allow the Essay to be published as soon as possible. Of this step we highly approved, provided Mr. Darwin did not withhold from the public, as he was strongly inclined to do (in favor of Mr. Wallace), the memoir which he had himself written on the same subject, and which, as before stated, one of us had perused in 1844, and the contents of which we had both of us been privy to for many years. On representing this to Mr. Darwin, he gave us permission to make what use we thought proper of his memoir, &c; and in adopting our present course, of presenting it to the Linnaean Society, we have explained to him that we were not solely considering the relative claims to priority of himself and his friend, but the interests of science generally; for we feel it to be desirable that views founded on a wide deduction from facts, and matured by years of reflection, should constitute at once a goal from which others may start, and that, while the scientific world is waiting for the appearance of Mr. Darwin's complete work. Some of the leading results of his labours, as well as those of his able correspondent, should together be laid before the public.

We have the honour to be yours very obediently,

Charles Lyell
Jos. D. Hooker

J. J. Bennett, Esq.
Secretary of the Linnaean Society.

1. Extract from an unpublished Work on Species, by C. Darwin, Esq., consisting of a portion of a Chapter entitled, "On the Variation of Organic Beings in a state of Nature; On the Natural Means of Selection; on the Comparison of Domestic Races and true Species."

De Candolle, in an eloquent passage, has declared that all nature is at war, one organism with another, or with external nature. Seeing the contented face of nature, this may at first well be doubted; but reflection will inevitably prove it to be true. The war, however, is not constant, but recurrent in a slight degree at short periods, and more severely at occasional more distant periods; and hence its effects are easily overlooked. It is the doctrine of Malthus applied in most cases with tenfold force. As in every climate there are seasons, for each of its inhabitants, of greater and less abundance, so all annually breed; and the moral restraint which in some small degree checks the increase of mankind is entirely lost. Even slow-breeding mankind has doubled in twenty-five years; and if he could increase his food with greater ease, he would double in less time. But for animals without artificial means, the amount of food for each species must, *on an average*, be constant, whereas the increase of all organisms tends to be geometrical, and in a vast majority of cases at an enormous ratio. Suppose in a certain spot there are eight pairs of birds, and that *only* four pairs of them annually (including double hatches) rear only four young, and that these go on rearing their young at the same rate, then at the end of seven years (a short life, excluding violent deaths, for any bird) there will be 2048 birds, instead of the original sixteen. As this increase is quite impossible, we must conclude that birds do not rear nearly half their young, or that the average life of a bird is, from accident, not nearly seven years. Both checks probably concur. The same kind of calculation applied to all plants and animals affords results more or less striking, but in very few instances more striking than in man.

Many practical illustrations of this rapid tendency to increase are on record, among which, during peculiar seasons, are the extraordinary numbers of certain animals; for instance, during the years 1826 to 1828, in La Plata, when from drought some millions of cattle perished, the whole country actually *swarmed* with mice. Now I think it cannot be doubted that during the breeding-season all the mice (with the exception of a few males or females in excess) ordinarily pair, and therefore that this astounding increase during three years must be attributed to a greater number than usual surviving the first year, and then breeding, and so on till the third year, when their numbers were brought down to their usual limits on the return of wet weather. Where man has introduced plants and animals into a new and favorable country, there are many accounts in how surprisingly few years the whole country has become stocked with them. This increase would necessarily stop as soon as the country was fully stocked; and yet we have every reason to believe, from what is known of wild animals, that *all* would pair in the spring. In the majority of cases it is most difficult to imagine where the checks fall—though generally, no doubt, on the seeds, eggs, and young; but when we remember how impossible, even in mankind (so much better known than any other animal), it is to infer from repeated casual observations what the average duration of life is, or to discover the different percentage of deaths to births in different countries, we ought to feel no surprise at our being unable to discover where the check falls in any animal or plant. It should always be remembered, that in most cases the checks are recurrent yearly in small, regular degree, and in an extreme degree during unusually cold, hot, dry, or wet years, according to the constitution of the being in question. Lighten any check in the least degree, and the geometrical powers of increase in every organism will almost instantly increase the average number of the favored species. Nature may be compared to a surface on which rest ten thousand sharp wedges touching each other and driven inwards by incessant blows. Fully to realize these views much reflection is requisite. Malthus on man should be studied; and all such cases as those of the mice in La Plata, of the cattle and horses when first turned out in South America, of the birds by our calculation, &c., should be well considered. Reflect on the enormous multiplying power *inherent and annually in action* in all animals; reflect on the countless seeds scattered by a hundred ingenious contrivances, year after year, over the whole face of the land; and yet we have every reason to suppose that the average percentage of each of the inhabitants of a country usually remains constant. Finally, let it be borne in mind that this average number of individuals (the external conditions remaining the same) in each country is kept up by recurrent struggles against other species or against external nature (as on the borders of the Arctic regions, where the cold checks life), and that ordinarily each individual of every species holds its place, either by its own struggle and capacity of acquiring nourishment in some period of its life from the egg upwards; or by the struggle of its parents (in short-lived organisms, when the main check occurs at longer intervals) with other individuals of the *same* or *different* species.

But let the external conditions of a country alter. If in a small degree, the relative proportions of the inhabitants will in most cases simply be slightly changed; but let the number of inhabitants be small, as on an island, and free access to it from other countries be circumscribed, and let the change of conditions continue progressing (forming new stations), in such a case the original inhabitants must cease to be as perfectly adapted to the changed conditions as they were originally. It has been shown in a former part of this work, that such changes of external conditions would, from their acting on the reproductive system, probably cause the organization of those beings which were most affected to become, as under domestication, plastic. Now, can it be doubted, from the struggle each individual has to obtain subsistence, that any minute variation in structure, habits, or instincts, adapting that individual better to the new conditions, would tell upon its vigour and health? In the struggle it would have a better *chance* of surviving; and those of its offspring which inherited the variation, be it ever so slight, would also have a better *chance*. Yearly more are bred than can survive; the smallest grain in the balance, in the long run, must tell on which death shall fall, and which shall survive. Let this work of selection on the one hand, and death on the other, go on for a thousand generations, who will pretend to affirm that it would produce no effect, when we remember what, in a few years, Bakewell effected in cattle, and Western in sheep, by this identical principle of selection?

To give an imaginary example from changes in progress on an island:— let the organization of a canine animal which preyed chiefly on rabbits, but sometimes on hares, become slightly plastic; let these same changes cause the number of rabbits very slowly to decrease, and the number of hares to increase; the effect of this would be that the fox or dog would be driven to try to catch more hares: his organization, however, being slightly plastic, those individuals with the lightest forms, longest limbs, and best eyesight, let the difference be ever so small, would be slightly favored, and would tend to live longer, and to survive during that kind of a year when food was scarcest; they would also rear more young, which would tend to inherit these slight peculiarities. The less fleet ones would be rigidly destroyed. I can see no more reason to doubt that these causes in a thousand generations would produce a marked effect, and adapt the form of the fox or dog to the catching of hares instead of rabbits, than that greyhounds can be improved by selection and careful breeding. So would it be with plants under similar circumstances. If the number of individuals of a species with plumed seeds could be increased by greater powers of dissemination within its own area (that is, if the check to increase fell chiefly on the seeds), those seeds which were provided with ever so little more down, would in the long run be most disseminated; hence a greater number of seeds thus formed would germinate, and would tend to produce plants inheriting the slightly better-adapted down.

Besides this natural means of selection, by which those individuals are preserved, whether in their egg, or larval, or mature state, which are best adapted to the place they fill in nature, there is as a second agency at work in most uni-sexual animals, tending to produce the same effect, namely, the struggle of the males for the females. These struggles are generally decided by the law of battle, but in the case of birds, apparently, by the charms of their song, by their beauty or their power of courtship, as in the dancing rock-thrush of Guiana. The most vigorous and healthy males, implying perfect adaptation, must generally gain the victory in their contests. This kind of selection, however, is less rigorous than the other; it does not require the death of the less successful, but gives to them fewer descendants. The struggle falls, moreover, at a time of the year when food is generally abundant, and perhaps the effect chiefly produced would be the modification of the secondary sexual characters, which are not related to the power of obtaining food, or to defense from enemies, but to fighting with or rivalling other males. The result of this struggle amongst the males may be compared in some respects to that produced by those agriculturists who pay less attention to the careful selection of all their young animals, and more to the occasional use of a choice mate.

2. Abstract of a Letter from C. Darwin, Esq., to Prof. Asa Gray, Boston, U.S., dated Down, September 5th, 1857.

1   It is wonderful what the principle of selection by man, that is the picking out of individuals with any desired quality, and breeding from them, and again picking out, can do. Even breeders have been astounded at their own results. They can act on differences inappreciable to an uneducated eye. Selection has been *methodically* followed in *Europe* only for the last half century; but it was occasionally, and even in some degree methodically followed in the most ancient times. There must have been also a kind of unconscious selection from a remote period, namely in the preservation of the individual animals (without any thought of their offspring) most useful to each race of man in his particular circumstances. The "roguing," as nurserymen call the destroying of varieties which depart from their type, is a kind of selection. I am convinced that intentional and occasional selection has been the main agent in the production of our domestic races; but however this may be, its great power of modification has been indisputably shown in later times. Selection acts only by the accumulation of slight or greater variations, caused by external conditions, or by the mere fact that in generation the child is not absolutely similar to its parent. Man, by this power of accumulating variations, adapts living beings to his wants—may be said to make the wool of one sheep good for carpets, of another for cloth, &c.

2   Now suppose there were a being who did not judge by mere external appearances, but who could study the whole internal organization, who was never
capricious, and should go on selecting for one object during millions of generations; who will say what he might not effect? In nature we have some *slight*
variation occasionally in all parts; and I think it can be shown that changed
conditions of existence is the main cause of the child not exactly resembling its
parents; and in nature geology shows us what changes have taken place, and
are taking place. We have almost unlimited time; no one but a practical geologist
can fully appreciate this. Think of the Glacial period, during the whole of which
the same species at least of shells have existed; there must have been during this
period millions on millions of generations.

3   I think it can be shown that there is such an unerring power at work in *Natural
Selection* (the title of my book), which selects exclusively for the good of each
organic being. The elder De Candolle, W. Herbert, and Lyell have written ex-
cellently on the struggle for life; but even they have not written strongly enough.
Reflect that every being (even the elephant) breeds at such a rate, that in a few
years, or at most a few centuries, the surface of the earth would not hold the
progeny of one pair. I have found it hard constantly to bear in mind that the
increase of every single species is checked during some part of its life, or during
some short recurrent generation. Only a few of those annually born can live to
propagate their kind. What a trifling difference must often determine which shall
live, and which perish!

4   Now take the case of a country undergoing some change. This will tend to
cause some of its inhabitants to vary slightly—not but that I believe most beings
vary at all times enough for selection to act on them. Some of its inhabitants will
be exterminated; and the remainder will be exposed to the mutual action of a
different set of inhabitants, which I believe to be far more important to the life
of each being than mere climate. Considering the infinitely various methods which
living beings follow to obtain food by struggling with other organisms, to escape
danger at various times of life, to have their eggs or seeds disseminated, &c.,
&c., I cannot doubt that during millions of generations individuals of a species
will be occasionally born with some slight variation, profitable to some part of
their economy. Such individuals will have a better chance of surviving, and of
propagating their new and slightly different structure; and the modification may
be slowly increased by the accumulative action of natural selection to any profitable
extent. The variety thus formed will either coexist with, or, more commonly, will
exterminate its parent form. An organic being, like the woodpecker or misseltoe,
may thus come to be adapted to a score of contingences—natural selection accumulating those slight variations in all parts of its structure, which are in any way
useful to it during any part of its life.

5   Multiform difficulties will occur to every one, with respect to this theory.
Many can, I think, be satisfactorily answered. *Natura non fecit saltum* answers
some of the most obvious. The slowness of the change, and only a very few in-

dividuals undergoing change at any one time, answers others. The extreme imperfection of our geological records answers others.

6   Another principle, which may be called the principle of divergence, plays, I believe, an important part in the origin of species. The same spot will support more life if occupied by very diverse forms. We see this in the many generic forms in a square yard of turf, and in the plants or insects on any little uniform islet, belonging almost invariably to as many genera and families as species. We can understand the meaning of this fact amongst the higher animals, whose habits we understand. We know that it has been experimentally shown that a plot of land will yield a greater weight if sown with several species and genera of grasses, than if sown with only two or three species. Now, every organic being, by propagating so rapidly, may be said to be striving its utmost to increase in numbers. So it will be with the offspring of any species after it has become diversified into varieties, or subspecies, or true species. And it follows, I think, from the foregoing facts, that the varying offspring of each species will try (only few will succeed) to seize on as many and as diverse places in the economy of nature as possible. Each new variety or species, when formed, will generally take the place of, and thus exterminate its less well-fitted parent. This I believe to be the origin of the classification and affinities of organic beings at all times; for organic beings always *seem* to branch and sub-branch like the limbs of a tree from a common trunk, the flourishing and diverging twigs destroying the less vigorous—the dead and lost branches rudely representing extinct genera and families.

This sketch is *most* imperfect; but in so short a space I cannot make it better. Your imagination must fill up very wide blanks.

C. Darwin

3. On the Tendency of Varieties to depart indefinitely from the Original Type. By Alfred Russel Wallace.

One of the strongest arguments which have been adduced to prove the original and permanent distinctness of species is, that *varieties* produced in a state of domesticity are more or less unstable, and often have a tendency, if left to themselves, to return to the normal form of the parent species; and this instability is considered to be a distinctive peculiarity of all varieties, even of those occurring among wild animals in a state of nature, and to constitute a provision for preserving unchanged the originally created distinct species.

In the absence or scarcity of facts and observations as to the *varieties* occurring among wild animals, this argument has had great weight with naturalists, and has led to a very general and somewhat prejudiced belief in the stability of species. Equally general, however, is the belief in what are called "permanent or true varieties,"—races of animals which continually propagate their like, but which differ so slightly (although constantly) from some other race, that the one is considered to be a *variety* of the other. Which is the *variety* and which the original *species*, there is generally no means of determining, except in those rare cases in which the one race has been known to produce an offspring unlike itself and resembling the other. This, however, would seem quite incompatible with the "permanent invariability of species," but the difficulty is overcome by assuming that such varieties have strict limits, and can never again vary further from the original type, although they may return to it, which, from the analogy of the domesticated animals, is considered to be highly probable, if not certainly proved.

It will be observed that this argument rests entirely on the assumption, that *varieties* occurring in a state of nature are in all respects analogous to or even identical with those of domestic animals, and are governed by the same laws as regards their permanence or further variation. But it is the object of the present paper to show that this assumption is altogether false, that there is a general principle in nature which will cause many *varieties* to survive the parent species, and to give rise to successive variations departing further and further from the original type, and which also produces, in domesticated animals, the tendency of varieties to return to the parent form.

The life of wild animals is a struggle for existence. The full exertion of all their faculties and all their energies is required to preserve their own existence and provide for that of their infant offspring. The possibility of procuring food during the least favourable seasons, and of escaping the attacks of their most dangerous enemies, are the primary conditions which determine the existence both of individuals and of entire species. These conditions will also determine the population of the species; and by a careful consideration of all the circumstances we may be enabled to comprehend, and in some degree to explain, what at first sight appears so inexplicable—the excessive abundance of some species, while others closely allied to them are very rare.

The general proportion that must obtain between certain groups of animals is readily seen. Large animals cannot be so abundant as small ones; the carnivora must be less numerous than the herbivora; eagles and lions can never be so plentiful as pigeons and antelopes; the wild asses of the Tartarian deserts cannot equal in numbers the horses of the more luxuriant prairies and pampas of America. The greater or less fecundity of an animal is often considered to be one of the chief causes of its abundance or scarcity; but a consideration of the facts will show us that it really has little or nothing to do with the matter. Even the least prolific of animals would increase rapidly if unchecked, whereas it is evident that the animal population of the globe must be stationary, or perhaps, through the influence of man, decreasing. Fluctuations there may be; but permanent increase except in restricted localities, is almost impossible. For example, our own observation must convince us that birds do not go on increasing every year in a geometrical ratio, as they would do, were there not some powerful check to their natural increase. Very few birds produce less than two young ones each year, while many have six, eight, or ten; four will certainly be below the average; and if we suppose that each pair produce young only four times in their life, that will also be below the average, supposing them not to die either by violence or want of food. Yet at this rate, how tremendous would be the increase in a few years from a single pair! A simple calculation will show that in fifteen years each pair of birds would have increased to nearly ten millions! whereas we have no reason to believe that the number of the birds of any country increases at all in fifteen or in one hundred and fifty years. With such powers of increase the population must have reached its limits, and have become stationary, in a very few years after the origin of each species. It is evident, therefore, that each year an immense number of birds must perish—as many in fact as are born; and as on the lowest calculation the progeny are each year twice as numerous as their parents, it follows that, whatever be the average number of individuals existing in any given country, *twice that number must perish annually*,—a striking result, but one which seems at least highly probable, and is perhaps under rather than over the truth. It would therefore appear that, as far as the continuance of the species and the keeping up the average number of individuals are concerned, large broods are superfluous. On the average all above *one* become food for hawks and kites, wild cats and weasels, or perish of cold and hunger as winter comes on. This is strikingly proved by the case of particular species; for we find that their abundance in individuals bears no relation whatever to their fertility in producing offspring. Perhaps the most remarkable instance of an immense bird population is that of the passenger pigeon of the United States, which lays only one, or at most two eggs, and is said to rear generally but one young one. Why is this bird so extraordinarily abundant, while others producing two or three times as many young are much less plentiful? The explanation is not difficult. The food most congenial to this species, and on which it thrives best, is abundantly distributed over a very extensive region, offering such differences of soil and climate, that in one part or another of the area the supply never fails. The bird is capable of a very rapid and long-continued flight, so that it can pass without fatigue over the whole of the district it inhabits, and as soon as the supply of food begins to fail in one place is able to discover a fresh feeding-ground. This example strikingly shows us that the procuring a constant supply of wholesome food is almost the sole condition requisite for insuring the rapid increase of a given species, since neither the limited fecundity, nor the unrestrained attacks of birds of prey and of man are here sufficient to check it. In no other birds are these peculiar circumstances so strikingly combined. Either their food is more liable to failure, or they have not sufficient power of wing to search for it over an extensive area, or during some season of the year it becomes very scarce, and less wholesome substitutes have to be found; and thus, though more fertile in offspring, they can never increase beyond the supply of food in the least favorable seasons. Many birds can only exist by migrating, when their food becomes scarce, to regions possessing a milder, or at least a different climate, though, as these migrating birds are seldom excessively abundant, it is evident that the countries they visit are still deficient in a constant and abundant supply of wholesome food. Those whose organization does not permit them to migrate when their food becomes periodically scarce, can never attain a large population. This is probably the reason why woodpeckers are scarce with us, while in the tropics they are among the most abundant of solitary birds. Thus the house-sparrow is more abundant than the redbreast, because its food is more constant and plentiful,—seeds of grasses being preserved during the winter, and our farm-yards and stubble-fields furnishing an almost inexhaustible supply. Why, as a general rule, are aquatic, and especially seabirds, very numerous in individuals? Not because they are more prolific than others, generally the contrary; but because their food never fails, the sea-shores and river-banks daily swarming with a fresh supply of small mollusca and crustacea. Exactly the same laws will apply to mammals. Wild cats are prolific and have few enemies; why then are they never as abundant as rabbits? The only intelligible answer is, that their supply of food is more precarious. It appears evident, therefore, that so long as a country remains physically unchanged, the numbers of its animal population cannot materially increase. If one species does so, some others requiring the same kind of food must diminish in proportion. The numbers that die annually must be immense; and as the individual existence of each animal depends upon itself, those that die must be the weakest—the very young, the aged, and the diseased,—while those that prolong their existence can only be the most perfect in health and vigour—those who are best able to obtain food regularly, and avoid their numerous enemies. It is, as we commenced by remarking, "a struggle for existence," in which the weakest and least perfectly organized must always succumb.

Now it is clear that what takes place among the individuals of a species must also occur among the several allied species of a group,—viz. that those which are best adapted to obtain a regular supply of food, and to defend themselves against the attacks of their enemies and the vicissitudes of the seasons, must necessarily obtain and preserve a superiority in population; while those species which from some defect of power or organization are the least capable of counteracting the vicissitudes of food, supply, &c., must diminish in numbers, and, in extreme cases, become altogether extinct. Between these extremes the species will present various degrees of capacity for insuring the means of preserving life; and it is thus we account for the abundance or rarity of species. Our ignorance will generally prevent us from accurately tracing the effects to their causes; but could we become perfectly acquainted with the organization and habits of the various species of animals, and could we measure the capacity of each for performing the different acts necessary to its safety and existence under all the varying circumstances by which it is surrounded, we might be able even to calculate the proportionate abundance of individuals which is the necessary result.

If now we have succeeded in establishing these two points—1st, *that the animal population of a country is generally stationary, being kept down by a periodical deficiency of food, and other checks*; and 2nd, *that the comparative abundance or scarcity of the individuals of the several species is entirely due to their organization and resulting habits, which, rendering it more difficult to procure a regular supply of food and to provide for their personal safety in some cases than in others, can only be balanced by a difference in the population which have to exist in a given area*—we shall be in a condition to proceed to the consideration of *varieties*, to which the preceding remarks have a direct and very important application.

Most or perhaps all the variations from the typical form of the species must have some definite effect, however slight, on the habits or capacities of the individuals. Even a change of colour might, by rendering them more or less distinguishable, affect their safety; a greater or less development of hair might modify their habits. More important changes, such as an increase in the power or dimensions of the limbs or any of the external organs, would more or less affect their mode of procuring food or the range of country which they inhabit. It is also evident that most changes would affect, either favourably or adversely, the powers of prolonging existence. An antelope with shorter or weaker legs must necessarily suffer more from the attacks of the feline carnivora; the passenger pigeon with less powerful wings would sooner or later be affected in its powers of procuring a regular supply of food; and in both cases the result must necessarily be a diminution of the population of the modified species. If, on the other hand, any species should produce a variety having slightly increased powers of preserving existence, that variety must inevitably in time acquire a superiority in numbers. These results must follow as surely as old age, intemperance, or scarcity of food produce an increased mortality. In both cases there may be many individual exceptions; but on the average the rule will invariably be found to hold good. All varieties will therefore fall into two classes—those which under the same conditions would never reach the population of the parent species, and those which would in time obtain and keep a numerical superiority. Now, let some alteration of physical conditions occur in the dictrict—a long period of drought, a destruction of vegetation by locusts, the irruption of some new carnivorous animal seeking "pastures new"—any change in fact tending to render existence more difficult to the species in question, and tasking its utmost powers to avoid complete extermination; it is evident that, of all of the individuals composing the species, those forming the least numerous and most feebly organized variety would suffer first, and, were the pressure severe, must soon become extinct. The same causes continuing in action, the parent species would next suffer, would gradually diminish in numbers, and with a recurrence of similar unfavourable conditions might also become extinct. The superior variety would then alone remain, and on a return to favorable circumstances would rapidly increase in numbers and occupy the place of the extinct species and variety.

The *variety* would now have replaced the *species*, of which it would be a more perfectly developed and more highly organized form. It would be in all respects better adapted to secure its safety, and to prolong its individual existence and that of the race. Such a variety *could not* return to the original form; for that form is an inferior one, and could never compete with it for existence. Granted, therefore, a "tendency" to reproduce the original type of the species, still the variety must ever remain preponderant in numbers, and under adverse physical conditions *again alone survive*. But this new, improved, and populous race might itself, in course of time, give rise to new varieties, exhibiting several diverging modifications of form, any of which, tending to increase the facilities for preserving existence, must, by the same general law, in their turn become predominant. Here, then, we have *progression and continued divergence* deduced from the general laws which regulate the existence of animals in a state of nature, and from the undisputed fact that varieties do frequently occur. It is not, however, contended that this result would be invariable; a change of physical conditions in the district might at times materially modify it, rendering the race which had been the most capable of supporting existence under the former conditions now the least so, and even causing the extinction of the newer and, for a time, a superior race, while the old or parent species and its first inferior varieties continued to flourish. Variations in unimportant parts might also occur, having no perceptible effect on the life-preserving powers; and the varieties so furnished might run a course parallel with the parent species, either giving rise to further variations or returning to the former type. All we argue for is, that certain varieties have a tendency to maintain their existence longer than the original species, and this tendency must make itself felt; for though the doctrine of chances or averages can never be trusted to on a limited scale, yet, if applied to high numbers, the results come nearer to what theory demands, and, as we approach to an infinity of examples, become strictly accurate. Now the scale on which nature works is so vast —the numbers of individuals and periods of time with which she deals approach so near to infinity, that any cause, however slight, and however liable to be veiled and counteracted by accidental circumstances, must in the end produce its full legitimate results.

Let us now turn to domesticated animals, and inquire how varieties produced among them are affected by the principles here enunciated. The essential difference in the condition of wild and domestic animals is this,—that among the former, their well-being and very existence depend upon the full exercise and healthy condition of all their senses and physical powers, whereas, among the latter, these are only partially exercised, and in some cases are absolutely unused. A wild animal has to search, and often to labour, for every mouthful of food—to exercise sight, hearing, and smell in seeking it, and in avoiding dangers, in procuring shelter from the inclemency of the seasons, and in providing for the subsistence and safety of its offspring. There is no muscle of its body that is not called into daily and hourly activity; there is no sense or faculty that is not strengthened by continual exercise. The domestic animal, on the other hand, has food provided for it, is sheltered, and often confined, to guard it against the vicissitudes of the seasons, is carefully secured from the attacks of its natural enemies, and seldom even rears its young without human assistance. Half of its senses and faculties are quite useless; and the other half are but occasionally called into feeble exercise, while even its muscular system is only irregularly called into action.

Now when a variety of such an animal occurs, having increased power or capacity in any organ or sense, such increase is totally useless, is never called into action, and may even exist without the animal ever becoming aware of it. In the wild animal, on the contrary, all its faculties and powers being brought into full action for the necessities of existence, any increase becomes immediately available, is strengthened by exercise, and must even slightly modify the food, the habits, and the whole economy of the race. It creates as it were a new animal, one of superior powers, and which will necessarily increase in numbers and outlive those inferior to it.

Again, in the domesticated animal all variations have an equal chance of continuance; and those which would decidedly render a wild animal unable to compete with its fellows and continue its existence are no disadvantage whatever in a state of domesticity. Our quickly fattening pigs, short-legged sheep, pouter pigeons, and poodle dogs could never have come into existence in a state of nature, because the very first step toward such inferior forms would have led to the rapid extinction of the race; still less could they now exist in competition with their wild allies. The great speed but slight endurance of the race horse, the unwieldy strength of the ploughman's team, would both be useless in a state of nature. If turned wild on the pampas, such animals would probably soon become extinct, or under favorable circumstances might each lose those extreme qualities which would never be called into action, and in a few generations would revert to a common type, which must be that in which the various powers and faculties are so proportioned to each other as to be best adapted to procure food and secure safety,—that in which by the full exercise of every part of his organization the animal can alone continue to live. Domestic varieties, when turned wild, *must* return to something near the type of the original wild stock, *or become altogether extinct*.

We see, then, that no inferences as to varieties in a state of nature can be deduced from the observation of those occurring among domestic animals. The two are so much opposed to each other in every circumstance of their existence, that what applies to the one is almost sure not to apply to the other. Domestic animals are abnormal, irregular, artificial; they are subject to varieties which never occur and never can occur in a state of nature: their very existence depends altogether on human care; so far are many of them removed from that just proportion of faculties, that true balance of organization, by means of which alone an animal left to its own resources can preserve its existence and continue its race.

The hypothesis of Lamarck—that progressive changes in species have been produced by the attempts of animals to increase the development of their own organs, and thus modify their structure and habits—has been repeatedly and easily refuted by all writers on the subject of varieties and species, and it seems to have been considered that when this was done the whole question has been finally settled; but the view here developed renders such an hypothesis quite unnecessary, by showing that similar results must be produced by the action of principles constantly at work in nature. The powerful retractile talons of the falcon- and the cat-tribes have not been produced or increased by the volition of those animals; but among the different varieties which occurred in the earlier and less highly organized forms of these groups, *those always survive longest which had the greatest facilities for seizing their prey*. Neither did the giraffe acquire its long neck by desiring to reach the foliage of the more lofty shrubs, and constantly stretching its neck for the purpose, but because any varieties which occurred among its antitypes with a longer neck than usual *at once secured a fresh range of pasture over the same ground as their shorter-necked companions, and on the first scarcity of food were thereby enabled to outlive them.* Even the peculiar colours of many animals, especially insects, so closely resembling the soil or the leaves or the trunks on which they habitually reside, are explained on the same principle; for though in the course of ages varieties of many tints may have occurred, *yet those races having colours best adapted to concealment from their enemies would inevitably survive the longest.* We have also here an acting cause to account for that balance so often observed in nature,—a deficiency in one set of organs always being compensated by an increased development of some others— powerful wings accompanying weak feet, or great velocity making up for the absence of defensive weapons; for it has been shown that all varieties in which an unbalanced deficiency occurred could not long continue their existence. The action of this principle is exactly like that of the centrifugal governor of the steam engine, which checks and corrects any irregularities almost before they become evident; and in like manner no unbalanced deficiency in the animal kingdom can ever reach any conspicuous magnitude, because it would make itself felt at the very first step, by rendering existence difficult and extinction almost sure soon to follow. An origin such as is here advocated will also agree with the peculiar character of the modifications of form and structure which obtain in organized beings—the many lines of divergence from a central type, the in-creasing efficiency and power of a particular organ through a succession of allied species, and the remarkable persistence of unimportant parts such as colour, texture of plumage and hair, form of horns or crests, through a series of species differing considerably in more essential characters. It also furnishes us with a reason for that "more specialized structure" which Professor Owen states to be a characteristic of recent compared with extinct forms, and which would evidently be the result of the progressive modification of any organ applied to a special purpose in the animal economy.

We believe we have now shown that there is a tendency in nature to the continued progression of certain classes of *varieties* further and further from the original type—a progression to which there appears no reason to assign any definite limits—and that the same principle which produces this result in a state of nature will also explain why domestic varieties have a tendency to revert to the original type. This progression, by minute steps, in various directions, but always checked in balance by the necessary conditions subject to which alone existence can be preserved, may, it is believed, be followed out so as to agree with all the phenomena presented by organized beings, their extinction and succession in past ages, and all the extraordinary modifications of form, instinct, and habits which they exhibit.

Ternate, February, 1858.

Industrial Melanism in the Lepidoptera and its Contribution to our Knowledge of Evolution

by H. B. D. KETTLEWELL

Industrial melanism refers to the phenomenon, at present taking place in the Lepidoptera of many countries, in which whole populations are changing from light to dark coloration. It is in fact the most striking evolutionary change ever witnessed in our life time. It has been referred to as a transient polymorphism: but polymorphism, wherever found, must be accepted as offering an opportunity for research. The fact that two or more forms of a species exist within a population must surely suggest alternative advantages, or disadvantages, for each, and these are, quite definitely, not limited to colour differences alone, but to the whole behaviour and physiological pattern of the individuals concerned. In transient polymorphism, we are witnessing a situation in its acute phase. Much more frequently we meet it in a balanced state in which the environment, with comparatively little change, governs the proportions of the two or more forms in a population. Industrial melanism may, therefore, be regarded as an expression of the degree of change which has taken place due to the impact of civilization. It also reflects the speed at which living organisms can adapt themselves to a changed situation.

In England, since the middle of the last century, black forms of many species have been becoming increasingly common, and at the present moment more than seventy species in the British Isles are in the process of changing. One of the earliest to do this was *Biston betularia* L, the Peppered Moth (Fig. 1, left 1, 2 and 3). Its all black form, *carbonaria* Jordan, was first recorded about 1845 from Manchester, when at its highest frequency it could not have been more than one per cent of the population. By 1895, however, it formed about 99 per cent. J. B. S. Haldane (1924) has shown that this represents an approximate 30 per cent advantage of the black form over the light for this period, a figure hitherto unknown in selective advantages. Since then, the same has taken place in scores of other species, but it must be noted that these are limited to those which depend for survival on their cryptic coloration, species which rely on their colour protection and pass the day concealed sitting motionless on lichened tree trunks, boughs or rocks. Industrial melanism does not normally occur among species which depend on other types of defence, such as warning or flash coloration, nor amongst those which simulate dead leaves or green foliage.

In nearly every case it has been shown that the new black mutant is inherited as a simple Mendelian dominant, and in no case so far investigated has a recessive

H. B. D. Kettlewell, "Industrial Melanism in the Lepidoptera and its Contribution to our Knowledge of Evolution," *Proceedings of the 10th International Congress of Entomology,* 1956 **2** (1958), 831–841. Reprinted by permission.

Fig. 1. *Examples of British industrial melanica with their typical forms.*
Left row: 1, Biston betularia *L. f.* typical; *2,* Biston betularia *f.* carbonaria *Jordan; 3,* Biston betularia *f.* insularia, *Th.-Mieg.; 4,* Gonondontis bidentata *Cl., 5,* Gonondontis bidentata *f.* nigra *Prout; 6,* Hemerophila abruptaria *Thun.; 7,* Hemerophila abruptaria *f.* fuscata *Tutt.* *Right row: 1,* Colocasia coryli *L.; 2,* Colocasia coryli *f.* melanotica *Haverkampf; 3,* Alcis rhomboidaria *Schf.; 4,* Alcis rhomboidaria *f.* nigra *Adkin; 5,* Alcis repandata *L; 6,* Alcis repandata *f.* nigra *Tutt; 7,* Semiothisa liturata *Cl.; 8,* Semiothisa liturata *f.* nigrofulvata *Collins.*

melanic spread through the population. Recessive melanics do, however, occur, but these are for the most part confined to non-cryptic species. They are rare, semi-lethal and are maintained by recurrent mutation.

Industrial melanism is not confined solely to Britain, where, because of the degree of industrialization and also its isolation, it has become more manifest than elsewhere. It is common in North Germany and in most of the other European manufacturing centres. It appears to have arisen at a much later date in North America, where today it is affecting about 100 species in the Pittsburgh area alone. That more has not been learnt about this rapid evolutionary change in its earliest stages is, therefore, a story of missed opportunity. Canada may thus offer us a further chance to exploit what has hitherto been missed. Melanic forms of many species are occurring at the present time around Montreal, Toronto and other centres. They are likely to spread in view of Canada's ambitious industrial programme.

Figure 1 shows, as well as *Biston betularia*, six other species with their melanic forms. They will serve as examples of how melanism has spread in England.

The present position of *Biston betularia* in Britain and its two melanics can been seen from Fig. 2. Three points can be elicited from it. First, there is correlation between a high proportion of the *carbonaria* form and industrial areas. Secondly, in western England, which is still unpolluted, *betularia* are 100 per cent of the *typical* light form; and, thirdly, there is a high proportion of melanics in the eastern counties, though far removed from industrial centres. In my opinion, the reason for this last group is that, with the prevailing southwesterly wind, the whole of eastern England is constantly subject to pollution fall-out as far as the coast and probably further. Moreover, this is substantiated by leaf washings which, even though conducted on a small scale so far, nevertheless show contamination and also by the absence of lichens in the vegetative form from most kinds of tree trunks. A comprehensive analysis of this map is about to go to press (Kettlewell, 1958).

Gonodontis bidentata (Fig. 2, left 4 and 5) has very different habits to the last species; it would appear not to fly nearly so actively. This year, I have been able to show that *betularia* regularly flies two miles and probably more in the course of a night, and this habit must favour gene-flow. The distribution of *bidentata*, f. *nigra* Prout, is local and patchy. Thus in the centre of Birmingham this mutation appears not yet to have taken place, and all the specimens are *typicals* but darker than normal. Twenty miles outside, however, in the colliery area of Cannock Chase, *nigra* forms about 40 per cent of the population.

Hemerophila abruptaria Thun (Fig. 3, left 6 and 7) has its melanics centred on London, but more recently it has appeared further north in Bedfordshire and Northamptonshire, most likely having its origin from a separate mutation and where, no doubt, it will now rapidly spread.

Colocasia coryli L., about 1926 the first melanics were bred from larvæ collected after being blown down by a severe storm in the Chilterns near Tring. Subsequently, melanic moths captured at light continued to increase so that today about 45 per cent taken at light are melanics in this district. In regard to

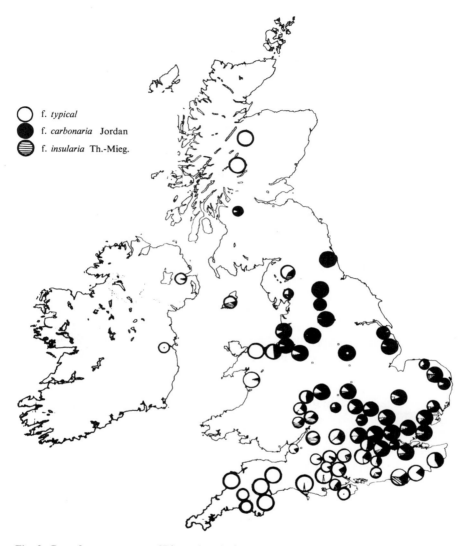

Fig. 2. *Gene frequency map of* Biston betularia *and its two melanics.*

possible behaviour differences, it is of interest to note that on several occasions larvæ have been beaten in some numbers from the lower boughs of beech (*Fagus sylvatica*) in this same district but, it is alleged, on each occasion all produced normal *typical coryli* only. However, more recently, following another high wind, larvæ were collected as they ascended the tree trunks after being blown down. These once again produced a proportion of melanics. If the evidence provided by the individuals concerned is correct, it would appear that there may be a

Fig. 3. Biston betularia *f.* typical *and f.* carbonaria *at rest on lichened oak trunk, Dean End Wood, Dorset.*

behaviour difference between the two forms, larvæ of the melanics feeding on the tops of the trees more frequently, and the typicals on the lower boughs. This example must also draw attention to the fact that in other species we have found behaviour differences between the two forms.

Alcis rhomboidaria Schf. (Fig. 1, right 3 and 4) is common throughout England but, although a darker form of the *typical perfumaria* (Newman) replaced the normal population in the London area many years ago, the all black form *nigra* (Adkin) was for many years found only in the Norwich area of East England. *Alcis repandata* L. (Fig. 1, right 5 and 6) has replaced its *typical* form by a melanic in many industrial areas in the midlands up to 90 per cent of the population. This species will be referred to again later in this paper.

Semiothisa liturata Cl. (Fig. 1, right 7 and 8) is a final example of where throughout central and the eastern half of England the black form is superseding the light. It will be seen from the seven species referred to that the appearance of a melanic form in a particular district is dependent on three factors:—first, the mutation rate for the particular locus; second, the suitability of the environment for receiving it; and, third, its capacity for spread depending on the habits of the species. In regard to the first, it is probable that the mutation rates of different melanics vary greatly. For example, it appears that it may be high in *Biston betularia*, where the *carbonaria* form has arisen separately both in Belfast and

Dublin in Ireland, and more recently again near Torquay in Devon, in each case in towns entirely surrounded by unpolluted countryside and harbouring 100 per cent of the *typical* form. On the other hand, *Ectropis consonaria* Hb. must surely have a very low mutation rate for its melanic form *nigra* Banks. In England it has been driven out of many built up areas but the melanic occurs in two widely separated areas, first near Maidstone in Kent, and secondly near Stroud in Gloucestershire. The melanic has, therefore, not had an opportunity of invading industrial areas before being eliminated in its *typical* form. In North Germany, however, f. *nigra* is an industrial melanic.

The small noctuid moth *Procus literosa* Haw. provides an example of where a species has for a time been eliminated in its *typical* form, but subsequently has regained lost territory as a melanic. For many years, this moth has been absent from Sheffield, but recently it has reappeared but in its melanic state. The same applies to *Apamea characterea* Hb.

Apart from mutation rate, dispersal can, on occasions, play an important part. In the species *Tethea ocularis* L., with one exception, no melanic was known in this country prior to 1947, though it was well known in Northern Europe. In that year throughout Eastern England odd specimens of its dark form were taken for the first time. Since then, it has gone ahead, and today the melanic forms about 50 per cent of the population in Cambridge (where *Biston betularia* is 85 per cent black).

All these examples bring home to one the great flexibility of species, and any preconceived idea of fixation must surely have been born of knowledge based on a study of species living in a comparatively unchanging environment.

The impact of industrial melanism on science did not actually take place until about 1890 even though it must have been occurring before Darwin's eyes. In this year, J. W. Tutt (1890), Chapman, Cooke and others vied with each other in differing explanations, the emphasis, in each case with a Lamarckian bias, being on the direct effect of the environment on the insect. It must be remembered that at this date Mendel's Laws, though conceived, did not receive recognition till 1900. In the 1920's J. W. Heslop-Harrison produced a series of papers (Harrison, 1927) in which he claimed that he had induced melanic mutations to the level of 8 per cent (Fisher, 1932) in *typical* stock treated with manganous sulphate and lead nitrate. More recently (Harrison, 1956), he has created the name "melanogen" which signifies a specific mutagenic agent present in air pollution, which gives rise to the black forms. Although repeated by several competent workers, these results have so far never been corroborated, nor in my opinion are they likely to be. In the laboratory, with the most potent weapon known, irradiation, a mutation rate of one in several thousands is the highest known. It is unlikely, in fact, that the effect of pollution on "soma" or "germplasm", as he calls it, can have any bearing on the origin or spread of industrial melanism.

Using *Biston betularia*, we have recently been able to show the important part played by natural selection. By releasing known numbers of marked individuals into first of all an industrial area, where the local population consisted of nearly

Fig. 4. Biston betularia, *f.* typical *and f.* carbonaria *at rest on oak trunk in industrial area, Birmingham.*

90 per cent melanics (Kettlewell, 1955a), and secondly into unpolluted countryside, where there were no melanics (Kettlewell, 1956), the selective advantages of the two forms in each case have been ascertained (Figs. 3 and 4). Of 584 individuals (447 *carbonaria* and 137 *typical*) freed into the Birmingham area, we got back three times more *carbonaria* than *typical* (Table 1). However, in the release of 969 *betularia* into an unpolluted wood in Dorset, we found exactly the reverse and recovered three times more of the *typical* light form than *carbonaria* (Table 2). Furthermore, Dr. Niko Tinbergen was able to film six species of birds in the act of taking the moths at rest and *they did this selectively* (Tables 3 and 4). By eliminating other considerations, it was possible to show that selective predation was

Table 1. *Release experiments for* B. betularia *(males only) Rubery near Birmingham, 1955. The Letters C, T, and I stand for* carbonaria, typical *and* insularia *respectively throughout this paper.*

Date	Releases			Total	Catches			Total	Recaptures			Total
	C	T	I		C	T	I		C	T	I	
8.7	54	23	(5)	82	62	7	5	74	—	—	—	—
9.7	—	—	—		73	11	1	85	33	11	0	44
10.7	100	41	(4)	145	51	5	2	58	3	2	0	5
11.7	—	—	—		50	7	2	59	46	2	(2)	50
12.7	—	—	—		89	7	5	101	0	1	0	1
13.7	—	—	—		25	4	0	29	—	—	—	
14.7	—	—	—		53	2	1	56	—	—	—	
15.7	—	—	—		20	2	2	24	—	—	—	
16.7	—	—	—		13	2	0	15	—	—	—	
17.7	—	—	—		20	2	0	22	—	—	—	
18.7	—	—	—		15	2	2	19	—	—	—	
19.7	—	—	—		5	1	0	6	—	—	—	
20.7	—	—	—		10	1	0	11	—	—	—	
Totals	154	64	(9)	227	486	53	20	559	82	16	(2)	100

	1955			Total	1953			Total
	C	T	I		C	T	I	
Wild Birmingham population Per cent phenotype	86.94	9.48	3.58	559	85.03	10.14	4.83	621
Per cent return of releases = recaptures	53.25	25	(22.2)	100	27.5	13.0	(17.4)	149

responsible for the deficiency in each case. In my opinion, there can be no longer any doubt of the part played by birds in the selective elimination of those individuals which do not conform to their backgrounds.

But this need not necessarily be the only difference between the black and the light forms. The gene responsible for the changed line of chemistry of the pigment is also responsible for other, maybe equally important, physiological and behaviour differences. We have attempted to analyse some of these. E. B. Ford has previously shown that when subjected to a degree of starvation, the melanic form of *Alcis repandata* f. *nigra* is more hardy than its *typical* form (Ford, 1937). By spraying pollution, obtained from air filters in London, on to leaves, we have been able to feed backcross broods of *B. betularia* on foliage similar to that found in industrial areas late in the year. The evidence so far accumulated by this method does suggest that a higher proportion of *carbonaria* forms survive than of the *typical*, but the

Table 2. *Release experiment figures for* Biston betularia *(males only) Dean End, Dorset, 1953.*

Date (1953)	Releases			Totals	Catches			Totals	Recaptures			Totals
	C	T	I		C	T	I		C	T	I	
(13.6)	(37)	(38)	(9)	(84)	—	—	—	—	—	—	—	—
14.6	8	17	2	27	4	17	2	23	(4)	(1)	(1)	(6)
(15.6)	(8)	(25)	(1)	(34)	2	27	5	34	2	9	(3)	14
(16.6)	(22)	(40)	(0)	(62)	1	34	2	37	(0)	(0)	(0)	(0)
17.6	—	—	—	—	7	58	3	68	(7)	(7)	(0)	(14)
18.6	42	65	(3)	110	0	30	1	31	0	1	0	1
19.6	39	72	0	111	2	26	1	29	2	6	0	8
20.6	24	57	0	81	1	44	2	47	1	3	0	4
21.6	42	29	0	71	1	13	2	16	1	4	0	5
22.6	—	—	—	—	5	13	1	19	5	4	0	9
23.6	—	—	—	—	No releases				No captures			
24.6	—	—	—	—	No releases				No captures			
25.6	82	43	0	125	1	11	0	12	0	0	0	0
26.6	—	—	—	—	3	8	1	12	2	2	0	4
27.6	51	28	0	79	0	8	0	8	0	0	0	0
28.6	22	22	0	44	1	20	0	21	1	5	0	6
29.6	17	18	0	35	0	14	0	14	0	5	0	5
30.6	24	11	0	35	4	11	1	16	3	6	0	9
1.7	—	—	—	—	2	9	0	11	2	2	0	4
2.7	—	—	—	—	0	7	0	7	0	0	0	0
3.7	—	—	—	—	—	—	—	—	—	—	—	—
4.7	55	31	0	86	—	—	—	—	—	—	—	—
5.7	—	—	—	—	0	9	0	9	0	7	0	7
Totals	473	496	15	984	34	359	21	414	30	62	4	96

	C	T	I	Totals
Wild Dean End population	(4)	297	17	318
Per cent phenotype	(Possible Escapes)	94.6	5.4	
Release after 1 day of self-determination	2	4	(1)	
Per cent phenotype				
Per cent return of releases	6.34	12.50	(26.67)	

issue has been complicated by the rearing of small numbers only in each brood due to the ravages of virus disease. However, six backcross broods gave 108 *carbonaria* to 65 *typical*, which by chance would happen on only one in 100 occasions.

There is some evidence that in certain backcross broods originating from

industrial areas those larvæ which fed up rapidly and pupated first, produced a
high proportion of *typical betularia*, whilst those that fed slowly and pupated late
in the summer were mostly of the *carbonaria* form. This it has been possible to

Table 3. *Observation on predation of* B. betularia
*by Redstarts for 2 days only (by Dr. N. Tinbergen
from his hide). Birmingham, 1955.*

	Typical	Carbonaria	Total
19.7 a.m.	12	3	15
20.7 a.m.	14	3	17
p.m.	17	9	26
Total	43	15	58

Note: On all occasions these observations commenced with equal numbers of both phenotypes.
We replaced them when all of one phenotype
had been taken.

Table 4. *Direct observation on predation by five species of birds. Dean End Wood,
Dorset, 1955.*

	Observer	Carbonaria	Typical
Spotted Flycatcher	N.T.	46	8
(*Muscicapa striata* L.)	H.B.D.K.	35	1
Nuthatch	N.T.	22	8
(*Sitta europœa* L.)	H.B.D.K.	9	0 (first day)
	H.B.D.K.	9	3 (second day)
Yellow Hammer	N.T.	8	0
(*Emberiza citrinella* L.)	H.B.D.K.	12	0
Robin	N.T.	12	2
(*Erithacus rubecula* L.)			
Thrush	N.T.	11	4
(*Turdus ericetorum* L.)			
			Total
Total Predation observed		164	26 190
(for days when records were kept)			

Note: On all occasions these observations commenced
with equal numbers of both phenotypes. We replaced them
when all of one phenotype had been taken.

Table 5. B. betularia. *Speed of reaching larval full-growth.*
A comparison of f. typical *and f.* carbonaria. *(Brood B/4/52.)*

Pupation date		*Typical*	*Carbonaria*
"Earliest"	Aug. 1st	9	1
"Early"	Aug. 8th	26	15
Main fraction	September	?	?
"Late"	October	0	5
Laboratory controls	Aug.–Oct.	19	17

check by segregating all larvæ that pupated at weekly intervals. Table 5 shows one such example. In regard to this brood, after the first two pupal containers, which produced 35 *typical* and 16 *carbonaria*, had been collected in August, mice ate the main and third group in September. However, seven larvæ, which survived and were still feeding in October, produced five moths, all *carbonaria*. If a differential feeding rate exists between the two forms, it can be accounted for by two hypotheses: first, that selection has favoured those *typicals* which fed up rapidly, thereby avoiding the heavier pollution which takes place late in the year; or, alternatively, *carbonaria* may be capable of getting rid of toxic substances. Slow feeding and a capacity for excreting noxious materials have been demonstrated frequently in other instances. In this light, industrial melanism may confer on a species a capacity for extending its larval life later in the season than would otherwise be the case.

A further behaviour difference may be found in regard to the assembling habits of newly hatched females. Sib females of the same day of hatching, one of f. *carbonaria* and the other f. *typical*, were placed in muslin cages which were hung up 3 to 5 feet apart. The work was conducted in a locality where the *betularia* were 100% of the *typical* form. Throughout the night males were collected as they fluttered on the outside of the assembling cages, and were segregated according to whether the female of choice was of the black or the light form. Table 6 shows the results obtained. It appears from this short experiment that *carbonaria* females may be more effective on warm nights and *typical* females on cold ones. Alternatively, the scent molecule may be slightly different. Sheppard (1952) has shown that preferential matings take place in another dimorphic species, *Panaxia dominula*.

Lastly, there may be a difference between the two forms in regard to their choice of resting site by day. Into a large barrel which presented alternate surface areas of black and white, equal numbers of each form of *B. betularia* were introduced at night; and at daybreak they were scored for correct or incorrect positions. Those individuals which were on the edges or the top or bottom of the container were eliminated. Table 7 shows the result. Of 118 releases which qualified, 77 chose correct positions, and 41 incorrect. (Kettlewell, 1955b.) It is likely, therefore, that the two forms are sensitive to the background they choose, having regard to

Table 6. B. betularia *female assembling differences between f.* typical *and f.* carbonaria.

Date	T. males to typical females	T. males to carbonaria females
Warm (above 60°F.)		
14.6.55	2	7
15.6.55	1	8
29.6.55	0	7
Total warm	3 (8%)	22 (92%)
Cold below (50°F.)		
17.6.55	10	5
20.6.55	4	4
28.6.55	10	5
30.6.55	6	1
Total cold	30 (67%)	15 (33%)
Cool (60–60°F.) 7 nights	21	38
Total All Weathers	54	75

Table 7. Background recognition in Biston betularia.

	Black (= carbonaria)	White (= typical)	Total
Black background	38	20	58
White background	21	39	60
Total	59	59	118

From this it can be seen that 77 *betularia* chose correct positions (38 *carbonaria* and 39 *typical*) and 41 incorrect. The 2×2 table gives $a \, x^2(1) = 10.9$, for which P is approximately 0.001.

their own colour. The same mechanism could account for their behaviour in each case. It is possible that contrast differences between the colour of the scales surrounding the eyes, and the light reflected from the background on which they sit, are appreciated and gauged by the different segments of the eye. In over 2,000 releases of *B. betularia* in the field, I have frequently noted that the insects take up the best possible position presented locally, and before settling down finally, they revolve on their own axis at the same time as they flatten their wings against the trunks. It is possible that during this procedure they are testing contrast differences.

These then, apart from changed pigmentation, are indications of the existence of behaviour differences between the dark and light forms. It must be emphasized, however, that in none of these have investigations been carried out, so far, on a scale large enough to admit conclusive results. If these differences really exist, some conferring benefits, others disadvantages, a state of balanced polymorphism may be expected to be attained in many species, and this is the more likely if the heterozygous melanic is at an advantage to both the homozygous forms.

Lastly, we have attempted to formulate a theory for the origin of the industrial melanics and the reason for their being Mendelian dominants in nearly every case. Dominance suggests that the gene-complex must have, at some time in the past, had previous experience of the particular mutation, that it was successful, and that during this period the state of dominance was achieved. It in no way assumes, however, that the conditions under which these melanics flourished, bear any relationship to those found today as the result of industrialization. Conversely, it could be argued that a recessive melanic has previously on no occasion conferred benefits on the species and hence, in a gene-complex not fitted to receive it, it is driven into the recessive state.

Is there any evidence available therefore that, in the past, melanic forms have succeeded in contributing to the survival of a species? In order to answer this, it is necessary to examine the situation in areas of relict countryside unchanged by man, and in Britain the old Caledonian forests in Scotland provide excellent material for investigation. This summer (1956) I spent several weeks working the Black Wood of Rannoch in Scotland, which is far removed from any industrial area, and one of the few indigenous pine forests left in this country, and without doubt similar to those which covered much of England 4,000–6,000 years ago. In this wood I found no fewer than seven species of Lepidoptera with melanic forms in a state of balanced polymorphism. One of these, *Alcis repandata* L., previously referred to, passes the day resting on pine trunks, and in a random sample of 428 recorded by me, 10 per cent were of the melanic form, *nigra* Tutt, a figure which is 5 per cent more than one recorded from the same wood in 1942 (Williams, 1949). Furthermore, this melanic form is similar to the industrial melanic which is spreading through built up areas in many parts of England. It may, in fact, provide a connecting link between the "ancient" or "geographic" melanics and present-day industrial melanism. Of the seven polymorphic species, *Alcis repandata* was obviously the one to choose for a fuller study and very early in our investigations I and three other observers noted that on taking flight, f. *nigra* was practically impossible to follow on the wing for more than a short distance, whereas f. *typical* could be seen flying up to a distance of one hundred yards or more. In order to learn more about the normal habits of this species, each morning many hundreds of pine trunks were searched and each *repandata* was scored for camouflage efficiency, and a white indicator label was pinned a foot to its right. The pine trunks offered two backgrounds, a light lichen covered one and a dark one; nevertheless, the majority of f. *nigra* were scored as inconspicuous and nearly all f. *typical* were assessed as inconspicuous and, in fact, the latter could frequently only be recognized on fanning the trunks with a net, thereby causing the wings to move momentarily. Later in the day the same trunks were examined and a record made of those which were missing. By this means it was found that on certain days as many as 50 per cent of the *repandata* had vacated the positions that they had occupied in the morning. On closer study it was apparent that these had taken flight due to disturbance by the large black ant (*Formica rufa* group) or due to direct sunlight which at this latitude strikes two-thirds of each trunk in the course of a day. We have, therefore, a situation in which the majority of melanics are at a slight cryptic disadvantage when at rest, but gain a very considerable benefit whilst on the wing. Furthermore, in this locality, large numbers of both forms have, in the course of a day, to fly because of disturbances from one cause or another. When this happens they may travel a considerable distance passing in and out of the shade, but eventually nearly always taking up position again on a pine trunk. During these excursions we actually witnessed three specimens captured on the wing by birds, all f. *typical*. This may well be part of the explanation of the presence of these melanic forms in these ancient woods, and it is my belief that the same species which today exhibit industrial melanism, have, in some previous era, found use for their melanic forms under conditions very different to those of today. This fact is again borne out by the Lepidoptera of Canada where, due to a very different reason, melanic forms are common in the extreme north. Or again further south in the genus *Zale*, occasional melanic forms turn up sporadically in many species and in at least one industrial melanism has developed. In another, *Z. undularis*, the melanic form appears to have become fixed, the light patterned form *umbripennis* occurring in the population as a rarity. Melanism is, in fact, not a recent phenomenon, but very old.

REFERENCES

Fisher, R. A. 1932–33. *Proc. Roy. Soc.* (B) CXII: 407–16.
Ford, F. B. 1937. *Biol. Rev.* 12: 461.
Haldane, J. B. S. 1924. *Trans. Cam. Phil. Soc.* 23: 26.
Harrison, J. W. H. 1928. *Proc. Roy. Soc.* (B) CII: 346.
Harrison, J. W. H. 1956. *Ent. Rec.* 68: 172–81.
Kettlewell, H. B. D. 1955a. *Heredity* 9:323–342.
Kettlewell, H. B. D. 1955b. *Nature* 175: 943.
Kettlewell, H. B. D. 1956. *Heredity* 10:287–301.
Kettlewell, H. B. D. 1958. *Heredity*. In press.
Sheppard, P. M. 1952. *Heredity* 6: 239–41.
Tutt, J. W. 1890. *Ent. Rec.* 1: 5–325.
Williams, H. B. 1949. *Ent. Rec.* 61: 5.

Aspects of Polymorphism in Man

by A. C. ALLISON

INTRODUCTION

When considering the factors which affect the frequency of a gene in a natural population, particular attention must be paid to the conditions favoring a constant gene frequency or equilibrium. Most common contrasting alleles are in or near equilibrium with one another; otherwise, with certain exceptions which will be described, they would not have survived to be observed. Three main types of genetic equilibrium can be distinguished: neutral, stable and unstable. These can be represented by diagrams of the type illustrated in Figure 1; in practice, the curves are seldom symmetrical as illustrated. The mean selective value must tend to a maximum, so that the gene frequency in the population will change in the direction of the arrows, and there is an equilibrium at points e on the curves shown. In a *neutral equilibrium*, the genes segregate and assort themselves at random according to the Hardy-Weinberg principle. The essential condition for equilibrium is that no genotype shall have any selective advantage, expressed either in terms of fecundity or vitality, over any other genotype. Gene frequency changes which take place by chance (random drift)—usually in small populations—remain permanent. In *stable equilibrium*, the gene ratio tends to be restored to the equilibrium value whenever it is disturbed from this value in either direction. This type of equilibrium depends on opposed forces and can be produced in three main ways: (a) recurrent mutation and elimination of an unfavourable gene; (b) when a heterozygote has a selective advantage over both hemozygotes; and

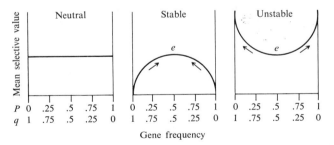

Fig. 1. Diagrams representing the three types of genetic equilibrium: neutral, stable and unstable. There is an equilibrium at all gene frequencies in the case of the neutral equilibrium. In the other two diagrams the gene frequency will change in the direction of the arrows and there will be equilibrium at points e, e.

Abridged from A. C. Allison, "Aspects of Polymorphism in Man," *Cold Spring Harbor Symposium on Quantitative Biology* **20** (1955), 239–255. Reprinted by permission.

(c) when two or more groups of alleles interact in such a way as to alter one another's selective values, for example, with alleles P, p and Q, q controlling contrasting characters, when P is at an advantage to p in the presence of Q but disadvantageous in combination with q while Q is advantageous with p but not with P (Fisher, 1930).

Provided that the sequence of fitnesses of the several genotypes is not disturbed, a change in the magnitude of the selective forces will not make such an equilibrium unstable: it will merely alter the gene frequency at which stability is achieved. There is no such restitution to the previous state when deviation from an *unstable equilibrium* takes place: on the contrary, the further the gene frequency departs from the stable value, the greater the instability. In other words, an equilibrium of this kind is easily destroyed, the commoner gene becoming universal at the expense of its allele. An unstable equilibrium is produced when a heterozygote is at a disadvantage to both homozygotes, by some chromosomal abnormalities and in the presence of certain types of social selection. These generalizations can now be applied to human populations.

Man is one of the most variable of animal species. This is partly geographical variation: any species can assume distinct forms in different regions. But even in the same region, man shows a great deal of variability, which has both genetic and environmental components. The genetic component can be divided for analysis into four classes (Ford, 1940): (1) disadvantageous varieties maintained at a low level by recurrent mutation of the genes controlling them; (2) variation due to the effects of genes neutral as regards survival value; (3) variation dependent on genes maintained by a balance of selective forces; and (4) advantageous varieties controlled by genes spreading through the population and displacing their allelomorphs.

The first class includes the numerous hereditary abnormalities, affecting every bodily organ, listed in the textbooks of medical genetics. Since the spread of genes giving rise to even small disadvantages tends to be checked at an early stage (Fisher, 1930), each of the genes in this class is maintained at a low stable equilibrium through recurrent mutation. Nevertheless, because of the enormous number of loci involved, the total variability produced in this way is considerable. The selection against the gene will, of course, be greater and the equilibrium frequency will be correspondingly lower for 'dominant' characters (*i.e.* those controlled by genes with observable effects in the heterozygous phase) than for fully recessive genes producing effects of comparable severity. Important though these conditions are from the point of view of medical practice and eugenics, they are of only limited interest in population genetics.

It is not known how much the second class contributes to the variability of man. However, Fisher (1930) has shown that for a gene to be effectively neutral, that is, for a neutral equilibrium to be maintained, the balance of advantage between the gene and its allelomorph must be very exact. Moreover, the chances or random survival of such mutant genes are small. Human genes have usually been placed in this class through ignorance of their selective effects. Thus, the human blood group genes were supposed for 40 years to be neutral as regards selective value, but more recent evidence indicates that this interpretation is incorrect.

Since mutation rates are low, of the order of 10^{-5} per gene per generation in man (Haldane, 1949), mutation alone cannot greatly accelerate the spread of neutral genes through a population. Hence, when any form is found to occupy as much as a few percent of a fairly numerous population it can generally be assumed that its increase has been facilitated by selection. In this way the third and fourth classes mentioned above, which constitute polymorphism, are produced. Polymorphism can be defined as the occurrence together in the same habitat of two or more discontinuous forms of a species in such frequencies that the rarest of them cannot be maintained by recurrent mutation (Ford, 1940). The term polymorphism covers two conditions which are produced by quite different genetic mechanisms although they are often difficult to distinguish from one another in practice. The fourth class, transient polymorphism, continues until the gene determining the advantageous variety has so far displaced its allelomorph that the latter is preserved only by recurrent mutation. An instance of transient polymorphism in man is the presence of the sickle cell gene in the colored population of the United States. Another example may be the polymorphism of Rh-positive and Rh-negative individuals in Western Europe, where the former are gradually replacing the latter according to Haldane (1942) and Wiener (1942). These examples will be discussed more fully below.

In a balanced polymorphism two or more forms of a species coexist in a population in stable proportions through the effects of opposing selective agencies. When a single pair of alleles is involved, one allele has a selective advantage until a certain gene ratio is established, above which the advantage is converted into a disadvantage. The simplest stable equilibrium of this kind occurs when a heterozygote has a selective advantage over either homozygote: this may be due to linkage of the gene to a lethal recessive, or to a difference in the effects of a gene when in single and double dose. Striking examples of linkage to lethal recessives are quite numerous in insects (Ford, 1945) but are so far unknown in man. However, one of the most fully investigated examples of the latter situation is that of the sickle cell gene in Africans.

SICKLE CELL POLYMORPHISM

It was demonstrated by Neel (1949) that persons who are heterozygous for the sickle cell gene have the sickle cell trait, which does not produce a significant morbidity, while those who are homozygous for the gene suffer from a hemolytic disease, sickle cell anemia. In the same year, Pauling, Itano, Singer and Wells (1949) discovered that the sickling phenomenon was produced by an abnormal hemoglobin, which they named sickle cell hemoglobin, in the erythrocytes of affected individuals. The genetic and biochemical evidence was united by their demonstration that in persons with sickle cell anemia the hemoglobin is all of the sickle cell type whereas in carriers of the sickle cell trait there is a mixture of normal and sickle cell hemoglobins in approximately equal proportions. The dilution of sickle cell hemoglobin in the cells of heterozygotes prevents the sickling phenomenon—with attendant hemolysis—from taking place in the circulating blood.[1] This rule of inheritance is now universally accepted, but requires qualification. Diseases very similar to sickle cell anemia occur in individuals who are heterozygous for both the sickle cell gene and another gene controlling hemoglobin synthesis, notably the thalassemia gene and the hemoglobin C gene. These conditions will be considered more fully below.

Analyses of the proportion of sickle cell hemoglobin in homozygotes and heterozygotes has yielded further information on the quantitative expression of the sickle cell gene. From the pattern obtained by electrophoresis of a hemoglobin specimen the genotype and also the quantitative expression of the genes concerned can usually be read directly: this must be one of the most favourable known cases for precise analysis of the effects of a mutant gene and its normal allele. The main results of such tests are summarized in Figure 2.

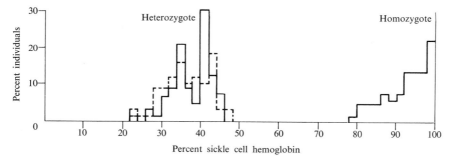

Fig. 2. *Frequency distribution curves of the proportion of sickle cell hemoglobin in sickle cell homozygotes and heterozygotes. The continuous line represents heterozygotes in the United States (data of Wells and Itano, 1951); the interrupted line represents heterozygotes of the Luo tribe from Kenya (Allison, unpub.).*

Wells and Itano (1951) found that some cases of sickle cell anemia have, in addition to a large component of sickle cell hemoglobin, a small hemoglobin component of apparently normal electrophoretic mobility. This component does not appear to be normal adult hemoglobin, and it has all the properties of fetal hemoglobin (Singer, Chernoff and Singer, 1951; Itano, 1953). Indeed, synthesis of normal adult hemoglobin would not be expected in the absence of the normal allele of the sickle cell gene, whereas the synthesis of fetal hemoglobin appears to be under independent genetic control (Allison, 1954c). Thus biochemical variability in the sickle cell homozygote depends upon the proportion of fetal hemoglobin synthesized, which rarely exceeds 20 per cent of the total hemoglobin. This appears to be true in all the population so far investigated—in the United

---

[1] Sickling would be expected to occur *in vivo* when the proportion of abnormal hemoglobin is about 65 per cent or higher.

States, Africa and Greece. It is remarkable that higher proportions of fetal hemoglobin do not occur, since sickle cell homozygotes producing more fetal hemoglobin (of the order of 40 % of the total) might be protected to a considerable extent from hemolysis; and they might therefore be expected to have a greater fitness than homozygotes producing little or no fetal hemoglobin. Why the proportion of fetal hemoglobin should always be so restricted in sickle cell anemia is unknown; in thalassemia major the total quantity of fetal hemoglobin synthesized is much larger, so that in some cases it comprises all the circulating hemoglobin (Rich, 1952). Nevertheless, the consequence of this fact—that the biochemical variability of the sickle cell homozygote is quite strictly limited and that all homozygotes are liable to develop hemolytic disease, though not all do so to the same extent—is important in reducing the fitness of the genotype.

Some years ago many investigators in Africa thought that sickle cell anemia was an uncommon and rather mild disease in that country. Comparing the relatively few cases of sickle cell anemia then described with the very high trait frequencies known to be present, Raper (1950) was led to suppose that "the appearance of sickle cell anemia depends not only upon the extent to which the trait is present in the community, but also on the extent to which admixture with other genetic strains has occurred." Since 1950 many hundreds of cases of sickle cell anemia have been reported from Africa, and the number of affected children identified in different populations is close to the number of sickle cell homozygotes expected from the known heterozygote frequency (Labotte-Legrand and Lambotte-Legrand, 1951; Vandepitte, 1954; Welbourn and Raper, 1954). Moreover, Neel (1953) was unable to find any correlation between the severity of sickle cell anemia and the estimated degree of non-Negro admixture in homozygotes in the United States. From published reports it appears that the mortality from sickle cell anemia in African children is at least as great as it is in the United States. A few sickle cell homozygotes can be recognized in the young adult population of East Africa (Allison, 1954c). There is, however, evidence that their fecundity is low: Dr. Gillian Jacob kindly allows me to state that she has found one homozygote in electrophoretic tests of specimens from 184 pregnant Baganda women and 82 pregnant women from other tribes whose blood showed sickle cells; and there were no homozygotes among the mothers of 261 children with sickle cell anemia reported from the Belgian Congo by Vandepitte (1954). Hence the conclusion (Allison, 1954c) that the genetic fertility of the sickle cell homozygote in Africa, as in the United States, is not more than one quarter that of the heterozygote seems to be fully justified.

The sickle cell heterozygote shows a somewhat greater range of variability, in accordance with the rule that the heterozygote tends to be more variable than either homozygote, while of the latter the abnormal is more variable than the normal. The proportion of sickle cell to normal adult hemoglobin varies in different individuals, presumably owing to the relative rates of synthesis of the two pigments, but tends to be constant in any one individual. In 42 heterozygotes from the colored population of the United States, Wells and Itano (1951) found that the frequency distribution curve of the proportion of sickle cell hemoglobin lay between 24 and 45 per cent and appeared to be bimodal (Fig. 2). These and other data were statistically analysed by Neel, Wells and Itano (1951), who reported that there were highly significant differences between the mean values for families and concluded that influences exist, probably at least in part genetic, which are capable of modifying the proportion of abnormal pigment present in an individual heterozygous for the sickle cell gene. From inspection of the data published by Neel and his colleagues it appears highly probable that the modifier or modifiers of the sickle cell gene are autosomal and independent of the gene.

My own observations on 38 heterozygotes from the Luo tribe in East Africa are included in Figure 2 for comparison. The technique used (filter paper electrophoresis, with dye elution) was different from that used by Wells and Itano (free electrophoresis) so that the absolute values are not strictly comparable; but the variations in both the American and African groups are consistent and reproducible, and lie far beyond variation due to technique alone. The American and African curves resemble one another quite closely; both cover approximately the same range and both appear to be bimodal, although the possibility of further modes cannot be excluded. Dr. Gillian Jacob kindly allows me to state that she has obtained a similar distribution curve, covering a somewhat higher range and possibly showing several modes in addition to the two primary ones, in heterozygotes of the Baganda tribe.

It can therefore be concluded that the proportion of sickle cell hemoglobin formed in heterozygotes varies and is itself under genetic control; the sickle cell gene acts as a switch mechanism determining that some of the hemoglobin formed shall be of the sickle type, while the proportion of sickle cell hemoglobin synthesized is regulated by modifying factors. The variation is not, however, great; heterozygotes with less than 20 per cent sickle cell hemoglobin are known (Singer and Fisher, 1952) but are rare, as are heterozygotes with more than 50 per cent sickle cell hemoglobin. This range seems to be optimal in permitting the selective advantage of the heterozygote to be effective while keeping the proportion of abnormal pigment below that which would bring about the sickling process *in vivo*, with consequent hemolysis and decreased fitness.

The central problem from the point of view of population genetics can now be stated: how can such high heterozygote frequencies—up to 40 per cent—be maintained in African tribes despite rapid elimination of genes through death of homozygotes? It has been calculated that to replace the loss of sickle cell genes by mutation alone a mutation rate of about 10^{-1} per gene per generation would be necessary (Allison, 1954c). This is of the order of 5,000 times as great as other estimated mutation rates in man, (Haldane, 1949), and approximately 60 times as great as the upper limit of mutation to the sickle cell condition estimated from limited data by Vandepitte, Zeulzer and Neel (1955). Furthermore, to explain the restricted distribution of the sickle cell gene such abnormally high mutation rates would have to be confined not only to one or two races of mankind but to isolated groups of individuals within these races. Hence it is reasonable to exclude an increased mutation rate as an explanation of the remarkably high heterozygote frequencies which are known to be present.

The occurrence of the sickle cell trait must therefore be regarded as a true polymorphism, and the remarkably constant upper limit to the heterozygote frequencies observed suggests that in Africa it is a balanced polymorphism. The stable equilibrium which this implies could not be produced by reproductive over-compensation, that is, replacement of children lost through sickle cell anemia in susceptible families, as suggested by Foy, Kondi, Timms, Brass and Bushra (1954); but it could be achieved through selective advantage of the hetero-zygote. There is direct evidence that heterozygotes are at an advantage in Africa since they suffer from subtertian malaria less frequently and less severely than normal individuals. That possessors of the sickle cell trait might be resistant to malaria had been suggested by Brain (1952) and by Mackey and Vivarelli (1952); substantial evidence in support of this view was presented by Allison (1954a), who studied the parasite rates and densities in children under natural conditions and obtained large differences in the response to artificial infection of susceptible volunteers with and without the sickle cell trait. Further observations which seem to establish beyond reasonable doubt that children with the sickle cell trait are resistant to malaria have recently been published by Raper (1955), who effectively answers critics of this interpretation. In the age group of one to three years, which is the age of maximum susceptibility to and mortality from malaria, Raper found that the *P. falciparum* rate was significantly lower in the sickle cell trait group than in those without the trait; parasite counts were very much lower in sickling than in non-sickling subjects. It is therefore highly probable that in regions where malaria is hyperendemic (*i.e.* transmission of *Plasmodium falciparum* continues throughout the greater part of the year, so that the population is constantly re-infected and susceptible individuals suffer from severe and pro-longed disease) children who possess the sickle cell trait will tend to survive while some of those without the trait will be eliminated before they acquire immunity to malaria.

It should prove possible eventually to make direct estimates of the fitness of sickle cell heterozygotes in malarious regions. Calculations indicate that the advantage possessed by the heterozygote under these conditions must be great. The highest equilibrium frequency of heterozygotes attained in African popula-tions—when maximal heterosis balances elimination of genes through death of homozygotes—appears to be around 40 per cent; all frequencies up to this limit are observed in East Africa and the limit is reached in several widely separated communities but never exceeded (Allison, 1954b). Assuming that three quarters of the homozygotes die without reproducing, an equilibrium frequency of 40 per cent heterozygotes implies that the fitness of the heterozygote must be about $1.26 \times$ that of the normal homozygote (Allison, 1954c). This is not quite so surprising when it is remembered that the infant mortality is about 200–500 per 1000. With selective forces of this magnitude operating in a population, the rate of increase or decrease of the adult sickle cell carrier frequency from low or high

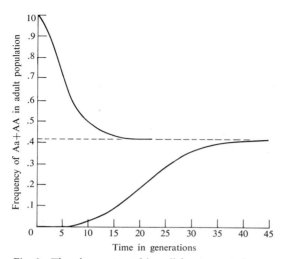

Fig. 3. *The change in sickle cell homozygote-heterozygote frequency in the adult population which would occur from a high or a low level when the fitness of the normal homozygote, sickle cell homozygote and heterozygote are 0.95, 1.19 and 0.30 respectively. The interrupted horizontal line represents an equilibrium of 40 per cent heterozygotes.*

values to the limiting value is shown in Figure 3.

The equilibrium would be stable, of course, only when the population is constantly exposed to subtertian malaria. It would therefore be expected that tribes living in malarious environments should have higher sickle cell trait frequencies than those living in environments free from malaria. In East Africa, which forms a convenient testing ground for the hypothesis because of the great diversity of climate, rainfall and malarial severity encountered there, this is indeed the case. In 35 East African tribes from widely different environments the incidence of the sickle cell trait was found to be invariably about 10 per cent in the tribes suffering from hyperendemic malaria and less than 10 per cent in tribes living in regions where malaria is absent or epidemic: this difference cuts across racial, linguistic and ethnographic barriers (Allison, 1954b, see Fig. 4). In general, high trait frequencies are found in Central Africa, where malaria is prevalent, but not in Northern or Southern Africa, where subtertian malaria is less common and is partially replaced by benign tertian malaria. There are, however, in the marginal zones tribes exposed to subtertian malaria of varying degrees of severity who do not have the sickle cell trait or have it in low frequencies; this is true of the Northern Nilotes in the Sudan (Foy, Kondi, Timms and Bushra, 1954; Robers and Lehmann, 1955) and of the Zulus of South Africa (Budtz-Olsen and Burgers, 1955). Little is known about the past histories of these tribes, who may have entered malarious habitats only a few generations ago; and they may not have acquired, or may only recently have acquired, the sickle cell gene. Even under conditions of maximum heterosis, the increase in frequency of the sickle cell gene in such populations would at first be slow (Fig. 3); later it would be more rapid,

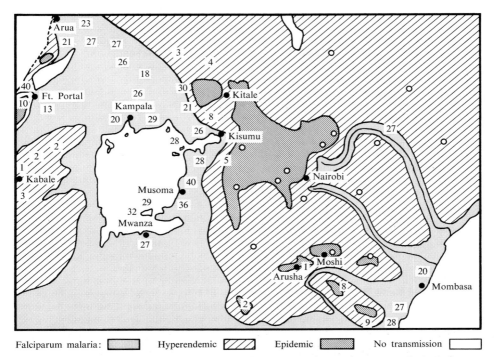

Falciparum malaria: ▨▨ Hyperendemic ▨▨ Epidemic ▨▨ No transmission ☐

Fig. 4. Sketch map of East Africa, outlining the regions where subtertian malaria is hyperendemic (i.e., transmitted throughout the greater part of the year), epidemic (i.e., seasonal or present near water) and absent. The observed percentages of indigenous Africans with the sickle cell trait in different localities are superimposed.

falling again as the limit is approached. That the trait is rare or absent in other races exposed to severe subtertian malaria (*e.g.* in Thailand) is also remarkable, but an explanation for this is suggested below. It is much more significant that high sickle cell trait frequencies do not occur in populations who have not been exposed to subtertian malaria. Thus, the high frequencies of the trait recorded in the aboriginals of South India (Lehmann and Cutbush, 1952), in the Greeks of Lake Copais (Choremis, Ikin, Lehmann, Mourant and Zannos, 1953) and in some southern Turks (Askoy, 1955) all occur in notoriously malarious regions.

The comparatively high incidence of the sickle cell trait observed in the colored population of the United States cannot be regarded as an exception to this generalization, since there is evidence that the frequency is unstable. The incidence of the trait in the slave population was probably at least 22 per cent (Allison, 1954c). Anthropologists estimate that "the average Negro is about one third white and Indian" which is in accordance with blood group data (Glass and Li, 1953). Given a population with 22 per cent carriers of the sickle cell trait and a one third admixture of strains having no sickle cell, a trait frequency of 15.4 per cent would be expected. In fact, the incidence of the sickle cell trait in United States Negroes is not over 9 per cent (Neel, 1951). Hence a significant fall in the frequency

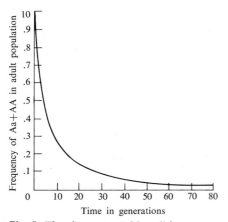

Fig. 5. *The change in sickle cell homozygote + homozygote frequency in the adult population which would occur when the fitness of the sickle cell homozygote is 0.25 and there is no heterosis, i.e., the fitness of the heterozygote and of the homozygote is 1.0.*

of the trait seems to have occurred among West Africans living in the United States. Such a fall would have taken place in about 12 generations, that is, 300 to 350 years, which fits the historical records of slave importations into the New World satisfactorily (Fig. 5).

If this interpretation is correct, the sickle polymorphism in the United States is a transient one, with the level of the sickle cell gene falling in each successive generation. The rate of fall would now be slow and the gene would be expected to persist in the population in low frequencies almost indefinitely, but eventually to be balanced only by recurrent mutation.

EFFECTS OF GENES FOR OTHER ABNORMAL HEMOGLOBINS

One of the remarkable features of the distribution of the sickle cell trait in Africa is the higher maximum frequency attained in East Africa, where several tribes have 40 per cent with the trait, than in West Africa, where all the tribes so far observed have trait frequencies below 30 per cent. This was, indeed, one of the points which led Lehmann (1954) to conclude that the sickle cell gene had been introduced into Africa from the North-East.

There is no reason to suppose that mortality from malaria is any lower in West Africa than in East Africa. Recently, however, another important factor has come to light. The hemoglobin C trait has been found in 12 per cent of Africans from the Gold Coast (Edington and Lehmann, 1954) and also in Africans from Ibadan, Nigeria, by Dr. N. A. Barnicot and Mr. J. Garlick. On the other hand, the hemoglobin C gene seems to be absent from Uganda (Jacob, 1955), the Sudan and Tanganyika (Roberts and Lehmann, 1955) and Kenya (Allison, unpublished). Now, it is known that individuals who are heterozygous for both the sickle cell gene and the hemoglobin C gene sometimes develop a disease similar to, though rather less severe than, sickle cell anemia (Kaplan, Zuelzer and Neel, 1951; Smith and Conley, 1954). Hence in a population where the two genes are present the sickle cell gene will be eliminated through failure of both sickle cell homozygotes and the double heterozygotes to reproduce, that is, the rate of elimination will be greater than in a population where only the sickle cell gene is present. It follows that if the selective advantage of the sickle heterozygote is the same in both populations, the stable equilibrium frequency, at which heterosis exactly counterbalances elimination, will be reached at a lower level in the population with hemoglobin C than in the population without it. Here, then, is a ready explanation for the lower limiting frequency imposed on the sickle cell gene in West Africa: there is no need to have recourse to hypothetical migration of populations.

Penrose (1955) has recently shown theoretically that three or more alleles will be in equilibrium provided that all homozygotes have a fitness below average, that is, the heterozygotes are at an advantage. A genotype table for a West African population where the sickle cell heterozygote frequency is 30 per cent and the hemoglobin C heterozygote frequency is 12 per cent is included in the appendix to this paper. The values for the fitness of the sickle cell heterozygote and homozygote agree quite well with those previously calculated for East Africans (Allison, 1954c)—1.19 and 0.30 respectively. The fitness of the sickle cell:hemoglobin C double heterozygote is about 0.51; in other words, the individual with sickle cell:hemoglobin C disease would have at least twice as great a chance of reaching reproductive age and bearing children as the individual with homozygous sickle cell anemia. This seems to be a reasonable estimate, and is one which could be confirmed or disproved by direct observation on hemoglobin types in the reproducing population.

That some individuals who are homozygous for the hemoglobin C gene are liable to develop disease is also known (for references see Singer, Chapman, Goldberg, Rubinstein and Rosenblum, 1954). It follows that in the West African population the hemoglobin C gene must be eliminated through death of sickle cell: hemoglobin C and homozygous hemoglobin C cases before reproductive age. It is highly probable, therefore, that the polymorphism is balanced through selective advantage of the hemoglobin C heterozygote. If the hemoglobin C homozygote has a fitness of 0.74 in the genotype table presented in the appendix, the fitness of the hemoglobin C heterozygote would be 1.12. We have no knowledge of any advantage possessed by the hemoglobin C heterozygote, but clearly the possibility of a relationship to malaria should be explored first. The limited available data again suggest that the stability of the equilibrium was destroyed when the West Africans were transferred to the New World. The frequency of the hemoglobin C heterozygotes in the slave population was probably of the order of 10 per cent, whereas in the colored population of the United States today it is only 1.8 to 3 per cent (Smith and Conley, 1953; Schneider, 1953).

Similar problems are raised in connexion with the polymorphism of the thalassemia gene in Italy, Greece and Thailand and that of the hemoglobin E gene in Thailand. It is now universally accepted that individuals homozygous for the thalassemia gene suffer from a very severe disease which reduces their fitness nearly to zero; in addition, heterozygotes are often mildly anemic. In spite of the great selective disadvantage to the thalassemia gene which this implies, the frequency of heterozygotes in many Italian districts is four per cent or higher, reaching 18 per cent in the Ferrara region (Bianco, Montalenti, Silvestroni and Siniscalco, 1952). It was first suggested by Bianco and her colleagues that the loss of genes might be compensated to some extent by increased fecundity of matings between heterozygotes; later some evidence was obtained that the heterozygotes in Italy have a selective advantage (Montalenti, 1954). The figures presented for normals and heterozygotes, however, show an insignificant difference and the advantage is too small to keep the gene frequency equilibrium stable at its present high level in Ferrara. If the fitness of the abnormal homozygote is 0.1 and that of the normal homozygote is 0.95 the fitness of the heterozygote where the heterozygote frequency is stable at 18 per cent would be 1.077, that is, the advantage must be of the order of nine percent. The position is thus still far from clear and has been complicated by the discovery that thalassemia is relatively common in Thailand (Minnich, Na-Nakorn, Chongchareonsuk and Kochaseni, 1954). In Thailand the thalassemia gene appears to be at an even greater disadvantage than in Italy owing to the reduced fitness of individuals, who are doubly heterozygous for this gene as well as for the hemoglobin E gene (Na-Nakorn, Minnich and Chernoff, 1955). According to Na-Nakorn and his colleagues, the frequency of hemoglobin E heterozygotes in the Thai population is 12.5 per cent. Since some of those who are homozygous for the hemoglobin E gene also develop disease, the situation is similar to the coexistence of the sickle cell gene and hemoglobin C gene in West Africa, the two abnormal homozygotes as well as those heterozygous for both abnormal genes being at a disadvantage.[2] The most probable explanation of the fact that the thalassemia gene has become common in two widely separated populations, and for the continued and apparently stable polymorphism of this gene together with the hemoglobin E gene in Thailand, is that both heterozygotes are at an advantage, or have been at an advantage until recently.

In a similar way the thalassemia and sickle cell genes interact to produce a diseased double heterozygote (Silvestroni and Bianco, 1946; Powell, Rodarte and Neel, 1950; Smith and Conley, 1954). Hence if both genes are present in a population, each would tend to check the frequency of the other. It is possible that the relatively low maximum frequencies of the sickle cell trait recorded in Greece (17.8 per cent, Choremis, Ikin, Lehmann, Mourant and Zannos, 1953) and in Turkey (13.3 per cent, Askoy, 1955) are due to the known coexistence of the thalassemia gene in these countries, but the populations investigated may not have reached a stable equilibrium in respect of the sickle cell gene frequency under conditions of maximum heterosis.

The apparent rarity of the hemoglobin D and hemoglobin G, H, I, and K genes, on the other hand, may imply that the heterozygotes have little or no

---

[2] Since the thalassemia and hemoglobin E genes are probably not allelic, however, the two situations are not identical genetically.

advantage, and the same is probably true of another globin abnormality described by Hörlein and Weber (1948), which may be termed hemoglobin M. It has recently been discovered that both sheep and goats have electrophoretically different hemoglobin types (Harris and Warren (1955). If the formation of these hemoglobin types proves to be under independent genetic control, these species must be polymorphic for the genes concerned. It may then be possible to make a direct experimental analysis of the mechanism by which this polymorphism is maintained.

BLOOD GROUP POLYMORPHISM

For many years it was widely held held that the human blood groups were neutral from the point of view of natural selection and that the different frequencies observed in different parts of the world were due to genetic drift (see, for instance, Wright, 1940). Fisher and Ford have long maintained that the stability of the blood group polymorphism must in all probability be due to the action of selective agencies (Ford, 1945). The discovery that immunization of an Rh-negative (d/d) mother by a heterozygous Rh-positive (D/d) fetus could produce hemolytic disease of the newborn established beyond doubt that these blood groups have selective value. In this case, selection acts against the heterozygote, which—as Haldane (1942) and Wiener (1942) pointed out—would lead to an unstable equilibrium and eventually bring to a low level the rarer of the two genes, the Rh-negative (d) gene. If this is so, the Rh polymorphism in Western Europe is of the transient type. To explain the high frequency of the Rh-negative gene still present, both Haldane and Wiener suggested that the Western Europeans might be descended from the products of intermarriage between a race predominantly Rh-positive (as in the populations of Africa and Asia) and a race predominantly Rh-negative. The subsequent discovery that the Rh-negative (d) gene is approximately twice as frequent in the Basques as in other Europeans (Etcheverry, 1947; Chalmers, Ikin and Mourant, 1948) made this interpretation more plausible, but cannot be accepted as confirmation of it. There is an unresolved difficulty: if one of the Rh genes arose as a mutation from the other, it is theoretically improbable that such a mutant gene, if devoid of selective value and disadvantageous in the heterozygous phase, could have become predominant in certain populations. The alternative view, that the Rh polymorphism is balanced and relatively stable, has been taken by Fisher, Race and Taylor (1944).

These authors suggested one way in which the intensity of selection against the Rh-negative gene through hemolytic disease might be reduced. Where the father is heterozygous in families with hemolytic disease, only half of the children will be affected; the unaffected children will be homozygous Rh-negative, so that even a partial replacement of children lost will help to compensate for the loss of Rh-negative genes. Glass (1950) has some evidence that white Rh-negative, immunized mothers have a higher average number of pregnancies than either Rh-negative non-immunized or Rh-positive mothers. Glass found no such difference in the colored population investigated, and this type of over-compensation would only be expected where there is effective control over family size. It seems very dubious whether such over-compensation was significant in the past and could have operated constantly enough to produce more or less uniform Rh frequencies over the greater part of Western Europe. The loss of Rh-negative genes may be partially compensated in other ways. One association which has recently been found is the apparently decreased susceptibility of Rh-negative individuals to squamous carcinoma of the bronchus (McConnell, Clarks, and Downton, 1954). However, since deaths from bronchial carcinoma usually take place after reproductive age, the higher mortality among Rh-positive individuals would not confer much selective advantage on the Rh-negative gene.

It is not sufficiently recognized that, however effective such compensation for the loss of Rh-negative genes might be, it could not lead to a stable equilibrium and a balanced polymorphism; the best it could do—in the improbable event of its exactly counterbalancing elimination—would be to produce a neutral equilibrium. A stable equilibrium could be produced through the possession of a selective advantage by the heterozygote, which would have to be large so as to overcome the disadvantage in hemolytic disease, or through strong interaction with other genes in the way described above. The heterozygote cannot, unfortunately, be recognized serologically on a wide scale, so that it would be difficult to collect data regarding its selection coefficient. This important investigation should nevertheless be attempted. Only two Rh genes (*D* and *d*) which are most commonly involved in hemolytic disease have so far been considered. The same general principle, selection against the heterozygote, applies equally to immunization by other Rh antigens.

On the other hand, there is some evidence for an interaction between the Rh and other blood groups. In hemolytic disease of the newborn due to Rh immunization, the parents are much more often compatibly mated as regards ABO blood groups, in the sense that the husband could be a donor to his wife, than would be expected (Race and Sanger, 1954). And Grubb and Sjöstedt (1955) found in a series of marriages with two or more pregnancies terminating in intra-uterine death for unknown reasons a highly significant excess of ABO incompatibility in the mating combination Rh-positive : Rh-positive but not in other Rh combinations. These findings illustrate the interdependence of different blood group systems in the genesis of disease—which is direct evidence that the selective forces acting on one system of blood group genes will be influenced by the presence or absence of blood group genes belonging to different systems, as they doubtless are by many other genes. Whether these interactions are of sufficient magnitude to be a significant factor in producing a stable equilibrium through the mechanism analysed mathematically by Fisher (1930) remains to be seen.

From what has been said, and from the fact that hemolytic disease of the newborn is sometimes produced by ABO incompatibility (Race and Sanger, 1954), it will be clear that the ABO blood group genes, also can no longer be regarded as devoid of selective value. Other unexpected, and at present inexplicable, associations between the ABO groups and disease have recently come to light. Struthers (1951) compared the ABO groups, in a consecutive series of young

West Scottish children coming to autopsy, with the groups of the adult population to which the parents belonged. A significant deficiency of group O was found among the infants, especially those with autopsy evidence of broncho-pneumonia. More firmly established is the finding that the frequency of group A is greater and the frequency of O is less in patients suffering from cancer of the stomach than in the general population of the locality in which they live (Aird, Bentall and Fraser Roberts, 1953). More recently (Aird, Bentall, Mehigan and Fraser Roberts, 1954), the ABO groups in three other cancers—colon, rectum and breast—were found not to differ significantly from the population controls. Patients suffering from peptic ulceration, however, showed a higher incidence of group O and a correspondingly lower incidence of the other three groups than the controls; if their series is typical—which it seems to be, judging from confirmatory Norwegian evidence (Westlund and Heistö, 1955)—persons of group O are about 35 per cent more liable to develop peptic ulceration than persons of the other groups. McConnell, Clarke and Downton (1954) found a barely significant excess of A at the expense of O in patients with oat-cell tumours of the lung but not in other types of lung cancer. And Pike and Dickens (1954) reported a significant excess of women with group O among 541 cases of toxemia of pregnancy compared with the groups of 3651 admissions to a maternity hospital.

Most of the studies of blood groups and disease so far published are, however, rather superficial and the results do not necessarily imply that the associations found are due to pleiotropic effects of the blood group genes. They might equally well be due to other factors, for example, population stratification. In the investigation of Pike and Dickens the question of maternal age and parity, which was not considered, might be very relevant. Nevertheless, the demonstration of significant associations between the incidence of certain blood groups and resistance or susceptibility to a variety of diseases is important, since disease is probably the most potent agent producing natural selection in man. Other selective agents which deserve attention are those affecting fecundity. Here the evidence of a relationship to blood groups is less clear. In a much-quoted paper, Waterhouse and Hogben (1947) asserted that there was a highly significant deficiency of A offspring of the mating of father A × mother O; their conclusions have, however, been criticized on statistical grounds by Bennett and Brandt (1954). No significant deficiency of A newborn children of O mothers could be found among 2000 London mother-infant combinations (Boorman, 1950) or 7856 such Australian combinations published by Bryce, Jakobowicz, McArthur and Penrose (1950). The table comparing Japanese parents and children presented by Matsunuga (1955) shows fewer O parents than O children and more AB parents than AB children. Similar deficiencies of AB children were found by Boorman and by Bryce and her colleagues. Allen (1953) reviewing his own and other data, concludes that the fecundity of individuals with different blood groups—that is, the mean number of offspring—is not equal.

It is therefore probable, though not satisfactorily proven, that the ABO blood group genes do not appear at random among the offspring of different matings. Through differences in respect of such features as well as susceptibility to disease, each of the blood groups would be at an advantage in certain situations and at a disadvantage in others. But this alone would not establish a stable equilibrium. The search for increased fitness of the heterozygotes, which would keep the system in equilibrium, has not yet been intensively pursued. There are, however, some pointers: the increased susceptibility of persons with group O to peptic ulcer and perhaps toxemia of pregnancy during reproductive age can be quoted as an instance of selection against one homozygote; and the excess of AB mothers in the series cited could be attributable to increased fitness of one heterozygote.

The great majority of human populations possess all three antigens, which suggests that the polymorphism is balanced. However, the frequencies are far from uniform: in fact, they show quite wide variations over relatively small distances. Mourant (1954) suggests that the ABO groups may be adaptive, in the sense that they are subject to environmental selection, whereas the remarkably uniform frequencies of most blood group genes over large areas of continental dimensions seems to imply a long-term stability not closely dependent on the varied external conditions provided by such an area. The evidence from distribution of the blood groups seems to be equivocal, however. In some instances populations of different racial origins living in the same region have the same ABO blood groups, as in the high B frequencies of Mongolians and Caucasians in Central Asia, whereas other populations known to have the same origin but living in different regions retain very similar blood group frequencies, for example, the gypsies quoted by Mourant.

Mourant also draws attention to the widespread distribution of ABO antigens and closely related substances among living organisms, and quotes evidence that part at least of the Rh and MN antigen systems seems to have been derived from an early primate stock. The very persistence of these antigens suggests that they may not be devoid of selective value; and once a population had become polymorphic in respect of such characters it might as a whole gain a versatility in resistance to disease advantageous for survival under unfavourable conditions.

A further instance of polymorphism in man which may be very ancient is that of the taste-deficiency gene, t, which has a frequency of about 53 per cent in Englishmen and 19.5 per cent in East Africans (Allison, 1951). Fisher, Ford and Huxley (1939) found that chimpanzees show definite differences in taste threshold for phenylthiocarbamide, as do humans. These authors concluded that our ancestors may have possessed both T and t genes in common with the ancestors of the anthropoids. In view of the apparent stability of the polymorphism, they believed that it was balanced by unknown selective forces—possibly an advantage possessed by the heterozygote. There is a somewhat suggestive relationship between the chemical structure of phenylthiocarbamide and that of certain antithyroid substances occurring in natural foods such as cabbages and turnips (Astwood, Greer and Ettlinger, 1949); and Harris, Kalmus and Trotter (1949) obtained evidence suggesting that non-tasters are more liable to develop nodular goiter than tasters.

REFERENCES

Aird, I., Bentall, H. H., and Fraser Roberts, J. A., 1953, Relationship between cancer of the stomach and the ABO blood groups. Brit. Med. J.. i: 779–780.

Aird, I., Bentall, H. H., Mehigan, J. A., and Fraser Roberts, J. A., 1954, The blood groups in relation to peptic ulceration and carcinoma of the colon, rectum, breast and bronchus. Brit. Med. J. ii: 315–321.

Allan, T. M., 1953, ABO blood groups and human fertility. Brit. J. Prev. Soc. Med. *7:* 220–226.

Allison, A. C., 1951, A note on taste-blindness in Kenya Africans and Arabs. Man *5:* 119–120.

——, 1954a, Protection afforded by sickle cell trait against subtertian malarial infection. Brit. Med. J. i: 290–292.

——, 1954b, The distribution of the sickle cell trait in East Africa and elsewhere, and its apparent relationship to the incidence of subtertian malaria. Trans. Roy. Soc. Trop. Med. Hyg. *48:* 312–318.

——, 1954c, Notes on sickle cell polymorphism. Ann. Hum. Genetics *19:* 39–57.

——, 1955, Notation for human hemoglobin types and genes controlling their synthesis. Science (in press).

Allison, A. C., Ikin, E. W., and Mourant, A. E., 1955, Further observations on blood groups in East African tribes. J. Roy. Anthrop. Inst. (in press).

Askoy, M., 1955, Sickle cell trait in South Turkey. Lancet *i:* 589–590.

Astwood, E. B., Greer, M. A., and Ettlinger, M. G., 1949, 1-5-vinyl-2-thiooxazolidone, an antithyroid compound from yellow turnip and from *Brassica* seeds. J. Biol. Chem. *181:* 121–130.

Bennett, J. H., and Brandt, J., 1954, Some more exact tests of significance for O-A maternal-foetal incompatibility. Ann. Eugen. Lond. *18:* 302–310.

Bianco, I., Montalenti, G., Silvestroni, E., and Siniscalco, M., 1952, Further data on the genetics of microcythaemia or thalassemia minor and Cooley's disease or thalassemia major. Ann. Eugen. Lond. *16:* 299–315.

Boorman, K. E., 1950, An analysis of blood types and clinical conditions of 2,000 consecutive mothers and infants. Ann. Eugen. Lond. *15:* 120–134.

Bryce, L. M., Jakobowicz, R. McArthur, N., and Penrose, L. S., 1950, Blood group frequencies in a mother and infant sample of the Australian population. Ann Eugen. Lond. *15:* 271–275.

Budtz-Olsen, O. E., and Burgers, A. C. J., 1955, The sickle-cell trait in the South African Bantu. S. Agr. Med. J. *29:* 109–110.

Chalmers, J. N. M., Ikin, E. W., and Mourant, A. E., 1948, Basque blood groups. Nature, Lond. *162:* 27.

Choremis, C., Ikin, E. W., Lehmann, H., Mourant, A. E., and Zannos, L., 1953, Sickle cell trait and blood-groups in Greece. Lancet ii: 909–911.

Cordeiro, A. R., and Dobhansky, Th., 1954, Combining ability of certain chromosomes in Drosophila willistoni and invalidation of the "wild-type" concept. Amer. Nat. *88:* 75–88.

Edington, G. M., 1953, Sickle cell anemia in the Accra district of the Gold Coast. Brit. Med. J. ii: 957–959.

Edington, G. M., and Lehmann, H., 1954a, A case of sickle cell hemoglobin C disease and a survey of hemoglobin C incidence in West Africa. Trans. Roy. Soc. Trop. Med. Hyg. *48:* 332.

——, 1954b, Hemoglobin. A new hemoglobin found in a West African. Lancet ii: 173–174.

Etcheverry, M. A., 1947, El factor Rh en personas de ascendencia Ibérica e Italica residentes en la Argentina. La Semana Médica. *2802:* 500–512.

Fisher, R. A., 1930, The Genetical Theory of Natural Selection. Oxford, pp. 376.

Fisher, R. A., Ford, E. B., and Huxley, J. S., 1939, Taste-testing the anthropoid apes. Nature, Lond. *144:* 750–751.

Fisher, R. A., Race, R. R., and Taylor, G. L., 1944, Mutation and the rhesus reaction. Nature, Lond. *162:* 27.

Ford, E. B., 1940, Polymorphism and taxonomy. In: The New Systematics. ed. J. S. Huxley, pp. 493–513. Oxford.

——, 1945, Polymorphism. Biol. Rev. *20:* 73–88.

Foy, H., Kondi, A., Timms, G. L., Brass, W., and Bushra, F., 1954, The variability of sickle cell rates in the tribes of Kenya and the southern Sudan. Brit. Med. J. i: 294–297.

Glass, B., 1950, The action of selection on the principal Rh alleles. Amer. J. Hum. Genet. *2:* 269–278.

Glass, B., and Li, C., 1953, The dynamics of racial intermixture—an analysis based on the American Negro. Amer. J. Hum. Genet. *5:* 1–20.

Grubb, R., and Sjöstedt, S., 1955, Blood groups in abortion and sterility. Ann. J. Hum. Genet. *19:* 183–194.

Haldane, J. B. S., 1942, Selection against heterozygosis in man. Ann. Eugen., Lond. *11:* 333–340.

——, 1949, The rate of mutation of human genes. Proc. VII Int. Cong. Genetics. Hereditas Supplement pp. 267–273.

Harris, H., Kalmus, H., and Trotter, W. R., 1949, Taste sensitivity to phenylthiourea in goitre and diabetes. Lancet ii: 1038–1039.

Harris, H., and Warren, F. L., 1955, Occurrence of electrophoretically distinct hemoglobin in ruminants. Biochem. J. (in litt.)

Hörlein, H., and Weber, G., 1948, Ueber chronische familiäre Methäemoglobinämie und eine neue Modifikation des Methäemoglobins. Dtsch. Med. Wsch. *73:* 746–762.

Itano, H. A., 1951, A third abnormal hemoglobin associated with hereditary hemolytic anemia. Proc. Nat. Acad. Sci. Wash. *37:* 775–784.

——, 1953. Human hemoglobin. Science *117:* 89–94.

Jacob, G. F., 1955, A survey for hemoglobins C and D in Uganda. Brit. Med. J. i: 521–522.

Kaplan, E., Zeulzer, W. W., and Neel, J. V., 1951, A new inherited abnormality of hemoglobin and its interaction with sickle cell hemoglobin. Blood *6:* 1240–1259.

Lambotte-Legrand, J., and Lambotte-Legrand, C., 1951, L'anémie a hématies falciformes chez l'enfant indigène du Bas-Congo. Mem. Inst. R. Col. Belge, Mem. 19, pp. 93.

Lehmann, H., 1954, Distribution of the sickle cell gene. Eugen. Rev. *46:* 3–23.

Lehmann, H., and Cutbush, M., 1952, Sickle cell trait in southern India. Brit. Med. J. i: 404–406.

Lerner, I. M., 1950, Population Genetics and Animal Improvement. 342 pp, Cambridge University Press.

McConnell, R. B., Clarke, C. A., and Downton, F., 1954, Blood groups in carcinoma of the lung. Brit. Med. J. i: 323–325.

Mackey, J. P., and Vivarelli, F., 1952, Annual Report of the Tanganyika Medical Laboratory.

Matsunuga, E., 1954, Intra-uterine selection by the ABO incompatibility of mother and foetus. Amer. J. Hum. Genet. *7:* 66–71.

Minnich, V., Na-Nakorn, Supa, Chongchareonsuk, S., and Kochaseni, S., 1954, Mediterranean anemia. A study of thirty-two cases in Thailand. Blood *9:* 1–23.

Montalenti, G., 1954, The genetics of microcythaemia. Caryologia, suppl. pp. 554–563.

Mourant, A. E., 1954, The Distribution of the Human Blood Groups. Oxford, Blackwell, 438 pp.

Na-Nakorn, Supa, Minnich, V., and Chernoff, A. I., 1955, Occurrence of abnormal hemoglobin E in Thailand. J. Lab. Clin. Med. (in press).

Neel, J. V., 1949, The inheritance of sickle cell anemia. Science *110:* 64–66.

——, 1951, The population genetics of two inherited blood dyscrasias in man. Cold Spr. Harb. Symp. Quant. Biol. *15:* 141–158.

——, 1953, Data pertaining to the population dynamics of sickle cell disease. Amer. J. Hum. Genet. *5:* 154–167.

Neel, J. V., Wells, I. C., and Itano, H. A., 1951, Familial differences in the proportion of abnormal hemoglobin present in the sickle cell trait. J. Clin. Invest. *30:* 1120–1124.

Pauling, L., Itano, H. A., Singer, S. J., and Wells, I. C., 1949, Sickle cell anemia, a molecular disease. Science *110:* 543–548.

Penrose, L. S., 1949, The meaning of "fitness" in human populations. Ann. Eugen. Lond. *14:* 301–303.

——, 1954, Short and long term influences of various factors on the frequency of genes which affect the characteristics of a population. Proc. World Population Conf. Rome, Meeting 53.

——, 1955, Personal communication.

Pike, A., and Dickins, A. M., 1954, ABO blood groups and toxaemia of pregnancy. Brit. Med. J. i: 321–323.

Powell, W. N., Rodarte, J. C., and Neel, J. V., 1950, The occurrence in a family of Sicilian ancestry of the traits for both sickling and thalassemia. Blood *10:* 887–897.

Race, R. R., and Sanger, R., 1954, Blood Groups in Man. Oxford, Blackwell, 2nd ed.

Ranney, H. M., 1954, Observations on the inheritance of sickle cell hemoglobin and hemoglobin C. J. Clin. Invest. *33:* 1634–1641.

Raper, A. B., 1950, Sickle cell disease in Africa and America—a comparison. J. Trop. Med. *53:* 49–53.

——, 1955, Malaria and the sickling trait. Brit. Med. J. i: 1186–1189.

Rich, A., 1952, Studies on the hemoglobin of Cooley's anemia and Cooley's trait. Proc. Nat. Acad. Sci. Wash. *38:* 187–192.

Roberts, D. F., and Lehmann, H., 1955, A search for abnormal hemoglobins in some southern Sudanese peoples. Brit. Med. J. i: 519–521.

Schneider, R. G., 1953, Paper electrophoresis of hemoglobin as a practical method of differentiating various types of sickle cell disease and of hemoglobin "C" trait. Texas Rep. Biol. and Med. *11:* 352–356.

Sheppard, P. M., 1953a, Polymorphism and population studies. Symp. Soc. Exp. Biol. *7:* 274–289.

——, 1953b, Polymorphism, linkage and the blood groups. Amer. Nat. *87:* 283–294.

Silvestroni, E., and Bianco, I., 1946, Una nuova entita nosologia: "la malattia micro-drepanocitica" Haematologica *29:* 455–488.

Singer, K., Chapman, A. Z., Goldberg, S., Rubinstein, H. M., and Rosenblum, S. A., 1954, Studies on abnormal hemoglobins. IX. Pure (homozygous) hemoglobin C disease. Blood *9:* 1023–1031.

Singer, K., Chernoff, A. I., and Singer, L., 1951, Idem. I. Their demonstration by means of alkali denaturation. Blood *6:* 412–428.

Singer, K., Kraus, A. P., Singer, L., Rubenstein, H. M., and Goldberg, S. R., 1954, Idem. X. Thalassemia-hemoglobin C disease. A new syndrome presumably due to the combination of the genes for thalassemia and hemoglobin C. Blood *9:* 1047–1054.

Singer, K., and Fisher, B., 1952, Idem. V. The distribution of type 5 (sickle cell) hemoglobin and type F (alkali resistant) hemoglobin within the red cell population in sickle cell anemia. Blood *7:* 1216–1226.

Smith, E. W., and Conley, C. L., 1953, Filter paper electrophoresis of human hemoglobin with special reference to the clinical significance of hemoglobin C. Bull. Johns Hopkins Hosp. *93:* 94–109.

——, 1954, Clinical features of the genetic variants of sickle cell disease. Bull. Johns Hopkins Hosp. *94:* 289–318.

Spaet, T. H., 1955, Personal communication.

Stern, C., Carson, G., Kinst, M., Novitski, E., and Uphoff, D., 1952, The viability of heterozygotes for lethals. Genetics *37:* 413–449.

Struthers, D., 1951, ABO groups of infants and children dying in the West of Scotland (1949–1951). Brit. J. Soc. Med. *5:* 223–228.

Vandepititte, J. M., 1954, Aspects quantitatifs et génétiques de la sicklanémie à Léopoldville. Ann. Soc. Belge de Med. Trop. *34:* 501–516.

Vandepitte, J. M., Zuelzer, W. W., Neel, J. V., and Colaert, J., 1955, Evidence concerning the inadequacy of mutation as an explanation of the frequency of the sickle cell gene in the Belgian Congo. Blood *10:* 341–350.

Waterhouse, J. A. H., and Hogben, L., 1947, Incompatibility of mother and foetus with respect to isoagglutinin a and its antibody. Brit. J. Soc. Med. *1:* 1–17.

Welbourn, H., and Raper, A. B., 1954, Sickle cell anemia in Uganda. Brit. Med. J. corr. *1:* 1440.

Wells, I. C., and Itano, H. A., 1951, Ratio of sickle cell anemia hemoglobin to normal hemoglobin in sicklemics. J. Biol. Chem. *188:* 65–74.

Westlund, K., and Heistö, H., 1955, Blood groups in relation to peptic ulceration. Brit. Med. J. i: 847.

Weiner, A. S., 1942, The Rh factor and racial origins. Science *96:* 407–408.

Wright, S., 1940, The statistical consequences of Mendelian heredity in relation to speciation. In: The New Systematics, ed. J. S. Huxley, pp. 160–183. Oxford.

Zuelzer, W. W., and Kaplan, E., 1954, Thalassemia-hemoglobin C disease. A new syndrome presumably due to the combination of the genes for thalassemia and hemoglobin C. Blood *9:* 1047–1054.

APPENDIX: CALCULATION OF FITNESS OF GENOTYPES IN A POPULATION HAVING THE SICKLE CELL AND HEMOGLOBIN C GENES

Penrose (1949) has discussed the question of fitness in a human population. He shows that in a random mating population in equilibrium the fitness of the genotypes AA, Aa, aa with frequencies p^2, $2pq$, q^2 can be expressed as $1-Kq^2$, $1+K$ pq, $1-Kp^2$, where K is a constant. By an extension of the argument, in a population with changing gene frequencies the fitness of the genotypes AA, Aa, aa can be expressed as $1-K\alpha^2$, $1+K\alpha\beta$, $1-K\beta^2$ where $\alpha+\beta = 1$ and at equilibrium $\alpha = p$, $\beta = q$. In East Africa, Allison (1954c) has presented evidence that there is an equilibrium point when frequency of trait carriers in the adult population is 40 per cent and when the survival rate of the sickle cell homozygote to reproductive age is not more than one quarter that of the heterozygote. Mrs. S. Maynard Smith, in a statistical appendix to the paper cited, has calculated that the fitnesses of the three genotypes Hb^A/Hb^A, Hb^S/Hb^A, Hb^S/Hb^S—that is, normal homozygote, heterozygote and abnormal homozygote—would then be 0.9482, 1.1908, 0.2977 (gene notation of Allison, 1955).

Zygotes				*Parents*				*Fitness*			
Geno-type	Hb^A	Hb^S	Hb^C	Geno-type	Hb^A	Hb^S	Hb^C	Geno-type	Hb^A	Hb^S	Hb^C
Hb^A	.5929	.1240	.0531	Hb^A	.5615	.1488	.0597	Hb^A	0.974	1.200	1.124
Hb^S	.1240	.0259	.0111	Hb^S	.1488	.0065	.0057	Hb^S	1.200	0.250	0.510
Hb^C	.0531	.0111	.0048	Hb^C	.0597	.0057	.0036	Hb^C	1.124	0.510	0.740
Total	.7700	.1610	.0690	Total	.7700	.1610	.0690				

The argument can be further extended to an equilibrium with three alleles. The appended tables give an equilibrium position for adult heterozygote frequencies $Hb^S/Hb^A = 30\%$, $Hb^C/Hb^A = 10\%$, which is the order of frequency of the genes for abnormal hemoglobins found in West Africa. The available data are insufficient to show the exact equilibrium position, and other equilibria are possible for the same heterozygote frequencies which give slightly different values for the fitness of Hb^S/Hb^C and Hb^C/Hb^C. The fitnesses as given compare quite well with those calculated previously for East Africans.

Section VI
The Origin of Life

Introduction

If the theory of evolution is true, then life must have originated in a very simple and primitive form at some time in the very distant past. Man has always had theories of how life began on earth, and every religion has its creation story. Yet only in the past forty years has a serious and reliable body of experimental evidence, in accordance with known physical and chemical laws, been obtained to suggest how life might have originated. The two papers reprinted in this section show two quite different approaches (in time and conception) to this problem.

The first paper, originally published by Louis Pasteur in 1861, is an attempt to refute the idea that living organisms arise spontaneously from simple organic substances. Prior to Pasteur's work, the familiar phenomena of decay, putrefaction, and fermentation of sugar were all held to be processes which generated the living corpuscles associated with them (we now recognize these corpuscles as yeast or bacteria). Pasteur felt that the idea of spontaneous generation was not in accordance with known biological and chemical laws, and could be supported by relatively little sound evidence. He maintained that yeast or bacteria could only come from the reproduction of preexisting microorganisms, and could not be produced spontaneously from nonliving material. He was not willing, however, to speculate about the origin of the first microorganisms on earth. Therefore, while discounting the idea of spontaneous generation as it was proposed in the eighteenth and nineteenth centuries, his work left the basic problem of the origin of life unsolved. For Pasteur had taken a logically impossible position: The possibility that somewhere at sometime a living corpuscle might arise spontaneously can never be ruled out; such is the nature of any statement insisting that such-and-such an event has the possibility of occurring. Pasteur's approach to the problem was to discredit in every way possible the examples brought forward as proof of the theory of spontaneous generation. By showing that the supposed examples of this phenomenon actually could be explained in other ways, he was doing his best to discredit, though he could not disprove, this theory.

The second paper, by Howard H. Pattee, summarizes some of the more recent experimental work aimed at throwing light on how complex organic molecules, or aggregates with certain quasi-biological properties, could arise spontaneously from simpler precursors. By accumulating an impressive array of experimental evidence, workers such as Pattee, Sidney Fox, Stanley Miller, and others have shown that "spontaneous generation" of a slightly different sort than that envisaged during the nineteenth century could indeed have occurred on the surface of the earth several billion years ago. Pattee's paper is less a presentation of experimental details than a review of much of the current work in a number of areas related to the origin-of-life problem. The paper is therefore of a type somewhat different in organization than most of the others included in this selection. Such review articles are of great importance in providing a general approach to, and summary of, the work in a particular field.

On the Organized Bodies which Exist in the Atmosphere; Examination of the Doctrine of Spontaneous Generation

by LOUIS PASTEUR

CHAPTER I. HISTORICAL. . . .

Chemists have discovered during the last twenty years a variety of really extra-ordinary phenomena which have been given the generic name of *fermentations*. All of these require the cooperation of two substances: one which is fermentable, such as sugar, and the other nitrogenous, which is always an albuminous sub-stance. But here is the universally accepted theory for this phenomenon: the albuminous material undergoes, when it comes in contact with air, an alteration, a particular oxidation of an unknown nature, which gives it the characteristics of a *ferment*. That is, it acquires the property of being able to cause fermentation upon contact with fermentable substances.

The oldest and the most remarkable ferment which has been known to be an organized being is the yeast of beer. But in all of the fermentations discovered since the beer yeast was shown to be organized, it has not been possible to demon-strate the existence of organized beings, even after careful study. Therefore, physiologists have gradually abandoned regretfully the hypothesis of M. Cagniard de Latour concerning a probable relation between the organized nature of this ferment and its ability to cause the fermentation. Instead, to beer yeast has been applied the following general theory: "It is not the fact that it is organized that makes the beer yeast active, rather it is because it has been in contact with air. It is the dead material of the yeast, that which has lived and is in the process of change, which acts on the sugar."

My studies have lead me to entirely different conclusions. I have found that all true fermentations—viscous, lactic, butyric, or those of tartaric acid, malic acid, or urine—only occur with the presence and multiplication of an organized being. Therefore, the organized nature of the beer yeast is not a disadvantage for the theory of fermentation. Rather, this shows that it is no different than other ferments and fits the common rule. In my opinion, the albuminous materials were never the ferments, but the nutrients of the ferment. The true ferments were organized beings.

This granted, it was known that the ferments originate through the contact of albuminous materials with oxygen gas. If this is so, there are two possibilities to explain this. Since the ferments are organized, it is possible that oxygen, acting as itself, is able to induce the production of the ferments through its contact with the nitrogenous materials, and therefore the ferments have arisen spontaneously. But, if the ferments are not spontaneously generated beings, it is not the oxygen gas itself which is necessary for their formation, but the stimulation by oxygen of a germ which is either carried with it by the air, or which already exists preformed in the nitrogenous or fermentable materials. At this point in my studies on fermentations, I wanted to arrive at an opinion on the question of spontaneous generation. I would perhaps be able to uncover a powerful argument in favor of my ideas on the fermentation themselves.

The researches which I will report here are only a digression made necessary by my studies on fermentations. . . .

CHAPTER II. EXAMINATION UNDER THE MICROSCOPE OF THE SOLID PARTICLES WHICH ARE DISSEMINATED IN THE ATMOSPHERE

My first problem was to develop a method which would permit me to collect in all seasons the solid particles that float in the air and examine them under the microscope. It was at first necessary to eliminate if possible the objections which the proponents of spontaneous generation have raised to the age-old hypothesis of the aerial dissemination of germs.

When the organic materials of infusions have been heated, they become populated with infusoria or molds. These organized bodies are in general neither so numerous nor so diverse as those that develop in infusions that have not been previously boiled, but they form nevertheless. But the germs of these infusoria and molds can only come from the air, if the liquid is boiled, because the boiling destroys all those that were present in the container or which had been brought there by the liquid. The first question to resolve is therefore: are there germs in the air? Are they there in sufficient numbers to explain the appearance of organized bodies in infusions which have been previously heated? Is it possible to obtain an approximate idea of the number of germs in a given volume of ordinary air? . . .

The procedure which I followed for collecting the suspended dust in the air and examining it under the microscope is very simple. A volume of the air to be examined is filtered through guncotton which is soluble in a mixture of alcohol and ether. The fibers of the guncotton stop the solid particles. The cotton is then treated with the solvent until it is completely dissolved. All of the particles fall to the bottom of the liquid. After they have been washed several times, they are placed on the microscope stage where they are easily examined. . . .

These very simple manipulations provide a means of demonstrating that there exists in ordinary air continually a variable number of bodies. Their sizes range from extremely small up to 0.01 or more of a millimeter. Some are perfect spheres, while others are oval. Their shapes are more or less distinctly outlined. Many are completely translucent, but others are opaque with granules inside. Those which are translucent with distinct shapes resemble the spores of common molds, and could not be told from these by the most skillful microscopist. Among the other forms present, there are those which resemble spherical infusoria and may be their cysts or the globules which are generally regarded as the eggs of these small organisms. But I do not believe it is possible to state with certainty that a particular object is a spore, or more especially the spore of a particular species, or that another object is an egg, and the egg of a certain microzoan. I will limit myself to the statement that these bodies are obviously organized, resembling in all points the germs of the lowest organisms, and so diverse in size and structure that they obviously belong to a large number of species.

By using a solution of iodine, it is possible to show unequivocally that amidst the bodies there are always starch granules. But it is easy to remove all globules of this sort by diluting the dust in ordinary sulfuric acid, which dissolves immediately all of the starch. Without a doubt the sulfuric acid alters and perhaps dissolves other globules, but there still remain a large number. Sometimes it is possible to distinguish more after treatment with sulfuric acid, because the acid dissolves the calcium carbonate and dilutes the other dust particles, so that many of the organized particles are freed from the amorphous debris which had prevented them from being seen well. It is well to make observations immediately after the small bubbles of carbonic acid have been dissipated, and before needles of calcium sulfate precipitate.

A wad of guncotton 1 centimeter long by $\frac{1}{2}$ centimeter in diameter was exposed to a current of air flowing at one liter per minute for 24 hours. After this time, examination revealed 20 to 30 organized bodies deposited per quarter of an hour (15 minutes). There are orinarily several bodies in the microscope field. It should be noted that the drop of dust mixture placed on the microscope slide is only a fraction of the total mixture obtained. . . .

CHAPTER III. EXPERIMENTS WITH HEATED AIR

We may conclude that there are always in suspension in the air, organized bodies which, from their shape, size and structure, cannot be distinguished from the germs of lower organisms, and without exaggeration, the number of these is quite large. Are there amongst these bodies really those which are capable of germinating? This is a very interesting question which I believe I have been able to solve with certainty. But before presenting the results of experiments which support in particular this argument, it is necessary to determine first if the results of Dr.

Schwann on the inactivity of air which has been heated red hot are correct. MM. Pouchet, Mantegazza, Joly and Musset contest this. Let us see which side is correct, especially since this will be fundamental to our later researches.

In a flask of 250–300 cc., I introduced 100–150 cc. of solution of the following composition: water, 100; sugar, 10; albuminous material and minerals from beer yeast, 0.2–0.7.

The neck of the flask is drawn out and connects with a platinum tube which is heated red hot, as shown in Figure 1. The liquid is boiled for two or three minutes, then it is allowed to cool completely. The flask is filled with ordinary air at atmospheric pressure, but all the air which has entered has been heated red hot first. Then the neck of the flask is sealed under a flame.

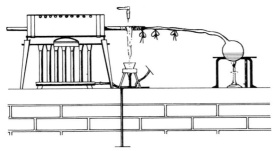

Fig. 1.

The flask so prepared is placed in a constant temperature chamber at 30°. It can be kept this way indefinitely without the liquid within showing the slightest alteration. Its clarity, odor, and slightly acidic character show not the slightest change. Its color darkens slightly after a time, which is undoubtedly due to a direct oxidation of the albuminous materials or the sugar.

I may say with the utmost sincerity that I have never had a single experiment which has given me the slightest doubt. Sugared yeast water heated to boiling for two or three minutes, then placed in contact with heated air, does not change in the slightest, even after 18 months at 25° to 30°. At the same time, if the flask is filled with ordinary air, it undergoes an extensive change within a day or two, and is full of bacteria, vibrios, or is covered with mucors.

The experiment of Dr. Schwann is therefore of irreproachable exactitude. . . .

CHAPTER VI. ANOTHER VERY SIMPLE METHOD TO DEMONSTRATE THAT ALL OF THE ORGANIZED BODIES IN INFUSIONS PREVIOUSLY HEATED ORIGINATE FROM BODIES WHICH EXIST IN SUSPENSION IN THE ATMOSPHERIC AIR

I believe I have rigorously established in the preceding chapters that all organized bodies in infusions which have been previously heated originate only from the solid particles carried by the air and which are constantly being deposited on all objects. In order to remove the slightest doubt in the reader, may I present the results of the following experiments.

In a glass flask I placed one of the following liquids which are extremely alterable through contact with ordinary air: yeast water, sugared yeast water, urine, sugar beet juice, pepper water. Then I drew out the neck of the flask under a flame, so that a number of curves were produced in it, as can be seen in Figure 2. I then boiled the liquid for several minutes until steam issued freely through the extremity of the neck. This end remained open without any other precautions. The flasks were then allowed to cool. Any one who is familiar with the delicacy of experiments concerning the so-called "spontaneous" generation will be astounded to observe that the liquid treated in this casual manner remains indefinitely without alteration. The flasks can be handled in any manner, can be transported from one place to another, can be allowed to undergo all the variations in temperature of the different seasons, the liquid does not undergo the slightest alteration. It retains its odor and flavor, and only, in certain cases, undergoes a direct oxidation, purely chemical in nature. *In no case is there the development of organized bodies in the liquid.*

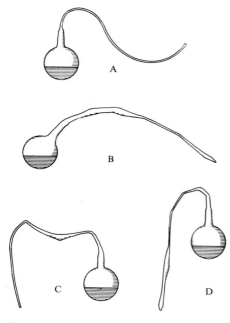

Fig. 2.

It might seem that atmospheric air, entering with force during the first moments, might come in contact with the liquid in its original crude state. This is true, but it meets a liquid which is still close to the boiling point. The further entrance of air occurs much slower, and when the liquid has cooled to the point where it will not kill the germs, the entrance of air has slowed down enough so that the dust it carries which is able to act on the infusion and cause the development of organized bodies is deposited on the moist walls of the curved tube. At least, I can see no other explanation for these curious results. For, after one or more months in the incubator, if the neck of the flask is removed by a stroke of a file, without otherwise touching the flask, molds and infusoria begin to appear after 24, 36, or 48 hours, just as usual, or as if dust from the air had been inoculated into the flask.

The same experiment can be repeated with milk, except here one must take the precaution of boiling the liquid under pressure at a temperature above 100° and allowing the flask to cool with the reentry of heated air. The flask can be allowed to stand in the open, just as before. The milk undergoes no alteration. I have allowed milk prepared in this manner to incubate for many months at 25 to 30°, without alteration. One notices only a slight thickening of the cream and a direct chemical oxidation.

I do not know any more convincing experiments than these, which can be easily repeated and varied in a thousand ways. . . .

At this moment I have in my laboratory many highly alterable liquids which have remained unchanged for 18 months in open vessels with curved or inclined necks. A number of these were deposited in the office of the Academy of Sciences during the meeting of 6 February 1860, when I had the honor of communicating to them these new results.

The great interest of this method is that it proves without doubt that the origin of life, in infusions which have been boiled, arises uniquely from the solid particles which are suspended in the air. Gas, various fluids, electricity, magnetism, ozone, things known or things unknown—there is absolutely nothing in ordinary atmospheric air which brings about the phenomenon of putrefaction or fermentation in the liquids which we have studied except these solid particles. . . .

The experiments of the preceding chapters can be summarized in the following double proposition:

1. There exist continually in the air organized bodies which cannot be distinguished from true germs of the organisms of infusions.

2. In the case that these bodies, and the amorphous debris associated with them, are inseminated into a liquid which has been subjected to boiling and which would have remained unaltered in previously heated air if the insemination had not taken place, the same beings appear in the liquid as those which develop when the liquid is exposed to the open air.

If we grant this, will a proponent of spontaneous generation continue to maintain his principles, even in the presence of this double proposition? This he can do, but he is forced to reason as follows, and I let the reader be the judge of it:

"There are solid particles present in the air," he will say, "such as calcium carbonate, silica, soot, wool and cotton fibers, starch grains, etc., and at the same time there are organized bodies with a perfect resemblance to the spores of molds and the eggs of infusoria. Well, I prefer to place the origin of the molds and infusoria in the first group of amorphous bodies, rather than in the second."

In my opinion, the inconsistency of such reasoning is self-evident. The entire body of my research has placed the proponents of spontaneous generation in this predicament.

Experimental Approaches
to the Origin of Life
Problem

by HOWARD H. PATTEE

I. INTRODUCTION

No question has aroused the curiosity of man for as long a time and provoked answers from so many disciplines as the primeval source of the persistent, localized, chemical reactions which we now recognize as living organisms. No doubt the question will continue to generate answers from many points of view for a long time to come. As a problem of experimental science it has stimulated only sporadic interest in the past, but for good reasons a general renewal of interest has grown in the last decade. First of all there are now many demonstrations that reasonable, primitive earth-like environments can produce most classes of molecules which are essential for present living organisms. Second, the immanent possibility of landing life-detection instruments on neighbouring planets has required some general thinking about a reasonable experimental strategy of extraterrestrial biological exploration. Third, the great advances in understanding the molecular basis of genetic replication and control of protein synthesis has raised deeper questions about the possible origin and evolution of these intricately connected macromolecular activities. Finally, there is a growing appreciation that the evolution of highly ordered systems from a chaos or cosmos poses a worthy fundamental problem in its own right, independent of what the physical or chemical representation of the systems we study may happen to be.

The present point of view of the author is that recent biological and abiological experiments which relate to the origin of life problem have so greatly reduced the gap between what are called "living" and "nonliving" states of matter that new questions must be asked and new experiments designed to help answer them. In some sense during the last decade we have learned to be less puzzled by the complexity of living matter and more puzzled by the complexity of nonliving matter. The general postulates of the biological theory of evolution, which in effect

Howard H. Pattee,"Experimental Approaches to the Origin of Life Problem," *Advances in Enzymology* **27** (1965), ed. F. F. Nord, 381–415. Reprinted by permission of John Wiley and Sons, Inc.

define what we mean by "living matter" (*cf.* Crick, 1961), have been reduced to molecular terms. Thus, blind mutation, self-replication, and the storage and expression of genetic information accumulated only by natural selection are described in terms of genetic, messenger, and transfer nucleic acids, protein synthesis, feedback control, the sequence hypothesis, and the central dogma. On the other hand, starting from the simplest molecules, such as water, carbon dioxide, and ammonia, it is possible to produce abiogenically many of the most essential biochemicals of present-day living organisms from common, nonspecific energy sources in a matter of hours (see Table 1). Some of these abiogenic polymers easily organize themselves into structured spheres which occasionally cleave or aggregate into more complex forms. (Fox and Yuyama, 1963a, b; 1964.) Furthermore, the simplest synthetic organic polymers can be precisely organized at the atomic level both in their primary linear structure (e.g., see Gaylord and Mark, 1959), as well as in their three-dimensional folding (e.g., see Geil, 1963) either autonomously or by the use of simple catalysts. Simplified models such as "perfect" crystals and "random" polymers are no longer of much use for explaining this behavior.

The main body of this chapter will be a brief review and discussion of recent experiments which have possible significance for the origin of life problem. These experiments raise many questions about the organization and behavior of collections of macromolecules which must be answered before any *non*biological theory of evolution can explain how simple molecules attain the intricate conditions necessary for biological evolution as we now observe it.

II. ABIOGENIC SYNTHESES IN SIMULATED PRIMEVAL ENVIRONMENTS

A. Review of Experiments

By far the greatest amount of experimental effort on the origin of life problem has been the search for reasonable reactions which produce biologically useful complex molecules from simpler starting materials which are likely to have occurred in abundance on the primitive, sterile earth. Most of these experiments are variations and extensions of experiments conceived first by Calvin (Garrison et al., 1951) and Urey (Miller, 1955). The phrase *chemical evolution* (e.g., see Calvin, 1956; Blum, 1961) is often used to describe this level of reaction in contrast to *biological evolution* by natural selection, although a precise definition of these terms in context is seldom given. Table 1 presents a brief summary of the data provided by abiogenic synthesis experiments showing the material synthesized, the starting compounds, the source of energy, and the reference. The column of materials synthesized is indeed a remarkable list of biochemicals which fully confirms the ideas first put forth by Oparin (1924) and Haldane (1929) that the primitive environment must have produced the organic materials which are essential for building up the first living organisms.

Several important additional points should be borne in mind when considering these data. In the first place, experiments of this type have been performed under

Table 1. *Abiogenic syntheses*[a]

Substances synthesized	Starting materials[b]	Energy source	References
Formic acid, formaldehyde	CO_2, H_2O, $(FeSO_4)$	Helium ions	Garrison et al. (1951)
Oxalic acid, fumaric acid	Glycine	Heat	Heyns and Pavel (1957)
Formic acid and higher fatty acids, urea	HCN, NH_4OH, H_2O	Heat	Lowe et al. (1963)
Glycolic acid, lactic acid, formic acid, acetic acid, propionic acid, α-hydroxybutyric acid, succinic acid, urea, methyl urea	CH_4, NH_3, H_2, H_2O	Electric discharge	Miller (1953, 1955, 1959); Miller and Urey (1959)
Glycolic acid, lactic acid, formic acid, glycinamide	Formaldehyde, hydroxylamine	Heat	Oró et al. (1959)

Amino Acids

Substances synthesized	Starting materials[b]	Energy source	References
α-Alanine, β-alanine, glycine, sarcosine	$CO_2(CO)$, $N_2(NH_3)$, H_2, H_2O	Electric discharge	Abelson (1956)
Aspartic acid, asparagine, arginine, glycine, serine, lysine, proline, histidine, valine	Paraformaldehyde, KNO_3, $(FeCl_3)$	Sunlight	Bahadur (1954, 1959)
Amino acids and amines (unidentified); Aspartic acid, alanine	CH_4, CO_2, NH_3, H_2, H_2O; Malic acid, urea	X-rays	Dose and Rajewsky (1957)
Glycine	Glucose urea, α-hydroxy-glutaric acid, NH_3	Heat	Fox (1960)
Glutamic acid; Aspartic acid, alanine	Ammonium fumarate, ammonium malate	Heat	Fox et al. (1955)
Glycine, alanine, sarcosine; Glycine, alanine, sarcosine, higher amino acids, amines	CH_4, NH_3, H_2O; C_2H_6, NH_3, H_2O	Ultraviolet	Groth (1957)
Aspartic acid, threonine, serine, glutamic acid, proline, glycine, alanine, valine, allo-isoleucine, isoleucine, leucine, tyrosine, phenylalanine, α-aminobutyric acid	CH_4, NH_3, H_2O	Heat	Harada and Fox (1964)

Products	Reactants	Energy source	Reference
Alanine, asparagine, glycylglycine	Glycine	Heat	Heyns and Pavel (1957)
Glycine, α-alanine, β-alanine, sarcosine, α-aminobutyric acid	CH_4, CO_2, NH_3, N_2, H_2, H_2S	Ultraviolet	Heyns et al. (1957)
Aspartic acid, threonine, serine, glutamic acid, glycine, alanine, isoleucine, leucine, β-alanine, α-β-diaminopropionic acid, α-aminobutyric acid and five others (unidentified)	HCN, NH_4OH, H_2O	Heat	Lowe et al. (1963)
Glycine, alanine, sarcosine, β-alanine, α-aminobutyric acid, N-methylalanine, aspartic acid, glutamic acid	CH_4, NH_3, H_2, H_2O	Electric discharge	Miller (1953, 1955, 1959); Miller and Urey (1959)
Glycine, alanine, aspartic acid, asparagine, isoleucine, proline and others (unidentified)	CH_4, C_2H_6, NH_4OH, H_2O	Electric discharge	Oró (1963)
Glycine, alanine, aspartic acid	HCN, NH_4OH	Heat	Oró and Kamat (1961)
Glycine, alanine, β-alanine, serine, aspartic acid, threonine	Formaldehyde, hydroxylamine	Heat	Oró et al. (1959)
Glycine and possibly alanine	$(NH_4)_2CO_3$	X-rays	Paschke et al. (1957)
Glycine, alanine, serine, glutamic acid, valine, isoleucine, phenylalanine, and basic amino acids (unidentified)	Formaldehyde, NH_4Cl, NH_4NO_3	Ultraviolet	Pavlovskaya and Pasynskii (1959)
α-Alanine, β-alanine and others (unidentified)	CH_4, CO, NH_3, H_2O (Al_2O_3, aluminosilicates, silicates)	Ultraviolet	Terenin (1959)

Polypeptides

Products	Reactants	Energy source	Reference
Polyglycine	Aminoacetonitrile, H_2O (kaolinite)	Heat	Akabori (1959)
Polyglycine with seryl or threonyl side chains	Polyglycine, formaldehyde or acetaldehyde (Kaolinite)	Heat	
Peptide infrared band	CH_4, NH_4Cl, H_2O, FeS	Ultraviolet	Ellenbogen (1958)

[a] The selection of entries in this table is illustrative rather than exhaustive. Inclusion in this table implies that some attempt has been made to simulate primitive earth or planetary conditions, even though many of these reactions have been known for years, and may have a large number of references in the literature of organic chemistry.

[b] Compounds in parentheses function as catalysts.

(cont.)

Table 1 (*continued*)

Substances synthesized	Starting materials	Energy source	References
Polypeptides (continued)			
Copolymers of aspartic acid with each of six other amino acids	Aspartic acid + other amino acids	Heat	Fox (1960)
"Panpolymers" of aspartic acid, glutamic acid, and 16 other amino acids	Aspartic acid, glutamic acid + other amino acids	Heat	Fox and Harada (1960)
Copolymers of glutamic acid or pyroglutamic acid and 6 or 7 other amino acids	Aspartic acid, glutamic acid + other amino acids	Heat	Harada and Fox (1958)
Copolymers of aspartic acid and glutamic acid	Aspartic acid, glutamic acid	Heat	Harada and Fox (1960)
Peptides (uncharacterized)	HCN, NH_4OH, H_2O	Heat	Lowe et al. (1963)
Polyglycine	Glycine, NH_4OH	Heat	Oró and Guidry (1961)
Polyarginine	Arginine (ethyl metaphosphate)	Heat	Schramm et al. (1962)
Poly(alanyl-glycyl-glycine)	Alanyl-glycyl-glycine (ethyl metaphosphate)	Heat	Schramm and Wissman (1958)
Purines, Pyrimidines, Nucleosides, Nucleotides			
Uracil	Malic acid, urea	Heat	Fox and Harada (1961)
Adenine, hypoxanthine	HCN, NH_4OH, H_2O	Heat	Lowe et al. (1963)
Adenine	CH_4, NH_3, H_2O	Electrons (4.5 m.e.v.)	Ponnamperuma et al. (1963)

Product	Starting materials	Energy	Reference
Adenosine	Adenine, ribose	Ultraviolet	Ponnamperuma et al. (1963)
ATP	Adenine, ribose, ethyl meta-phosphate Adenosine, ethyl meta-phosphate AMP, ethyl metaphosphate	Ultraviolet	Ponnamperuma et al. (1963)
Adenine	HCN (NH$_4$OH)	Heat	Oró and Kimball (1962)
Adenosine, deoxyadenosine	Adenine, ribose, deoxyribose (ethyl metaphosphate)	Heat	Schramm et al. (1962)
Polynucleotides			
Polyribonucleotides, e.g., poly-A, poly-U, poly-C, and various copolymers	Nucleoside 2'-, 3'-, or 5'-mono-phosphates	Heat	Schramm et al. (1962)
Polydeoxyribonucleotides, e.g. poly-dT	2'-Deoxynucleoside-5'-monophosphates (ethyl metaphosphate)	Heat	
Poly-C.	Cytosine 2'- or 3'-monophosphate (ethyl meta-phosphate)	Heat	Schwartz et al. (1964)
Sugars			
Ribose, deoxyribose	Formaldehyde	Ultraviolet	Ponnamperuma and Mariner (1963)
Cellibiose	Glucose, methyl glucose (ethyl metaphosphate)	Heat	Schramm et al. (1962)

[a] The selection of entries in this table is illustrative rather than exhaustive. Inclusion in this table implies that some attempt has been made to simulate primitive earth or planetary conditions, even though many of these reactions have been known for years, and may have a large number of references in the literature of organic chemistry.

[b] Compounds in parentheses function as catalysts.

(cont.)

Table 1 *(continued)*

Substances synthesized	Starting materials	Energy source	References
Polysaccharides			
Polyglucose	Glucose	Heat	Mora (1958, 1964)
Polyglucose	Glucose (ethyl metaphosphate)	Heat	Schramm et al. (1962)
Polyribose	Ribose	Heat	
Polyfructose	Fructose (ethyl metaphosphate)	Heat	
Other Substances			
Melanic polymers	Phenylalanine	Ultraviolet	Blois (1964); Blois and Kenyon (1964); Kenyon and Blois (1964)
Polymers which yield amino acids and urea upon hydrolysis	HCN, NH$_4$OH, H$_2$O	Heat	Lowe, Rees, and Markham (1963)
Porphine-like substances	Pyrrole + an aldehyde	Ultraviolet; x-rays	Szutka (1963, 1964)
High molecular weight hydrocarbon polymer	CH$_4$, NH$_4$OH, H$_2$O, H$_2$S, yeast ash	Electric discharge	Wilson (1960)

[a] The selection of entries in this table is illustrative rather than exhaustive. Inclusion in this table implies that some attempt has been made to simulate primitive earth or planetary conditions, even though many of these reactions have been known for years, and may have a large number of references in the literature of organic chemistry.
[b] Compounds in parentheses function as catalysts.

laboratory environments which represent possible primitive earth conditions. The best evidence available on these macroscopic conditions is very incomplete and leaves many possibilities open. Furthermore, although improved techniques and more imaginative searches, such as the paleobiochemical experiments of Abelson (1963), will greatly increase out historical knowledge, it is extremely unlikely that direct geochemical evidence can be found to provide the basis for what we might call "crucial" experiments (Rutten, 1962). Nevertheless, the geochemical ground rules provided the essential independent restrictions necessary to give these experiments more than hypothetical significance. Second, even if the precise macroscopic or thermodynamic conditions could be specified accurately, the details of the molecular environment may still be of the utmost importance. Although we may not know details with certainty, we are certain that the details were complex. Consider any primitive seashore with periodic waves and tides washing over many forms of sand and clay, and all bathed with ultraviolet and visible light; or consider an active volcanic region with high temperatures and high temperature gradients in complex mineral surfaces cooled by heavy rains which flow into warm stagnant pools or into the sea. Even though we do not know the details, we should recognize that only a few laboratory experiments approach this order of chemical, structural, or sequential complexity (e.g., Fox, 1964) and in this sense many realistic simulated primeval environments remain to be explored. Furthermore, probably only a few per cent of the organic material produced in these experiments has been identified, and there is no reason to believe that the unidentified material is biologically uninteresting or insignificant. Perhaps the most surprising general result of all these abiogenic syntheses is that so many complex organic and biochemical species are produced from such simple starting materials and in such a short time. As Fox (1964) has demonstrated, it is now a reasonable hypothesis that volcanic regions of the primitive earth produced significant quantities of high molecular weight heteropolyamino acids from simple gases in a matter of hours. All these general considerations when combined with the results in Table 1 reinforce the conclusion that almost any specified class of molecule which we consider essential for life is likely to be produced in a reasonable simulated environment representing some region of the primitive earth.

B. Discussion of Abiogenic Synthesis Experiments

What are the conclusions to be drawn from these abiogenic synthesis experiments, and to what type of future experiments do they lead? These experiments were based on the hypothesis that conditions on the primitive earth, whatever they may have been in detail, were at some place favorable for the production of many organic compounds which make up *life at the present time* (e.g., see Miller and Urey, 1959). The results of these experiments make this hypothesis extremely plausible.

   At the same time, these experiments show that an enormous number of other compounds were also produced. Which of these many materials were essential in forming the most primitive hereditary macromolecules which led to present forms of life has not been demonstrated. The most common working hypothesis is that those species of molecules which make up *present living matter* were also the *starting material*. This *biochemical similarity principle* is perhaps the simplest hypothesis, but there is no evidence as yet which excludes alternative possibilities. From the time of the first appearance on earth of such enormously complex chemical heterogeneity, which these abiogenic syntheses lead us to believe existed, there may have been a long period of evolution before the state of biochemical uniformity based on proteins and nucleic acids came into being (e.g., see Pirie, 1959). The fact that an experimenter who has done an abiogenic synthesis can pick out of such complex mixtures so many biochemicals is a valuable starting point for many theories, but it is not in itself sufficient to verify the biochemical similarity principle.

It is important that experiments on abiogenic synthesis continue until it is demonstrated which general sets of conceivable primitive earth conditions produce those chemicals which are considered essential for the different theories of evolving systems; for it may well be that the richness of organic material produced by simulating conditions on the surface of the primeval earth is sufficiently great that within certain limits most classes of biochemical and organic molecules may be found. The only obvious limit is set by the immense number of isomers in heteropolymers which could not all exist simply for lack of space. Furthermore, judging from results of abiogenic experiments using different energy sources and starting materials, the conditions required to produce any class of molecules may not be unique. It is therefore not likely, nor should it be necessary, that a final decision will be made on the basis of abiogenic synthesis experiments alone as to which particular set of primitive earth conditions existed, or which particular molecules were essential for the evolution of present life. The great value of these remarkable experiments is that they have given us a large amount of freedom in formulating reasonable theories for the first evolving molecular systems.

III. STUDIES OF ORGANIZED STRUCTURE

The complexity and diversity of biological structure is a striking characteristic which has historically often obscured the more fundamental biochemical uniformity at the molecular level. Even if we assume a *structural similarity principle* to guide our observations, the problem of evaluating the significance of "lifelike" structures which arise from abiogenic environments is more difficult than comparing *biochemical similarity*, not only because our knowledge of the formation and development of living structures is very small compared to our chemical knowledge, but also because no quantitative measure of "likeness" has been defined as it has in chemistry. A biologist observing the remarkable structures which are so easily produced with thiocyanates (Herrera, 1942), phospholipids (Nageotte, 1936), or polyamino acids (Fox, Harada and Kendrick, 1959) often finds it difficult to maintain an unbiased attitude. There is often a feeling that the structural complexity and behavioral similarity to living systems is so much greater than we should expect from such simple mixtures that some coincidence or even self-deception is involved, and as a consequence the whole observation is discounted as irrelevant to living systems. At best they are labeled as superficial likenesses, since no metabolism or reproduction is observed. But perhaps this is too strong a reaction. While it is likely that these organized structures contain no genetic information, and may not be precursors of life, on the other hand we actually have far too little detailed molecular knowledge of how genetic information determines the structure in living systems to judge the significance of morphological similarities. It is a lot to expect that we can understand how the conformation and function of an enzyme or a structural protein is affected by a linear sequence of bases in nucleic acids, when we do not even know why the simplest linear carbon chains fold into precise crystals, or why simple metal hydrides can effect the precise sequential positioning of subunits in tactic polymers. Just as there are many biochemical events which can be understood only by studying fundamental nonbiological chemical reactions, so there are probably many biological structures which will be understood only by learning more about molecular structure at a nonbiological level. To be of long-range significance, however, experiments on macromolecular morphology should be done at an elementary level; that is, the systems studied should yield explanations in physical and chemical terms (e.g., Bangham and Horne, 1964), not in biological terms. Morphological analogs of living structures certainly should not be discounted as superficial simply because they are not likely to come alive.

On the basis of abiogenic synthesis experiments already performed, it is reasonable to go a step further and consider the types of organization and structure which these high molecular weight materials produce. Fox has studied in detail the structure and behavior of microspherical particles formed in aqueous solutions of thermally polymerized amino acids (Fox et al., 1959; Fox and Yuyama, 1963a, b; 1964). These particles are several microns in diameter, often show simple internal structure, and occasionally divide in two. Demonstrations of this type are valuable guides to our concepts of the possible order which we can expect from primitive macromolecules, but their explanation will certainly require a more fundamental understanding of the structure and behavior of simple polymers than we now possess.

Considering the enormously rich possibilities for natural influence of reactions on the primitive earth such as mineral catalysis, photoreactions, natural isolation and mixing processes, concentration and temperature changes, there is no reason to exclude reasonably simple chemical mixtures only because they have not yet been demonstrated to occur in greatly oversimplified, primitive-earth simulation experiments. Following this approach and recognizing the conditional nature of such experiments, Oparin (1964) has introduced proteins, nucleic acids, and other polymers isolated from living matter into structural coacervate systems with the result that certain limited types of protometabolic reactions are observed along with increased structural complexity.

The introduction of extracted biological macromolecules into origin of life experiments must always be considered critically since the introduction of large quantities of evolutionary information is possible. If this happens, the behavior of the system may in some respects become quite lifelike, but it could not answer the basic question of the ultimate source of these evolutionary inventions. On the other hand, the use of non-enzymically synthesized polypeptides and poly-nucleotides in studying primitive structures and behavior is of great interest and is a logical extension of experiments, if the *biochemical similarity principle* is assumed as a working hypothesis. The only mandatory ground rule in testing this hypothesis is that no molecules be introduced in the experiments which represent large amounts of genetic information accumulated by natural selection. In effect these experiments increase the biochemical complexity of a simulated "primeval broth" and may demonstrate characteristics of structure or function which are in some sense "lifelike" beyond the mere sum of biochemicals which are present. How the likeness is to be defined and measured remains a serious conceptual problem without a clear distinction between what type of structures have or have not the potential for biological evolution. Again, a fundamental understanding of such complexity is beyond our reach without more basic studies of macro-molecular aggregations.

IV. THE SEARCH FOR EXTRATERRESTRIAL INFORMATION
A. Meteorites and Planetary Landings

The biochemical and structural similarity hypotheses have also been assumed in the interpretation of organized carbonaceous material in meteorites (Claus and Nagy, 1961; Nagy, Meinschien, and Hennessy, 1961). An enormous amount of technical discussion concerning the source and significance of these organized elements has taken place (e.g., see Urey, 1962 and following articles). The basic problem of evaluating these organized structures is deciding the essential differences expected in chemistry and structure between (*1*) extraterrestrial fossils of primitive organisms, (*2*) extraterrestrial prebiota, (*3*) extraterrestrial abiota, (*4*) terrestrial contamination, and (*5*) artifacts of specimen preparation. Whatever differences are assumed, there is the added problem of experimentally resolving these assumed differences on a very small amount of intractable material. Some of the most complex structures in meteorites have been traced to terrestrial contamination of pollen (Fitch and Anders, 1963), but *in situ* microchemical analysis of other organized regions has been interpreted by Nagy et al. (1963) as evidence that some of these organized structures have not originated on earth. In any case, even if some of these structures are of extraterrestrial origin, their significance for the origin of life is at present unknown (e.g., see Morrison, 1962; Fox and Yuyama, 1963b).

With the availability of large rockets and the complex technology of artificial satellite control and communication, there is now the possibility of landing instruments on the moon and nearby planets. Here again, the strategy of explora-tion is based on the biochemical similarity principle (e.g., Lederberg, 1960a), although gross structural similarity as viewed by televised images from high power telescopes landed on the surface would also be likely to reveal unmistakable characteristics of life if it exists. Other evidence gathered from the many observations of planets have often suggested the possibility of vegetation on Mars (e.g., Sinton, 1959), but as yet this information is so incomplete and conditional that further review is unproductive at this time (see Sagan, 1961).

B. Discussion of Extraterrestrial Experiments

In order to better imagine what the next stage of origin of life experiments should seek to discover, it may be useful to consider the possible outcomes of experiments involving planetary landings. One possibility is that earth-like forms of life exist on Mars. By "earth-like" we mean that there are interactions with the exploring instruments which we have predicted on the basis of known biochemical behavior on earth. To find life like our own on a distant planet would undoubtedly be considered the most notable discovery of the century, but, paradoxically, the more biochemical similarity any such extraterrestrial life might possess, the less we may actually learn from it concerning the primeval source of this complexity. For example, if genetic nucleic acids and protein enzymes are identifiable on Mars we might expect life there as we know it; but what else would we be likely to learn? Knowing that life on Mars is not essentially different from life on earth adds very little information to what we have already learned or what we may expect to learn of its origin from studying life and evolution on the earth. We may at least return to our terrestrial experiments knowing that we are missing no great evolutionary innovations.

More generally we must ask what are the minimum essential, remotely observable characteristics which would be acceptable to us as evidence of life? Since we have abiogenically produced protein-like and nucleic acid-like molecules on earth as well as organized structures which resemble living cells in many ways, we could not interpret similar finding on Mars as sufficient evidence that life exists there. As the biochemical list in Table 1 is gradually extended, abiogenically, there will be a corresponding reduction in the significance of finding such biochemicals on other planets.

Another possibility is that a sufficiently complex type of living system exists so that its outward appearance gives it away, such as tree-like growth or a body with a well-developed form of locomotion. The biochemical nature of such complex structures would be of profound interest, but not essential for the recognition of a live form of matter. However, the basic question of the *evolution* of such highly complex forms, by which we must ultimately define or recognize the living state of matter, would in all likelihood remain for a long time even more obscure than the source of life on earth where we have available an enormous amount of evolutionary information compared to what we may expect to obtain from any other planet. Therefore, there is as yet no very convincing reason why we should expect that a rudimentary knowledge of the existence and nature of life, in one form or another, on other planets should necessarily lead us directly to a nonbiological theory of the *origin* and evolution of this highly organized state of matter from chaotic primeval molecules. There is, of course, a remote possibility that an intelligent form of life on another planet has already solved the problem of its own origin and could in turn explain it to us.

V. THE APPROACH FROM MOLECULAR BIOLOGY

There is always the hope that as we learn to describe in more and more detail the functioning and evolution of living cells there will concurrently emerge some understanding of the origin of evolution of nonliving molecular complexity. In fact, many theories of the earliest form of life are in some sense attempts to simplify and abstract from our knowledge of living systems some characteristic features which, for one reason or another, appear to be the most essential or productive starting point for biological evolution. It is understandable that earlier theories, such as those of Oparin, reflected the biochemical interests of the time in metabolic pathways; later on, the origin of catalytic reactions was often emphasized, whereas today most theories reflect the nucleic acid–protein interaction which is now the center of so many productive experiments.

However, instead of providing greater understanding of the source of living complexity, what has actually happened is that our recent detailed understanding of the intricacies of DNA replication and control of protein synthesis through the elaborate mediation of many specific RNA's and enzymes has created a greater mystery; for it is now even less imaginable how all the necessary conditions for a biochemically similar ancestral threshold system could originate from the primeval broth.

A. Current Molecular Biological Theories

Many of the latest discussions of the origin of life have assumed or defined the minimum requirements for life in modern genetic terms involving mutable self-replication of nucleic acid-like macromolecules, and the *assumed* property of such systems of evolving only by the biological process of natural selection. This implies that the central dogma was still valid at this primitive level, i.e., that hereditary information is determined solely by its parental sequence and not by external acquisition.

These assumptions necessarily lead to what we may call *threshold* theories of the origin of life, since biological evolution by natural selection is defined only by assuming *at least* the preexistence of mutable self-replicating units. The origin of the first mutable, self-replicating unit can *not* therefore be explained by the evolutionary process of natural selection from simpler aggregations of molecules which are below this threshold. The term *chemical evolution* has come to mean those chemical processes which lead to increased complexity without assuming natural selection, but as yet there is no theory of chemical evolution, and consequently the term explains nothing. The lowest level of complexity of the threshold which would support persistent evolution by natural selection is usually set at the nucleic acid level (e.g., Muller, 1961), although Lederberg (1960b) has suggested that nucleic acids are more subtle and specific than we might reasonably expect from chemical evolution alone, or than we might select as a goal for our first attempts to synthesize an artificial replicating macromolecule. Lederberg pictures the minimal threshold as follows:

It must have a rigid periodic structure in which two or more alternative units can be readily substituted. It must allow for the reversible sorption of specific monomers to the units in its own sequence. Adjacent, sorbed monomers must then condense to form the replica polymer, which must be able to desorb from the template.

Crick (1961) and Rich (1962) discuss the necessity for a more elaborate threshold involving both nucleic acid replication and specific coupling with amino acid polymers. This symbiosis of the two types of polymer is, of course, the central theme of present-day molecular biology and it is difficult to imagine a more elementary threshold on which natural selection can operate. A similar point of view is expressed by Horowitz and Miller (1962), Schramm (1962), and Haldane (1964). Rich has emphasized in some detail the rather stringent requirements for the interactions of amino acids and polynucleotides which would be essential for a threshold with evolutionary potential.[1] In chemically less specific terms Calvin and Calvin (1964) have described the minimum threshold of life as

(*1*) the ability of such a molecular aggregate to transfer and transform energy in a directed way; and (*2*) its ability to remember how to do this, once having "learned" it, and to transfer, or communicate, that information to another system like itself which it can construct.

B. Discussion of Biological Approaches to the Origin of Life

These descriptions of possible ancestral thresholds for organisms evolving by natural selection are certainly great simplifications of the known organization of living cells, but they are still logically extremely sophisticated and leave an enormous gap beyond what has been demonstrated by chemical evolution. It is sometimes assumed that this gap can be bridged by chance. Thus, Wald (1954) has used the argument that the level of such a threshold makes its attainment highly improbable within the time available in laboratory experiments, but nearly inevitable by cosmic time scales. Whether or not such arguments are satisfying depends largely on the epistemological or esthetic standards one demands for scientific explanation. The logical complexity of any biological threshold would make a Maxwell demon appear as an elementary particle by comparison, but such constructs are not acceptable in scientific theories, except insofar as we assume they do not exist. In any case it is difficult to imagine how any theory which depends essentially on auspicious accidents could be experimentally tested (cf. Bridgman, 1954).

Haldane (1964) has pointed out two other difficulties with biological threshold theories. One difficulty involves the problem of the behavior of any "half-life" or prethreshold systems which would presumably contain catalysts arising by chemical evolution which are needed eventually for the threshold nucleic acid–protein system when it "goes critical." Such unorganized catalysts, like those in a

---

[1] As Commoner (1962) has pointed out, if the potential for biological evolution is the definition of the threshold of life, then nothing less than a whole live cell has been demonstrated to be alive.

dead cell, would be likely to release the energy of any metastable molecules—say, pyrophosphates or sugars—and thereby generally tend to spoil rather than enhance the gains of chemical evolution. The second difficulty is in reconciling the likely minimum biochemical threshold requirements of a specific polypeptide catalyst coupled to a replicating nucleic acid with the probability of attaining these requirements by a stochastic chemical evolution process. Thus a relatively short peptide of only 20 or 25 ordered amino acid residues found by random search might alone be expected to involve some 10^{31} trials, which is probably expecting too much for the space and time available on the earth.

A more general difficulty with any threshold theory is its implicit violation of the Principle of Continuity (e.g., see Weyl, 1949) which in the broadest sense is what any theory of origins should try to preserve. In seeking origins, it is certainly a reasonable strategy to extrapolate backwards from what is now known. In the case of living organisms, following the course of evolution into the past involves many guesses, but whatever hypothesis we choose to consider in our attempt to approach the conditions of the primeval abiogenic reservoir, we must preserve enough organization and function to assure the continuity of the evolutionary pathway that we have retraced. The restriction in this procedure is not the lack of facts about the course of evolution, but the assumption of the theory of evolution itself. This is a logical restriction, and has nothing to do with the truth of any particular theory. For example, if we define an evolutionary theory which depends on the properties of mutation, replication, and natural selection, then we may not extrapolate backwards beyond these properties using this theory. In effect, these properties determine a *conceptual threshold* beyond which we must either invent a new theory of evolution or else relinquish continuity and rely on accidents to organize matter up to this threshold of complexity. It is therefore reasonable to assume that knowledge of biological behavior, including the biological theory of evolution, will be necessary but not sufficient to formulate a theory of its own origin.

VI. ABIOLOGICAL APPROACHES

A. Future of Abiogenic Syntheses

There can be no doubt that abiogenic synthesis experiments have significantly narrowed the gap between inorganic and living matter, and have shown that many essential biochemicals have very primitive origins. Similarly, the demonstrations that some of these molecules when mixed under nonspecific conditions aggregate into formed structures of the size and shape of the simplest living cells certainly suggest that some of the structure of living matter may also be of very primitive origin. The productivity of this approach should stimulate many more experiments which in time will no doubt narrow the gap even further.

We may reasonably ask if we expect this approach to eventually close the gap; that is, do we expect that with the mixing together of more and more complex biochemicals we will continue to learn more about the origin of life? Do we expect to eventually produce a self-replicating macromolecule or aggregate of molecules which will evolve by natural selection?

One criticism of this approach is that while in principle this is possible, or actually happened on the earth, in practice the time and volume of matter necessary to reach the threshold of self-replication effective for biological evolution far exceeds any possibility for an experimental test. However, if the premise is correct then it is reasonable to accelerate the approach toward the replicating threshold by the careful guidance of the experimenter. This has already been done in abiogenic synthesis experiments in which the synthesis of a trace of one chemical in one experiment is followed by its introduction in concentration in subsequent experiments. This is justified by two arguments: (*1*) that the earth has an immense advantage in size and age over the laboratory, and (*2*) that natural catalysis or concentration is likely to occur in the much greater chemical and structural heterogeneity of the earth than in the oversimplified laboratory conditions. Very likely the size and age of the earth is an advantage only for a theory of prebiological evolution in which random reactions play an essential role. In other words, if, say, over 10^{30} small amino acid copolymers must be randomly synthesized in order to give a reasonable probability of producing the first polymerase-type catalyst, then the whole surface of the earth working for many millions of years would indeed be necessary to assure success. On the other hand, if we use the hypothesis that some form of prebiological evolution continuously produces increasing molecular order without essential dependence on accidents, then the value of enormous reaction volumes is difficult to imagine. Any mile of seashore (or any volcano) would be about as good as any other, since primitive molecular evolution which we presume went on in such regions would not be significantly influenced by neighboring areas. The value of long time intervals is even more questionable since even for accident-dependent theories the crucial time interval will be the half-life of the fortuitously polymerized catalysts once they appear rather than the time necessary to find them by trial and error. Continuous evolutionary theories, on the other hand, must by their nature depend on a temporal sequence, each element of which has some causal significance in the evolutionary process. In other words, if we are not assuming that accidents are essential for reaching the biological threshold, the size and age of the earth do not present an insurmountable experimental problem for abiogenic synthesis. In future abiogenic synthesis experiments it will be most interesting to more closely simulate the known complexity of the earth such as occurs at the seashore or in volcanic pools, where catalysis, periodic mixing, and natural concentration may all occur.

The question as to whether or not a stage of self-replication can be reached within a reasonable time span is not particularly relevant at this time for evaluating abiogenic synthesis experiments. As a practical matter the problem is really quite the opposite: *abiogenic syntheses have demonstrated more rapid molecular evolution than we can presently explain.* As we have pointed out, experiments have produced almost all essential types of biochemicals plus an even greater amount of unanalyzed organic material, as well as many structures which are beyond our ability to explain in any fundamental way. Therefore, while it is not at all unlikely that abiogenic syntheses will eventually produce a kind of replicating unit, if they have not done so already, this demonstration will be of little significance if we have no theory to explain it. Perhaps the most valuable abiogenic experiments of the future will be those which are designed to verify or disprove specific *non-biological theories of molecular evolution* rather than to demonstrate the increasing complexity of molecular aggregations supplied with steady energy sources.

B. Contributions of Polymer Chemistry

At present the gap between abiogenesis experiments and molecular biology experiments remains enormous. Some intermediate stage of complexity which could be studied experimentally would be of great value in linking the two approaches as well as in guiding the formulation of theories of molecular evolution. The most obvious possible link is the area of polymer chemistry. Historically, of course, polymer chemistry grew out of studies on biological polymers, and since the commercial availability of synthetic polymers, one of the principal goals of the polymer chemist has been to accomplish an "abiogenic synthesis" which would produce material similar in its properties to macromolecules produced by living systems (e.g., see Flory, 1953; Mark, 1964). Today, however, the gap between polymer chemists and molecular biologists has in many ways grown larger instead of smaller. Much fundamental work is being done on synthetic polypeptides and polynucleotides from the point of view of the molecular biologist both experimental (e.g., see Stahmann, 1962; Khorana, 1960) and theoretical (e.g., see Weissbluth, 1964), and an enormous effort from the chemists' point of view is stimulated by hope of improving the properties of commercial polymers (e.g., see Gaylord and Mark, 1959; Geil, 1963; Ke, 1964). There has been surprisingly little interaction between these groups even though many of the fundamental problems of polymer sequence and conformation are common to both.

Two discoveries have been recognized in the last decade about the behavior of simple linear polymers which are of great potential significance for any theory of molecular evolution. The first discovery is that single linear polymer molecules will spontaneously fold into precise conformations and aggregate with similar molecules to form three-dimensional crystals. The first evidence of this behavior is relatively old (Staudinger and Signer, 1929; Sauter, 1932; Storcks, 1938) but only more recently has work on single polymer crystals, beginning with Keller (1957), Fischer (1957), and Till (1957), produced a clear appreciation of the precision in the conformation of individual molecules in the crystal.

The second discovery is that the linear sequential control of the orientation of nonsymmetric monomers in a growing polymer may be precisely accomplished by simple heterogeneous catalysts. Although the concept of stereoregularity in polymers was clearly stated by Huggins (1944) many years ago, it was the discovery by Ziegler (1952) of catalysts exerting highly specific and detailed steric control of polymer propagation, and the studies by Natta and his coworkers (Natta et al., 1955) on the structures of these polymers that stimulated this new branch of polymer chemistry. Neither this folding of single polymer molecules into crystals nor the catalytic control of sequential orientation in linear polymers is understood, but the observations make it quite clear that both processes are not only possible, but also occur quite generally with a wide range of polymeric material.

Merely to state that polymers will form crystals does not give an adequate picture of polymer morphology, nor is the historical idea of a crystal entirely satisfactory for describing the behavior and structure of such polymers. The essential fact, based on the observation of many types of simple polymers, is that chain folding tends to occur in a *precise* form, probably to within atomic dimension, from either dilute solution or from the melt. The regularity of this chain folding, under fixed conditions, is sufficiently high to produce thin platelet crystals with a hollow pyramid shape. Typically, the thickness of a single platelet is about 100 A. and the platelet may be 1–10 microns across. The polymer chain is faked in a zigzag nearly perpendicular to the large faces of the platelet. Of course, the crystallization conditions will determine the morphology of the crystal habit. The range of structures from single crystals to highly twinned crystals, dendritic growths, and spherulitic textures, depend on primary nucleation rates, growth rate, and rate of generation of deformations, although these relationships are not generally understood (e.g., see Lindenmeyer, 1963). However, the significant point this demonstrates for any theory of molecular evolution is that even at the simplest level of organization in single macromolecules there is the possibility of precise, three-dimensional positioning of all the monomeric units without breaking the linear chain holding the monomers together. Although this may appear as an obvious or trivial property of chain molecules, nevertheless without this property it would be difficult to imagine molecular storage or transcription of order of any complexity.

Tactic polymerization, in which the positions of each monomer are determined with respect to the linear sequence, is, in effect, one-dimensional crystallization. The order which has been studied so far is extremely simple and may usually be described by Bernoulli statistics, as in isotactic order, or first-order Markov statistics, as in syndiotactic or alternating copolymer order (e.g., see Krigbaum, 1964). But here again, as with the simple polymer crystals, there is clear indication of the property of precise sequential ordering at a very simple macromolecular level.

Most of the work on tactic polymers and polymer crystals has been done from the point of view of the synthetic polymer chemist, and the attitudes and results may appear somewhat far removed from the biological approaches to macromolecular behavior as well as to origin of life studies. This is certainly the case with respect to the type of material which is studied, the descriptive terminology, and the goals of the research. However, with respect to the *elementary* operations involved in the control and propagation of sequential and conformational order in chain macromolecules there is no evidence to suggest that different physical or chemical laws are involved in a plastics factory than in a cell. The significant difference is the order of complexity which one chooses to emphasize in each case.

The description of any experiment must depend to a great degree on what type of order is resolvable by the experimental technique employed. Thus the characterization of a linear heteropolymer as "random" is seldom no more than a statement that the sequence order is unresolved and presumed to obey certain statistics. However, even though statistical models are useful in formulating theories of propagation, they do not as yet solve the problem of what type of order exists in polymers. Experimentally, all but one of the present tests for tacticity, including x-ray diffraction, melting point determination, mechanical and thermodynamic properties, dipole moments, infrared and nuclear magnetic resonance spectroscopy, etc., depend for their sensitivity to linear order only indirectly through the three-dimensional crystalline structure or conformation, which is conditionally dependent on the linear sequence (Krigbaum, 1964). This is also the case for tests of enzyme activity. Furthermore, the absence of detectable crystallinity does not preclude eutacticity, as is obvious from our knowledge of proteins. The only test which reveals linear structure directly is chemical sequence determination, which depends for its resolution on the sequential homogeneity of the polymer and highly specific degradation procedures. This has only been accomplished with proteins. The intimate dependence of three-dimensional structure on linear sequence is therefore experimentally difficult to resolve even at the most elementary level, but there can be little doubt that at all levels of organization of polymers the conformation will depend conditionally on the precise linear order of subunits in the chain.

　　This leads to the question of what determines the linear sequential order of polymers. From the theoretical point of view we may begin with a simple homo-polymerization in which order has no significance and the growth kinetics is represented by a propagation rate. Ideally, this rate is constant for a given set of external thermodynamic variables, monomer concentration, catalyst concentration, etc.; but the growing polymer itself represents a changing condition of the system, and its conformation and interactions with catalyst, monomers, and other polymer chains should influence the rate of monomer addition. Such a rate change is observed in the polymerization of amino acids where it has been interpreted as the consequence of a conformation change in the growing chain from an open structure to an α-helix (Lundberg and Doty, 1957; Idelson and Blout, 1957). In stereotactic or copolymers, the possibilities quickly become more complex. Assuming two distinguishable orientations or types of monomer, and their reaction rates dependent on only the last monomer type in the chain, there are four reaction rates to consider, each of which may change with the growing chain conformation. Furthermore, it is quite reasonable to consider monomer interactions with several end units (De Santis et al., 1962; Natta et al., 1962), or to postulate that the polymer itself has more than one state with different sets of probabilities of addition for each state (Coleman and Fox, 1962). Pattee (1964) has suggested that a higher degree of order could reasonably be expected if mono-mer addition rates were influenced by two or more polymer subunits widely separated from each other in the linear chain, but brought together by the precise three-dimensional folding, as for example in a helix or by zigzag folding. Such interactions would be favored by heterogeneous systems or in poor solvents

(Ham, 1959), but experimentally such order would be difficult to resolve since the sequential complexity could easily match that of proteins, even assuming very simple rules of sequence propagation (Pattee, 1961). However, the work of Fox and Harada (1960) shows clearly that thermally polymerized amino acids are not random with respect to terminal residues, and the fact that they exhibit catalytic activity which is thermally inactivatable in aqueous solution suggests some degree of preferred conformation (Fox et al., 1962). This might suggest some form of sequential order, but as yet no sequence analysis has been done.

These experiments on chain macromolecules are difficult to interpret, and there is no fundamental understanding of either chain crystallization or tactic polymerization. But certainly the elementary processes or precise conditional control of conformation and sequence in the simplest heteropolymers are basically similar to the conformation and sequence control of the more intricate type which has evolved in nucleic acid and protein interactions. In the last section we shall discuss some possible theories of how this intricate control could have evolved.

VII. THEORIES OF MACROMOLECULAR EVOLUTION

The experimental evidence now clearly substantiates the basic hypothesis of Oparin and Haldane that the primitive earth provided the essential starting materials for living systems. Consequently we may expect that the origin of life problem will shift away from the evolution of the building blocks and the elementary operations of joining them together, to the more difficult problem of the *evolution of control* in complex organizations. This problem is more difficult because the idea of "control" is not defined in the same sense as we can define biochemicals. Nevertheless, as biologists have so often emphasized, the essential characteristics of life cannot be separated from the total *process* of cellular activity, and as Weiss (1962) has put it, the elements of a complex process are not elementary particles or biochemicals, but elementary *processes*. A live cell and a dead collection of the identical biochemicals in the same structural organization differ essentially in the amount of intermolecular control that exists in each unit. From this point of view, the question of the origin of life becomes the problem of understanding elementary molecular control processes, and of formulating a theory of the evolution of molecular control.

What no one can say at this stage is how much effort should be aimed at gathering data in the hope that it will stimulate a good theory, and how much effort should be directed at formulating a theory which will generate some good experiments. Historically, a mixed strategy has often proven the most productive, and since the main body of this review discusses experimental approaches to the problem, a few ideas on experimentally testable theories of evolution may be of some value.

A. Order from Disorder

Perhaps the simplest physical example of ordering is the process of crystallization. Ideally we may picture a large collection of subunits confined within some kind of box. Initially these subunits move with a distribution of energy high enough to keep them in disarray. If the energy is now reduced by removing it from the box, the subunits will begin to appear ordered, by which we mean that we recognize some simple rule which relates one subunit to another. This type of order is explained physically by a combination of more general laws which include the inherent structure and forces of the subunits on each other, the minimum energy principle, statistical thermodynamics, or the general properties of three-dimensional Euclidean space, depending on the point of view. But since every subunit in the box must also be "ordered" by these same general physical principles, we may find it more instructive to consider carefully why we choose to "recognize" the particular order which we call a crystal. This is the point of view which Burgers (1963) has adopted in his discussion of the emergence of patterns of order in simple examples from classical physics, and which Ashby (1962) presents in analyzing the "self-organizing" system in general. It is difficult to escape the conclusion that the concept of "order" is not so much a property of the system as of the frame of mind of the observer. Furthermore, the frame of mind of an observer, especially one trained as a scientist, is often sensitive to some form of simplicity. We cannot pursue the idea of simplicity in an experimental sense, although its relationship to scientific generalization and physical laws is certainly fundamental (e.g., see Frank, 1957). However, there is discernible here some kind of paradox when we see that in our search for a theory of the evolution of complexity we tend to focus our attention on those aspects of a physical situation which are the *simplest*. There is some reason, then, to consider the possibility that complexity as we find it in living systems is the end result of a kind of divergent phenomenon which, although obeying physical laws, leaves us conceptually impotent with respect to the formulation of general theories. This pessimistic idea, once stated by Condon (1959), is a slightly better working hypothesis than any "accident" theory, since there is at least the possibility of significant experimental observations and formulation of partial theories up to the point where our conceptual mechanisms of abstraction fail. Elsasser (1963) has argued that the inhomogeneity or "individuality" of biological organisms requires a separate type of law which is not logically reducible to physical laws; but this approach is even farther from experimental test at this stage.

B. Order in Automata

One of the most promising experimental approaches to the evolution of complexity is by the construction of devices of complexity in which each element and operation is thoroughly understood beforehand. These automata may be designed or programmed to simulate the behavior of other complex systems which are not understood in detail, and with which they may be compared by some objective test (Turing, 1956). Such deterministic machines have the advantage that any abstract subjective "order" which an observer may find interesting can in principle be reduced to a set of objective "states" of the machine. Furthermore, the behavior of such complex automata does not depend in any essential way on the physical building blocks from which they are assembled. The logical "control" aspects of behavior are then more clearly separated from any particular physical representation, which in itself may be entirely too complex to efficiently describe in physical terms.

Von Neumann (1956) has formulated the control aspects of *self-reproduction* in terms of automata theory, based on the idea of the Turing machine (Turing, 1936), which may be thought of as the simplest type of automaton which is not limited by its elementary logical operations, although it may compute very slowly in comparison to more complicated automata. The conclusions of this analysis are discouraging from the point of view of a primitive theory of evolution; for although von Neumann designs a self-reproducing machine, his careful description also shows how logically complex the threshold of any complete self-replicating organization must be. Furthermore, he suggests that "complication" in some sense is degenerative below a certain level, and thereby places the concept of evolution up to such a level outside the scope of his theory. On the other hand, there is ample experimental evidence, such as shown in Table 1, that simple systems do form more complicated organization in a fairly persistent way, but we are inclined to expect that this degree of order can be explained by chemical statistics and the properties of the starting molecules, and that no additional theory of evolution is necessary up to this stage. The gap in theories of evolution is therefore between the levels of molecular complexity on the outskirts of statistical distributions representing chemical reaction probabilities and the threshold of persistent self-replicating units with the potential for evolution by natural selection.

C. Order Acquired by Learning

An obvious case of the evolution of complexity which occurs without self-replication is the process of learning. This may at first be considered a poor example on at least two counts: the first is the association of learning with highly evolved biological systems, and the second is that we do not understand the process of learning any better than evolution itself. In fact, several authors have used the analogy of biological evolution by trial and selection to explain the process of learning (e.g., Pringle, 1951; Bremermann, 1958; Campbell, 1960). However, an analogy may be used both ways. Furthermore, the recent contributions to the theory of learning in automata have reduced many aspects of learning to practical levels of simulation on general purpose computers (e.g., see Fiegenbaum and Feldman, 1963).

We have the same advantage in using the concept of learning at the macromolecular level as we do in using the concept of biological evolution, that is, we may attempt to reduce these ideas to their most primitive operations. We have reviewed the various hypothetical thresholds of molecular complexity which might support biological evolution in Section V-A, and pointed out the large gap that still exists between these thresholds and what we have observed in abiological experiments. What is the corresponding primitive threshold for a learning process?

Both learning and biological evolution certainly require the acquisition and storage of order or information, which is another way of saying that learning and evolution produce increasing complexity of control. The simplest information-storage structure which we can imagine is a linear chain with ordered, distinguishable subunits; and, as we have seen, this condition is fulfilled in the simplest abiogenic heteropolymers. The essential difference between the processes of learning and biological evolution at this elementary level is in the method of acquisition of order in such a linear chain. First of all, biological evolution requires chance alteration in sequence, whereas learning more often implies a predictable or causal change in order. Second, biological evolution requires self-replication of linear sequence without regard to the order being replicated, whereas learning only implies storage or propagation of order. Finally, biological evolution can be said to increase its order only by the natural selection process which does not involve any direct interaction of the environment with the replicated sequential order; whereas in the learning process, especially in the sense of "training," there is selection by direct feedback interaction of the environment with the newly acquired order. Therefore, in spite of our lack of detailed understanding of either learning or the behavior of simple polymers, we may more reasonably compare the elementary sequence and conformation control processes which are observed in polymers to the elements of learning rather than to a process of biological evolution. The question now becomes: can we formulate a theory which explains why a collection of growing linear sequences in the form of interacting heteropolymers should learn to control its molecular processes so that self-replication and natural selection becomes an effective method of evolution?

At this point we are at the fringe of our knowledge of both macromolecular behavior and theories of self-organizing systems. To proceed further will require first an experimental determination of the basic functional operations which are accomplished by tactic polymer sequence and conformation control. From what is already known of conditionality and specificity of polymer interactions, it is not unlikely that growing collections of heteropolymers behave like molecular automata (Pattee, 1961; Stahl and Goheen, 1963) but until these interactions are better understood no detailed theory is likely to be formulated.

On the other hand, general theories of learning in automata may be the most productive approach in deciding what type of experimental information about polymer interaction is most significant for molecular evolution. No general theory of self-organization exists at the present time, although many aspects of the problem have been analyzed (e.g., see Shannon and McCarthy, 1956; Yovits and Cameron, 1960; von Foerster and Zopf, 1962; Yovits et al., 1962). Ashby (1962) has postulated that reproduction in some sense is a dynamical state which will be reached in time by any "sufficiently large system" if it does not first reach equilibrium. We might also postulate that replication is favored by "the principle of the most unstable solution" by which Burgers (1963) accounts for the choice of particular patterns of order in certain hydrodynamic convection problems. There is also the analogy with learning in higher organisms with well-developed nervous systems, in which the most primitive learning is by rote, direct training, or simple, immediate interaction with the environment. Gradually, as the brain develops more conditional relationships, the learning process becomes increasingly similar to random search and selection (e.g., Hadamard, 1945; Campbell, 1960). This same strategy of learning has also proven effective for the programming of computers to simulate learning (e.g., Newell, 1962; Minsky, 1963). We might therefore consider this strategy as a valuable source of order at the molecular level (Pattee, 1964), beginning with learning order by direct feedback with the environment, and proceeding *continuously* through stages of increasing delay and hereditary isolation from the environment to the ultimate random search and natural selection process which is now observed in highly evolved organisms. At the present time any tests of such a theory must be simulated by computers, since no techniques of polymer characterization are likely to resolve such sophisticated behavior. However, experimental studies of the basic elements of control of polymer sequence and conformation are essential before any such computer-simulated process could be designed to represent actual macromolecular interactions.

VIII. CONCLUSION

The Oparin-Haldane theory of the origin of the organic molecules necessary for living organisms by abiogenic synthesis on the primeval earth has been largely confirmed by many experiments. We now face the problem of the evolution of the interaction and control of macromolecular sequence and conformation. Only recently have experiments shown that precise sequence control and conformation control is a general possibility in a wide variety of simple polymers, but much more experimental work must be done before these properties can be understood. Similarly, studies of the theory and behavior of automata suggest that many types of self-organization are possible with extremely simple, fundamental operations, not unreasonably different in a logical sense from the basic operations in collections of growing macromolecules. As we learn more of macromolecular control and theories of organization, we may not only expect a more fundamental understanding of biological behavior, but we may also fill in the gap between our present conceptions of chemical evolution and the process of biological evolution.

ACKNOWLEDGMENTS

The author wishes to acknowledge the contributions of Mr. D. Kenyon in the preparation of this paper, both his valuable discussions and the compilation of Table 1. This work has been supported in part by the Office of Naval Research, Contract Nonr 225 (68), and by the National Aeronautics and Space Administration, Grant No. NsG 218-62.

REFERENCES

Abelson, H. A., *Science, 124,* 935 (1956).

Abelson, P. H., in A. I. Oparin, ed., *Evolutionary Biochemistry,* Pergamon Press, New York, 1963, p. 52.

Akabori, S., in F. Clark and R. L. M. Synge, eds., *The Origin of Life on the Earth,* Pergamon Press, New York, 1959, p. 189.

Ashby, W. R., in C. A. Muses, ed., *Aspects of the Theory of Artificial Intelligence,* Plenum Press, New York, 1962, p. 9.

Bahadur, K., *Nature, 173,* 1141 (1954).

Bahadur, K., in F. Clark and R. L. M. Synge, eds., *The Origin of Life on the Earth,* Pergamon Press, New York, 1959, p. 140.

Bangham, A. D., and Horne, R. W., *J. Mol. Biol., 8,* 660 (1964).

Blois, M. S., in S. W. Fox, ed., *The Origin of Prebiological Systems,* Academic Press, 1964, p. 19.

Blois, M. S., and Kenyon, D. H., Paper presented at Fourth International Congress of Photobiology, Oxford, England, July 1964.

Blum, H. F., *Am. Scientist, 49,* 474 (1961).

Bremermann, H. J., *Tech. Rept. No. 1,* Contract Nonr 477(17), Dept. of Mathematics, University of Washington, Seattle, 1958.

Bridgman, P. W., *Science, 123,* 16 (1954).

Burgers, J. M., *Bull. Am Math. Soc., 69,* 1 (1963).

Calvin, M., *Am. Scientist, 44,* 248 (1956).

Calvin, M., and Calvin, G. J., *Am. Scientist, 52,* 163 (1964).

Campbell, D. T., in M. C. Yovits and S. Cameron, eds., *Self-Organizing Systems,* Pergamon Press, New York, 1960, p. 205.

Claus, G., and Nagy, B., *Nature, 192,* 594 (1961).

Coleman, B. D., and Fox, T. G., *Abstr. 142nd Am. Chem. Soc Meeting,* September, 1962, paper 14R.

Commoner, B., in M. Kasha and B. Pullman, eds., *Horizons in Biochemistry,* Academic Press, New York, 1962.

Condon, E. V., unpublished discussion, 1959.

Crick, F. H. C., in M. X. Zarrow, ed., *Growth in Living Systems,* Basic Books, New York, 1961, p. 3.

De Santis, P., Giglio, E., Liquori, A. M., and Ripamonti, A., *Nuovo Cimento, 26,* 616 (1962).

Dose, K., and Rajewsky, B., *Biochim. Biophys. Acta, 25,* 227 (1957).

Ellenbogen, E., *Abstr. Am. Chem. Soc. Meeting,* Chicago, 1958, paper 47C.

Elsasser, W. M., *J. Theoret. Biol., 4,* 166 (1963).

Feigenbaum, E., and Feldman, J., eds., *Computers and Thought,* McGraw-Hill, New York, 1963.

Fischer, E. W., *Z. Naturforsch., 12a,* 753 (1957).

Fitch, F. W., and Anders, E., *Science, 140,* 1097 (1963).

Flory, P. J., *Principles of Polymer Chemistry,* Cornell University Press, Ithaca, New York, 1953, p. 102.

Foerster, H. von, and Zopf, Jr., G. W., eds., *Principles of Self-Organization,* Pergamon Press, New York, 1962.

Fox, S. W., *Nature, 201,* 336 (1964).

Fox, S. W., and Harada, K., *J. Am. Chem. Soc., 82,* 3745 (1960).

Fox, S. W., and Harada, K., *Science, 133,* 1923 (1961).

Fox, S. W., Harada, K., and Kendrick, J., *Science, 129,* 1221 (1959).

Fox, S. W., Harada, K., and Rohlfing, D., in M. A. Stahmann, ed., *Polyamino Acids, Polypeptides, and Proteins,* University of Wisconsin Press, Madison, 1962, p. 47.

Fox, S. W., Johnson, J. E., and Middlebrook, M., *J. Am. Chem. Soc., 77,* 1048 (1955).

Fox, S. W., and Yuyama, S., *J. Bacteriol., 85,* 279 (1963).

Fox, S. W., and Yuyama, S., *Ann. N.Y. Acad. Sci., 108,* 487 (1963).

Fox, S. W., and Yuyama, S., *Comp. Biochem. Physiol., 11,* 317 (1964).

Frank, P., *Philosophy of Science,* Prentice Hall, Englewood Cliffs, N.J., 1957, p. 350.

Garrison, W. M., Morrison, D. H., Hamilton, J. G., Benson, A. A., and Calvin, M., *Science, 114,* 416 (1951).

Gaylord, N. G., and Mark, H. F., *Linear and Stereoregular Addition Polymers,* Interscience, New York, 1959.

Geil, P. H., *Polymer Single Crystals,* Interscience, New York, 1963.

Groth, W., in F. Daniels, ed., *Photochemistry in the Liquid and Solid States,* Wiley, New York, 1957.

Hadamard, J., *The Psychology of Invention in the Mathematical Field,* Princeton University Press, Princeton, N.J., 1945.

Haldane, J. B. S., *Rationalist Annual,* 1929.

Haldane, J. B. S., in S. W. Fox, ed., *Origin of Prebiological Systems,* Academic Press, New York, 1964, p. 11.

Ham, G., *J. Polymer Sci., 40,* 569 (1959).

Harada, K., and Fox, S. W., *J. Am. Chem. Soc., 80,* 2694 (1958).

Harada, K., and Fox, S. W., *Arch. Biochem. Biophys., 86,* 274 (1960).

Herrera, A. L., *Science, 96,* 14 (1942).

Heyns, K., and Pavel, K., *Z. Naturforsch., 12b,* 97 (1957).

Heyns, K., Walter, W., and Meyer, E., *Naturwiss, 44,* 385 (1957).

Horowitz, N. H., and Miller, S. L., *Fortschr. Chem. Org. Naturstoffe, 20,* 423 (1962).

Huggins, M. L., *J. Am. Chem. Soc., 66,* 1991 (1944).

Idelson, M., and Blout, E. R., *J. Am. Chem. Soc., 79,* 3948 (1957).

Ke, B., ed., *Newer Methods of Polymer Characterization,* Interscience, New York, 1964.

Keller, A., *Phil. Mag., 2,* 1171 (1957).

Kenyon, D. H., and Blois, M. S., *Photochem. Photobiol.,* (1964), in press.

Khorana, H. G., in E. Chargaff and J. N. Davidson, *The Nucleic Acids,* Academic Press, New York, 1960, p. 105.

Krigbaum, W. R., in B. Ke, ed., *Newer Methods of Polymer Characterization,* Interscience, New York, 1964, p. 1.

Lederberg, J., *Science, 132,* 393 (1960a).

Lederberg, J., *Science, 131,* 269 (1960b).

Lindenmeyer, P. H., *J. Polymer Sci.,* Pt. C, Polymer Symposium, No. 1, p. 1 (1963).

Lowe, C. U., Rees, M. W., and Markham, R., *Nature, 199,* 219 (1963).

Lundberg, R. D., and Doty, P., *J. Am. Chem. Soc., 79,* 3961 (1957).

Mark, H., *Biophys. J., 4,* No. 1, Pt. 2, 5 (1964).

Miller, S. L., *Science, 117,* 528 (1953).

Miller, S. L., *J. Am. Chem. Soc., 77,* 2351 (1955).

Miller, S. L., in F. Clark and R. L. M. Synge, eds., *The Origin of Life on the Earth,* Pergamon Press, New York, 1959, p. 123.

Miller, S. L., and Urey, H. C., *Science, 130,* 245 (1959).

Minsky, M., in E. A. Feigenbaum and J. Feldman, eds., *Computers and Thought,* McGraw-Hill, New York, 1963, p. 406.

Mora, P. T., in S. Fox, ed., *The Origins of Prebiological Systems,* Academic Press, New York, 1964, p. 39.

Mora, P. T., and Wood, J. W., *J. Am. Chem. Soc., 80,* 685 (1958).

Morrison, P., *Science, 135,* 663 (1962).

Muller, H. J., *Perspectives Biol. Med., 5,* 1 (1961).

Nageotte, J., *Morphologie des Gels Lipóides,* Hermann, Paris, 1936.

Nagy, B., Fredriksson, K., Urey, H. C., Claus, G., Andersen, C. A., and Percy, J., *Nature, 198*, 121 (1963).

Nagy, B., Meinschein, W. G., and Hennessy, D. J., *Ann. N.Y. Acad. Sci., 93*, 25 (1961).

Natta, G., Corrandini, P., and Ganis, J., *J. Polymer Sci., 58*, 1191 (1962).

Natta, G., Pino, P., Corrandini, P., Danusso, F., Mantica, E., Mazzanti, G., and Moraglio, G., *J. Am. Chem. Soc., 77*, 1708 (1955).

Neumann, J. von, in J. R. Newman, ed., *The World of Mathematics*, Simon and Shuster, New York, 1956, Vol. IV, p. 2070.

Newell, A., in M. C. Yovits, G. T. Jacobi, and G. D. Goldstein, eds., *Self-Organizing Systems 1962*, Spartan Books, Washington, D.C., 1962, p. 393.

Oparin, A. I., *Proiskhozhdenie zhizni*, Moscow: Izd. Moskovskiĭ Rabochiĭ, 1924. Transl. by S. Morgulis: *The Origin of Life*, Macmillan, New York, 1938.

Oparin, A. I., in S. W. Fox, ed., *Origins of Prebiological Systems*, Academic Press, New York, 1964, p. 331.

Oró, J., and Kimball, A. P., *Archiv. Biochem. Biophys., 96*, 293 (1962).

Oró, J., *Nature, 197*, 862 (1963).

Oró, J., and Guidry, C. L., *Archiv. Biochem. Biophys., 93*, 166 (1961).

Oró, J., and Kamat, S. S., *Nature, 190*, 442 (1961).

Oró, J., Kimball, A., Fritz, R., and Master, F., *Archiv. Biochem. Biophys., 85*, 115 (1959).

Paschke, R., Chang, R., and Young, D., *Science, 125*, 881 (1957).

Pattee, H. H., *Biophys. J., 1*, 683 (1961).

Pattee, H. H., in S. W. Fox, ed., *The Origin of Prebiological Systems*, Academic Press, New York, 1964, p. 385.

Pavlovskaya, T. E., and Pasynskii, A. G., in F. Clark and R. L. M. Synge, eds., *The Origin of Life on the Earth*, Pergamon Press, New York, 1959, p. 151.

Pirie, N. W., in F. Clark and R. L. M. Synge, eds., *The Origin of Life on the Earth*, Pergamon Press, New York, 1959, p. 76.

Ponnamperuma, C., Lemmon, R. M., Mariner, R., and Calvin, M., *Proc. Natl. Acad. Sci. U.S., 49*, 737 (1963).

Ponnamperuma, C., and Mariner, R., *Radiation Res., 19*, 183 (1963).

Ponnamperuma, C., Mariner, R., and Sagan, C., *Nature, 198*, 1199 (1963).

Ponnamperuma, C., Sagan, C., and Mariner, R., *Nature, 199*, 222 (1963).

Pringle, J. W. S., *Behavior, 3*, 174 (1951).

Rich, A., in B. Kasha and B. Pullman, eds., *Horizons in Biochemistry*, Academic Press, New York, 1962, p. 103.

Rutten, M. G., *The Geological Aspects of the Origin of Life on Earth*, Elsevier, Amsterdam, 1962.

Sagan, C., *Radiation Res., 15*, 174 (1961).

Sauter, E., *Z. Physik Chem., B18, 417* (1932).

Schramm, G., Grötsch, H., and Pollmann, W., *Angew. Chem., Intern. Ed., 1*, 1 (1962).

Schramm, G., and Wissman, H., *Chem. Ber., 91*, 1073 (1958).

Schwartz, A., Bradley, E., and Fox, S. W., in S. W. Fox, ed., *The Origins of Prebiological Systems,* Academic Press, New York, 1964, p. 317.

Shannon, C. E., and McCarthy, J., eds., *Annals of Mathematics Studies,* Princeton University Press, Princeton, N.J., 1956, Vol. 34.
Sinton, W. M., *Science, 130,* 1234 (1959).

Stahl, W. R., and Goheen, H. E., *J. Theoret. Biol., 5,* 266 (1963).

Stahmann, M. A., ed., *Polyamino Acids,.Polypeptides and Proteins,* The University of Wisconsin Press, Madison, 1962.

Staudinger, H., and Signer, R., *Z. Krist., 70,* 193 (1929).

Storcks, K. H., *J. Am. Chem. Soc., 60,* 1753 (1938).

Szutka, A., *Radiation Res., 19,* 183 (1963).

Terenin, A. N., in F. Clark, and R. L. M. Synge, eds., *The Origin of Life on the Earth,* Pergamon Press, New York, 1959, p. 139.

Till, P. H., *J. Polymer Sci., 24,* 301 (1957).

Turing, A. M., *Proc. London Math. Soc., 2–42,* 230 (1936).

Turing, A. M., in J. R. Newman, ed., *The World of Mathematics,* Simon and Shuster, New York, 1956, Vol. IV, p. 2099.

Urey, H. C., *Nature, 193,* 1119 (1962).

Wald, G., *Scientific American,* August 1954, p. 3.

Weiss, P., in J. M. Allen, ed., *The Molecular Control of Cellular Activity,* McGraw-Hill, New York, 1962, p. 1.

Weissbluth, M., ed., *Quantum Aspects of Polypeptides and Polynucleotide (Biopolymers Symp.,* No. 1), Interscience, New York, 1964.

Weyl, H., *Philosophy of Mathematics and Natural Science,* Princeton University Press, Princeton, N.J., 1949, p. 160.

Wilson, A. T., *Nature, 188,* 1007 (1960).

Yovits, M. C., and Cameron, S., eds., *Self-Organizing Systems,* Pergamon Press, New York, 1960.

Yovits, M. C., Jacobi, G. T., and Goldstein, G. D., eds., *Self-Organizing Systems,* Spartan Books, Washington, D.C., 1962.

Ziegler, K., *Angew. Chem., 64,* 323 (1952).